AN INTRODUCTION TO THE
BEHAVIOUR OF INVERTEBRATES

by J. D. Carthy

ANIMAL NAVIGATION

Second Impression 1957

FRONTISPIECE. A queen (*Chlamys opercularis*) swims upward at the approach of a starfish (*Asterias rubens*). Note the sensory tentacles and the eyes along the mantle edge of this close relative of the scallop (*Pecten* sp.).

(*Photo: D. P. Wilson*)

AN INTRODUCTION TO
THE BEHAVIOUR
OF INVERTEBRATES

BY

J. D. CARTHY

M.A., PH.D.

Lecturer in Zoology, Queen Mary College,
University of London

ILLUSTRATED

Ruskin House
GEORGE ALLEN & UNWIN LTD
MUSEUM STREET LONDON

FIRST PUBLISHED IN 1958
SECOND IMPRESSION 1962

PRINTED IN GREAT BRITAIN
BY BRADFORD AND DICKENS,
LONDON, W.C.1

To my Mother and Father

PREFACE

WHILE preparing this book, it has become obvious that greater attention has been paid to the behaviour and sensory physiology of insects than to the rest of the invertebrates. An attempt has therefore been made to strike a balance and as far as possible to draw conclusions which may be applicable throughout the invertebrate subkingdom—though the very diversity of those animals militates against this. The mass of work still waiting to be done on invertebrates other than insects stands accentuated once again.

I have not been concerned here with the pros and cons of terminology, such as the implications of the terms taxes and kineses, but have used the few which do appear as names for observational concepts without inferring anything more, nor, indeed, implying physiological or anatomical mechanisms, unless they have been discussed specifically.

The debt which this book must owe to its predecessors in this field is great and the help I have derived from Warden, Jenkins and Warner's *Comparative Psychology*, Fraenkel and Gunn's *Orientation of Animals* and W. von Buddenbrock's *Vergleichende Physiologie*, was invaluable, not least in introducing me to work which I had not encountered already.

It is always difficult for a non-systematist to be certain that the specific names he is using are the correct ones. With the help of various members of the staff of the British Museum of Natural History, I have brought the specific names up-to-date so far as possible. After the first mention, an animal is always referred to by its modern name though this may differ from that used in the original paper.

In the search for the literature many librarians have given me willing aid, but most particularly I have persistently troubled the Librarians and their staffs of Queen Mary College and the Zoological Society of London, never failing to get help and advice from them.

Several people have given their time to reading parts or all of this book and I hope I have met their criticisms. Of these persons, I would like to express my very grateful thanks to G. E. Newell, C. F. A. Pantin and J. E. Smith, without, in any way, wishing to suggest that they can be held responsible for any of the inadequacies of this book.

My wife gave me much practical help, as well as encouragement, when needed. Miss J. Hawkes aided in some of the final typing and the indices were prepared most efficiently by G. J. Peakin. A number of drawings were made by W. Tschernezky; their clarity speaks for itself.

I am indebted to the following authors for permission to reproduce text-figures: H. Autrum (120,121), G. P. Baerends (85), G. Benz (144), W. von Buddenbrock (4, 41, 43, 53, 74, 76, 79, 121, 128, 130), J. Crane (87, 88, 89), V. G. Dethier (132, 134, 135, 139), F. G. C. Evans (145), G. Fraenkel (146), G. Fraenkel and D. L. Gunn (22, 23, 27, 28, 35, 39, 44, 45, 48, 49, 108), D. L. Gunn (141), J. E. Harris (148), F. S. J. Hollick (136), N. Millott (19), H. Mittelstaedt (31, 77), R. J. Pumphrey (122), L. M. Roth (17, 123, 142), H. Schöne (50, 113, 114), G. M. Spooner (36), G. O. Stride (58), W. H. Thorpe (part of 9), N. Tinbergen (52, 99), D. M. Vowles (62), T. H. Waterman (63, 67), V. B. Wigglesworth (129), D. I. Williamson (73), W. G. Wellington (66, 143), and to the following for permission to reproduce plates: D. P. Wilson (frontispiece) and plate III (i), G. Fraenkel (plate I), P. T. Haskell (plate II) and E. W. Knight-Jones (plate III (ii)).

The following publishers gave permission also for the reproduction of figures and plates: Springer-Verlag (2, 31, 50, 56, 69, 70, 71, 106, 107, 113, 114); the Company of Biologists (9, 19, 20, 85, 126, 141 and plates II and III (ii)), the Wistar Institute of Anatomy and Biology (17, 29, 30, 33, 142); the University of Columbia Press (21, 104); the Clarendon Press, Oxford (22, 23, 27, 28, 35, 39, 44, 45, 48, 49, 52, 99, 108); Birkhaüser Verlag (34, 41, 43, 53, 74, 76, 79, 121, 128, 130); the Council of the Marine Biological Association of the United Kingdom (36, 73 and plate III (i)); Akademische Verlagsgesellschaft (37, 38, 47, 140); the Editor, *Biological Reviews* (46, 122); the Editor, *British Journal of Animal Behaviour* (58); Macmillan and Co. Ltd. (62, 66); the American Association for the Advancement of Science (63); the New York Zoological Society (87, 88, 89); Saunders and Co. (103); the Editors, the *American Midland Naturalist* (123); Cambridge University Press (129); the Rockefeller Institute for Medical Research (132, 134); the American Institute of Biological Sciences (135); the Royal Society of London (136, 148); Williams and Wilkins Co. (139); the Royal Society of Canada (143); the Editors, *Experientia* (144); Blackwell Scientific Publications Ltd. (145).

QUEEN MARY COLLEGE
March, 1958

CONTENTS

PLATES

CHAPTER I

INTRODUCTORY

THE behaviour of an animal is the result of information fed into the
co-ordination system, nervous or otherwise, relating to two sources,
one, the external conditions of the environment, and the second, the
state of the individual itself. Since the form of the information is
the stimulus received at a sense organ—where these exist—it has
become customary to consider the sense organs as exteroceptors and
interoceptors. However, this is an artificial distinction since no sense
organ receiving stimuli from outside can escape the influence of the
internal, physiological state of the body.

Nor is the pattern resulting from these stimuli determined solely
by them but is strongly influenced by this same internal state—
whether the animal is hungry or replete, old or young, in reproductive
condition or not, to take examples. Also there may be rhythmic
activity patterns inherent, and even innate, in the central nervous
system, which influence the expression of the sensory inflow as
motor action.

We shall be mainly concerned in this book with the behaviour of
invertebrates in response to external factors and the role which this
behaviour plays in the natural life of the animal. These factors which
characterize the external environment may be arbitrarily divided into
chemical and physical ones. From this arises the division of sense
organs into mechanoreceptors, receiving physical stimuli such as
pressure, radioreceptors, receiving stimuli in the form of radiant
energy, that is light and heat, and, finally, chemoreceptors stimulated
by chemicals. Both classifications are matters of convenience and
cannot be rigidly applied especially when it is not clear what sense
is involved. Thus, humidity differences could be detected either by
their effect on chemoreceptors or by changes in the physical properties of structures, these affecting mechanoreceptors. It is characteristic of all stimuli that they are forms of energy which can be transferred across a sensory cell surface and passed along a nerve as a
series of electrical and chemical changes.

In general, the physical factors are those of light, heat, gravity,
pressure. To these might be added electricity but since there is no
evidence at the moment that invertebrates require to react to this
stimulus under natural conditions, and indeed probably rarely
encounter conditions in which the stimulus is important outside the

1

laboratory, this will not be dealt with in this volume. But it must be admitted that the evidence of electrical sensitivity in the mormyrid fishes[336] makes it advisable not to be dogmatic concerning the unimportance of electric fields as stimuli in nature.

Different sense organs may react to different qualities of a single source of stimulation. Thus, animals may react to the wavelength characteristics of light, called by us, colour, or to the plane of the wave movement, as polarized light, or simply as a straight beam from the direction of movement of the constituent waves.

Both physical and chemical stimuli arise from living and from inanimate sources. All act as indicators of the state of the environment and thus of the ecological conditions in which the animal finds itself. Behaviour plays an important part in maintaining an animal in its optimum ecological environment. Obviously, indeed, as this is one essential for survival of the species, even if it is not necessarily so for the mere existence of the individual.

It may be true to say that the simpler the animal's requirements the simpler its responses, while the wider the range of conditions which it can tolerate the more complex become its responses, enabling it to make the fine adjustments necessary for existence in the different parts of its survival range. The behavioural responses of invertebrate animals to their surroundings are often very simple, consisting solely of random movement under particular stimulation (kineses) or of movement directed with respect to the source of stimulation (taxes). Simplicity of responses in these cases may be indicated by attention to one factor, or source of stimulation, at a time without evidence of choice of this factor. Choice, and its frequent accompaniment, the ability to learn, are not absent from the behaviour of invertebrates, most of whom possess these abilities to some degree, while they rise to a height among the cephalopods and among the social insects, where they appear to be accompanied by a process of abstraction and symbolization in the dances of honeybees superior to that of any other invertebrates.

Simplicity and rigidity of response is often coupled with simplicity of central nervous organization. The simple nerve net of coelenterates may form through-conduction tracts, as they do in the Actinozoa, but the greater part of the system retains its diffuse arrangement. It may be said that the more diffuse the nervous system the more stereotyped the response, for parts tend to be autonomous, depending upon local reflex arcs. Without central control variability of reaction may be reduced. Bi-lateral symmetry and anterior-posterior polarization of the body bring with them condensation of the nerve cells along the axis of the body with the formation of a nerve cord and brain. By a process of cephalization the sense organs become collected at the anterior end; with this end leading in movement this arrangement is functionally more efficient, in that food detecting and food collecting organs, for example, are often drawn together into the most advantageous position. The concentration of sense organs produces enlargement of that end of the central nervous system to form a brain. Its function is essentially to correlate the sensory inflow from the sense organs and on this information to channel the nervous activity into the appropriate motor outflows. Further increase in the relative size of the brain produces more complex and more variable behaviour, due to the great increase in the number of internuncial neurones enlarging the possible interconnections that can be made.

Behaviour is attuned to the normal conditions of the animal's life, that is, the conditions which occur with the greatest frequency in nature. Further, normal behaviour is apparently purposive because it has survival value or one supposes it would not achieve the level of development that the normal patterns do reach in the average animal. It is under the extraordinary conditions of an experiment, or under some unusual turn of events, that the behaviour, particularly that of the rigid, instinctive type, may appear to be useless or even directly fatal to the animal. These are important considerations when evaluating the results of experiments on the effects of different factors.

Since a major limiting factor on reaction to a particular stimulus is the ability of the sense organs to receive the stimulus, many behaviour experiments are, in fact, evaluations of the sensory abilities of the animals concerned. It is therefore appropriate to consider sense organs in general terms at the outset.

CHAPTER 11

THE SENSE ORGANS

MOST behaviour is initiated by the reception of stimuli by some sense organ or another. Indeed sense organs, being responsible for receiving and measuring the characteristics of the surroundings, are the means by which the animal keeps, often literally, in touch with the outside world. The extent of their ability to carry out this task imposes a limit on the range of an animal's behaviour. The essential parts of them all are the sensory cells which act as transducers translating the energy form of the stimulus, chemical or physical, into nerve impulses by a variety of paths. The ancillary apparatus of the simpler sense organs serves to increase the efficiency of this process by concentrating the stimulus on to the sensory surface. The temporal pattern of the stimulus can alone be perceived through such an organ but more complex ancillary apparatus may make the spatial pattern of the stimulus perceptible. Thus a light sensitive cell in the skin of an earthworm may react to consecutive light and dark, but a retina and the addition of focusing apparatus is required for the perception of images formed by the simultaneous presentation of light and dark patches (there is evidence, however, that image perception depends upon a temporal patterning of the stimulus, so that the details of an object cannot be perceived unless either the moving eye scans it or it moves itself when its details can be perceived through a stationary eye [586a]).

The impulses passing from the sense organs make their appearance on experimental apparatus as electrical impulses, accompanied by shifts of chemical substances which may be the result, or the cause, of the electrical changes. Conduction of excitation along nerves seems to depend upon these electrical effects. Thus the integration of the body into a functional whole by its nervous system will also depend upon electrical phenomena of this sort.

In this conversion the form of the information is also altered. The wave form of the light received by an eye is not reflected in the wave form of the electrical impulse passing down the nerve. Instead, if the nerve reacts at all, it reacts at maximum intensity (the all-or-nothing law) but with a frequency that is directly proportional to the strength of the stimulus, though as a result of adaptation this frequency may decrease with continued stimulation at the same strength. Thus reaction to light is indicated in the optic nerve by

pulses of electrical energy rising to a fixed level; as the light is in-
increased in brilliance, so the frequency of the pulses increases though
the height of each pulse remains the same. In this way not only is
the information that a particular source of stimuli is in the animal's
vicinity conveyed to the central nervous system but also the strength
of the stimuli emanating from it is measured.

The sensitivity of the receptor cells varies very greatly. A chain
of impulses will not leave the cell until the stimulation reaches a
definite value, the threshold, which is fixed for that particular type
of cell in that particular species of animal at the time of measurement. Two cells reacting to the same stimulus in two animals of
different species will not necessarily have the same threshold and
changes of the physiological state of an animal may alter the thresholds of its nerve cells. Once the information has reached the central
nervous system the reaction to it is not fixed. The motor directions
which leave the central nervous system will be affected by the other
sensory impulses arriving in the motor centres and also by the
physiological state of the animal. For example, the reactions of a
fully satisfied blood-sucking tick are different from those of a
hungry tick seeking a blood meal and the reactions of a planarian
worm to currents depend upon whether it is about to lay eggs, or
has already done so.

Though it may be clear from the behaviour of an animal that it is
receiving certain forms of stimulation, it may not always be possible
to single out any structures as those responsible for perceiving the
stimuli. Many insects retain a limited ability to behave towards
light stimuli even after their eyes and ocelli have been blackened.
The sensory apparatus for such behaviour has not been demonstrated. However, in general, there is good information about the
structure of the sense organs responsible for the various reactions
though the morphology of them is so varied in detail that it is impossible to give more than a general review here.

LIGHT RECEPTORS

The ability to react to light usually depends upon the existence
of definite organs or, in the case of non-cellular animals, organelles.
These receptors may be simply for the perception of the direction of
light, like the ocelli of insects, or light sensitive cells in the epidermis
of earthworms, in which case they can be termed 'euthoscopic'[420]
eyes. There is usually some structure masking the sensitive cells so
that light is perceived from one direction only, and a lens may be
developed to concentrate the light upon sensitive cells. But the
receptor has to become a more complex eye, when the pattern of

light is to be perceived, that is, when images are perceived. This is an 'eidoscopic' eye. This requires some method of moving the lens relative to the screen, in other words, a focusing device by which the shape of the lens can be altered, changing its focal length, so that a clear image falls upon the screen, which must be capable of resolving it.

The receptors may be unicellular or multicellular. The complex organization of the protozoan body may culminate in the complex specialization of parts for a variety of functions. As a result sense organelles are developed which are sensitive to light. One of the

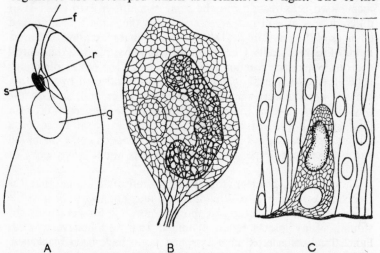

A   B   C

Fig. 1. Light receptors. A. Gullet and base of flagellum of *Euglena;* s, pigment spot; r, receptive area; f, flagellum; g, gullet (after Mast[363]) B, Light sensitive cell from epidermis of earthworm. And C, part of the epidermis showing a sensitive cell in position. (after Hesse[263])

simpler of these is found in *Euglena*. Here the sensitive spot is a hyaline enlargement near the base of the flagellum. This is shaded from one side by a yellowish-red cup lying in the cytoplasm (Fig. 1A), thus producing the masking essential in a light receptor which is to be used to obtain direction from light rays. The organelle may become more complex as in the dinoflagellate *Pouchetia*, whose amoeboid pigment spot is surmounted by a sphaerulitic lens, with, it is supposed, a light sensitive area lying between the two; the two considerations of masking for localization of the direction of the light and of concentration by means of a lens are fulfilled.

An example of single cells specialized for light reception are the photo-receptor cells scattered over the epidermis of the earthworm.

Each of these contains a hyaline lens which appears to concentrate light upon a neurofibrillar net surrounding the lens itself, fibrils also spreading throughout the cytoplasm (Fig. 1B). The cells rest upon the basement membrane and extend about half-way up between the neighbouring epidermal cells.[263] The cells surrounding the photo-receptors are slightly parted, a pinhole of light being permitted to fall upon the cell, so that light is accepted from one direction only. The sensitive areas are not evenly distributed over the worm's body

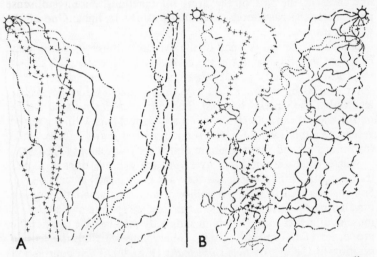

FIG. 2. Tracks of caterpillars of *Lymantria dispar* reacting to two candles, A, normal animals, B, blinded animals. (Lammert[326]).

for there is greater sensitivity at the head end, greatest on the pros-tomium and declining along the body for a few segments and then increasing in sensitivity to the tail. The dorsal region of any segment is more sensitive than the ventral.[262] Such isolated scattered sensitive cells are common among invertebrates where they are probably the cause of the generalized dermal light sense found in some insects. The cave beetle, *Anophthalmus*, though eyeless as its name implies, will still react to the light of a candle. [354] The caterpillars of various *Colias* species which are coloured to match their surroundings al-ways arrange themselves so that light falls on them from a particular angle. The perception of the direction of the incident light seems to be a property of their body surface, for lacquering their eyes does not affect the reaction. Indeed the caterpillars of a number of moths and butterflies can still orientate to lights with their ocelli covered (Fig. 2).[326] Cockroaches (*Blattella*[211] and *Periplaneta*[62]) though blinded by painting over their eyes will still choose a dark place rather than a light one.

These unicellular eyes are euthoscopic in function as are many of the simpler multicellular eyes. The plan of these simple eyes is a vesicle lined with light-sensitive cells from which nerves lead to the nervous system. Such vesicles occur among the coelenterates, on the margins of the bells of jellyfishes, for example, among annelid and other worms, usually at their anterior ends, among echinoderms, like those at the tips of the arms of starfishes, among molluscs, particularly the gastropods, and finally on the larvae and adults of various insects.

Sometimes the pit is open to the exterior, though its cavity may be full of secretion, as in the eye of *Haliotis*, the ormer. But the pit may also be closed by a transparent or translucent piece of the outer skin which may itself act as a lens, or may enclose a separate lens within the vesicle (Fig. 3A). The eyes of *Helix pomatia*, borne on the ends of the tentacles, contain a spherical lens within a closed vesicle, the inner wall of which is composed of sensitive cells, while the outer wall and the epithelium above are transparent (Fig. 3B).

Where the external layers overlying the eye are thickened and transparent, forming a lens, as they are in an insect's ocellus (Fig. 5B), there is clearly little possibility of any accommodation device for altering the focus. But where the lens is separate and enclosed, muscles attached to it directly or indirectly may be able to alter the properties of the optical system. Ciliary muscles sling the lens in position in the eye of *Sepia officinalis* (Fig. 4B). Their contraction moves the lens towards the retina, while contraction of the muscles of the ocular bulb squeezes the lens forward. Thus the eye can act eidoscopically, a clear image being produced on the retina. The process is indirect in the polychaete, *Alciopa* (Fig. 4A). Lens movement is brought about by the contraction of a fluid-filled ampulla which forces liquid into the optic vesicle, pushing the lens forward. Alteration in the shape of the lens can be produced by the muscles of the corneal bulge which contract upon the body of the lens.

Such vesicular eyes, whether open or closed, are usually backed by a pigment layer permitting light to fall upon the retina from one direction only. The amount of light may be further reduced by a pupillary device, like the stripes threading the surface surrounding the lens of *Alciopa*. In general the retinae have nerves leaving from the outside of the cup, but in the eyes of *Pecten*, the scallop, they leave the retina cells from within, for the cells point outwards, so that light must pass through the network before stimulating the retinal cells (Fig. 3C). The eyes are arranged around the mantle edge

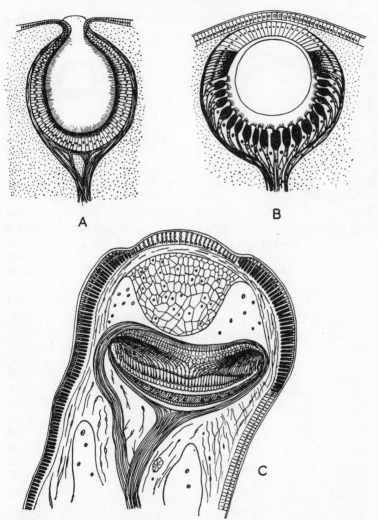

FIG. 3. Sections of the eyes of A, *Haliotis*, B, *Helix pomatia* and C, *Pecten* (from Hesse[263a])

which protrudes from the gaping shells. The retina of planarian worms is also of this type and the orientation of the cell to the light rays determines whether it shall be stimulated or not (see Chapter III).

One of the most efficient and the most widespread pattern of eidoscopic eye is that of the compound eye, found in most arthropods

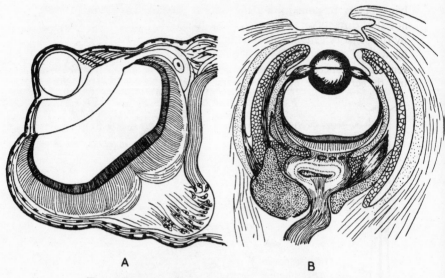

FIG. 4. Sections of the eyes of A, *Alciopa* and B, *Sepia*.

but particularly among insects. This is composed of units, the ommatidia, each of which is itself a receptor with a fixed focus lens system (Fig. 5A); thus no accommodation is possible within the individual unit. But the eye acts as a whole, all the ommatidia being used in concert. The numbers of these in an eye vary widely from one in the ant, *Ponera punctatissima*, to 10,000–28,000 in dragonflies. Each acts as a receptor for light, any image formed on the sensitive cells not apparently being received as such, but, rather, the image built up from all the units is appreciated. Thus a large number of ommatidia will give rise to an image of finer grain than a smaller number. Ideally for more accurate image perception a greater number of ommatidia are required. A limit is imposed, however, by the optical properties of the system of each individual unit and by the angle between it and the neighbouring ommatidia. Thus a point is reached where closer packing of ommatidia in the same eye, resulting in units of smaller cross-section will lead to a decrease in acuity because of diffraction. In fact examination of a number of eyes of hymenopterous insects has shown that the inter-ommatidial angle is always just below that for the limiting resolving power for the ommatidia in question.[26]

An ommatidium contains a corneal lens (equivalent to the thickening of the epidermis in closed vesicular eyes) with a crystalline cone

lying below it, constituting the optical system. This may or may
not abut directly on to the rhabdome, a refractile structure, secreted
by the sensory cells which surround it (Fig. 5A). These cells connect
by way of ganglionic layers with the optic lobe of the brain. The
remaining structures, accessory to the main ones, are the cells secret-
ing the crystalline cone. Surrounding the whole system, forming

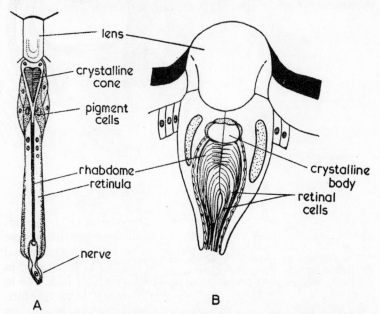

lens

crystalline
cone

pigment
cells

rhabdome
retinula

nerve

crystalline
body
retinal
cells

A   B

FIG. 5. Sections of A, the ommatidium of the beetle, *Cicindela*, and B,
a stemma (ocellus) from the caterpillar of *Gastropacha rubi* (from
Weber, *Lehrbuch der Entomologie*, 1933).

a sleeve of opaque pigment, the pigment cells lie in two groups, one
around the optical system, the other around the sensitive retina
cells.

An eye of this type with the optical system connecting directly
with the rhabdome is an apposition eye. The sleeve of pigment
isolates the ommatidium from its neighbours, so that its retinal
cells are stimulated only by light rays passing parallel or almost
parallel to its longitudinal axis. In this eye much light is wasted, for
if it enters the ommatidium at an angle it will be absorbed by the
pigment. Many nocturnal insects (e.g. lampyrid beetles, noctuid
moths), however, have eyes which utilize all the light, since the ommatidia are not necessarily isolated by pigment (Fig. 6). The optical

part of the eye connects with the rhabdome by means of a translucent filament. This is surrounded by secondary pigment cells, while the crystalline cone has a sleeve of primary pigment cells, as in the apposition eye. When the pigment granules are distributed throughout the secondary cells, the eye functions as an apposition eye, but in low light intensities, at twilight and during the night, the pigment migrates upwards in the cells surrounding the cone with

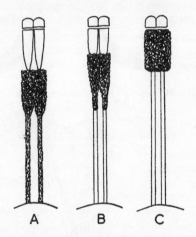

A   B   C

FIG. 6. Pigment movements in the eye of *Carpocapsa*; A, eye completely light-adapted; B, intermediate stage; C, completely dark adapted (from Wigglesworth, *Principles of Insect Physiology*).

a double sleeve of pigment and leaving the translucent filament uncovered. Then light entering a lens at an angle may pass through the structure of the ommatidium to stimulate the retinulae of its neighbour, thus this type of eye is called a superposition eye. Under these conditions the separateness of the spots of light comprising the image will be destroyed because light passing through the lens of one ommatidium, instead of stimulating only that one, forming a clearly defined dot, now stimulates neighbouring ommatidia forming a less clearly defined patch. The sharpness of the image must then be much reduced (though experiments on the compound eyes of some crustacea suggest (p. 124) that the pigment may not influence acuity as much as was believed[69a]). The part functioning as a superposition eye may be separate from the part forming an apposition eye. Among the mantids, who catch their prey by grasping it in their forelegs, an accurate appreciation of distance and distinct vision towards the front is required. The anterior-facing units of

their eyes are used for binocular fixation and are apposition ommatidia, while the lateral ommatidia function as superposition eyes.
Movement of the pigment is usually connected with the intensity
of the light falling on the eye (Fig. 6). In the mantids, just mentioned,
pigment of the superposition eyes spreads down the sides of the
ommatidia in daylight, but is withdrawn at night. This also applies
to Lepidoptera, in which ultra-violet light is as effective as normal
daylight in producing expansion of the pigment in nocturnal moths.
But there may also be an endogenous rhythm of movement, per-
sisting in complete darkness and unaffected by other factors, such
as temperature and humidity. The light-adapted arrangement may
be converted into the dark-adapted by shaking the insect. It is possible
that retraction of the pigment into the dark-adapted position may
be maintained by nervous excitation from the brain for when the
brain is removed the granules disperse into the light-adapted pattern.

HEAT RECEPTORS

All living cells react to heat, since it has an effect on the chemical
changes going on in cells and ultimately, at high temperatures, produces irreversible changes in proteins. So heat could be perceived
by its direct influence on the metabolism of a sensory cell. There is
no need for an intermediary between the cell and the heat waves.
Those cells which have been identified as heat receptors on the
bodies of invertebrates are invariably simple sensory cells, though
how the temperature differences produce their effect is, as yet,
unknown.

Recently some cell patches on the body of locusts and other
Acrididae have been located which seem to be responsible for perceiving heat.[493] They are segmentally arranged, the general pattern
being one pair on the head, as crescents below the bases of the antennae, a pair in the membrane connecting the head to the thorax
and a pair on meso- and metathoracic segments (Fig. 7). In addition
there are single pairs situated dorsally on the first seven segments
of the abdomen. They have been identified in over a hundred species
of short-horned grasshoppers.[494]

In *Locusta migratoria migratorioides,* they consist of a single
layer of cells closely pressed against the inside of patches of cuticle
which is rather thinner than on the rest of the body and consists
only of a layer of exocuticle (Fig. 7). The cells are cuboidal, inter-
digitating at their lower ends. Small nerves enter the patch at intervals and a larger nerve arises from a conspicuous mound of cells.
The distribution of the nerves and their connections within the
patch are difficult to make out. It is not clear, for example, whether

each cell is itself a receptor or whether some are sensitive and some auxiliary to them.[493]

In other insects, and ticks, the heat receptors are simple hairs with sensory cells at their bases. Extensions of these cells extend up the hairs. The hairs themselves are short and thick-walled differing

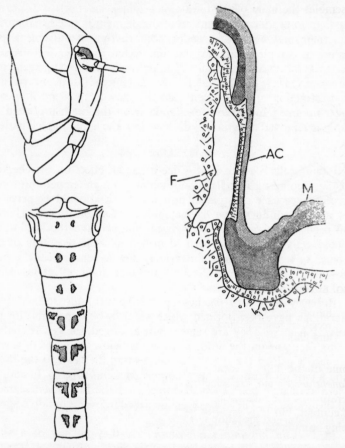

FIG. 7. Probable heat receptors of *Locusta migratoria migratorioides*. Left, upper, head of adult male showing the position of the antennal crescent (stippled). Left, lower, distribution of the fenestrae on the first seven abdominal segments of an adult male (dorsal view). Right, cross-section of lower region of antennal crescent. AC, antennal crescent; F, fat body; M, antennal membrane. Epidermis on either side of crescent pulled away from cuticle. Note thin cuticle and regular cell layer of crescent (Slifer[493]).

therefore from the longer tactile or the thinner walled chemoreceptive hairs. They are distributed sparsely over the body of the tick, *Ixodes reduvius* (= *I. ricinus*) but are more concentrated on the legs and especially the front pair,[329] being gathered onto the dorsal and lateral aspects of the legs particularly. But the receptors of *Rhodnius prolixus* are borne on the antennae. They are of two sorts, one of which resembles the hairs of the tick[574] (Fig. 8). Receptors, which may be

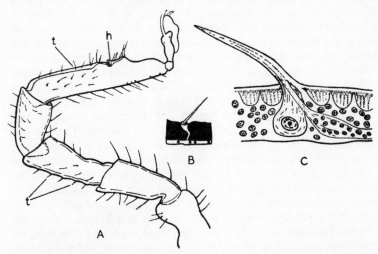

FIG. 8. Heat receptors. A, the foreleg of a female tick, *Ixodes reduvius*; t, temperature sensillum; h, Haller's organ. B, a temperature sensillum of a tick (both after Lees[329]) C, sensillum, probably a temperature receptor, from the antenna of *Rhodnius prolixus* (after Wigglesworth and Gillett[574]).

some of the hairs present on the tarsal joints and pulvilli of *Periplaneta americana*, are sensitive (below 13° C) to 1° C drop in temperature of the substratum with which the feet of the cockroach are in contact, but they seem to be less sensitive to rise of temperature being stimulated by 5° C increase.[299a]

PRESSURE RECEPTORS

The detection of pressure, however, usually requires some structure which on being deformed by an increase or decrease in pressure will stimulate sensory cells. Such organs are found best developed in aquatic animals as hydrostatic pressure receptors—thus acting as depth receptors. For, in air, atmospheric pressure differences play a very minor part in behaviour, no invertebrate orientating to an area of particular constant air pressure.

Though pressure receptors may be present in other animals it is the hydrostatic organs of aquatic insects that we know most about. Many of these incorporate an air bubble which, under the influence of the increased water pressure, alters its volume in direct proportion to the extent of the changes. This bubble often acts as an air store as well. Air is retained in two grooves roofed with hairs along the underside of the abdomen of nymphs of *Nepa* and *Ranatra* (Fig. 9). The hairs are hydrofuge and retain the thread of air beneath them. At intervals smaller sensitive hairs take the place of the larger retaining hairs. These also are hydrofuge and held in the air water interface so that when volume changes occur the curvature of this boundary is affected and the hairs are bent. This stimulates the nerve cells at their bases and signals an alteration in pressure.

Nepa adults have organs which are differently arranged and which function in a different manner. The spiracles in three of the abdominal segments open into a chamber roofed by a pliable membrane.[517] A pad of sensory cells lies beneath this. Some of these cells have flattened umbrella-like extensions which lie directly beneath the membrane (Fig. 9D). On an increase of pressure the membrane is pressed inwards and seems to stimulate these cells by contact. Other peg-like sensory hairs are arranged between them but the function of these is obscure. The three organs on one side are connected together by means of the tracheal system and the sensory equipment is sufficiently sensitive to enable very small differences in pressure between the fore, middle and hindmost of the organs to be detected. They do not, however, react to absolute changes of pressure but act as a differential manometer so that the position of the insect is indicated by the pressure differences between the three pairs of organs (Fig. 10). When horizontal, the three will be at equal pressures; when tilted head downwards, the anterior will have greater pressures imposed upon them than the middle pair and these in turn greater than the posterior pair. With the head upwards this relationship is reversed. The organs responsible for detecting the differences are of great sensitivity for with the body inclined at 45°, the topmost organ will be 1·5 mm above the lowest, the pressure difference being 0·00015 atmospheres. But increases in the total pressure bring about no response in the bug.

The receptors are of a different structure in *Aphelocheirus* which carries a thin film of air on the undersurface of its abdomen acting as a physical gill. There are two depressions on the underside of the second abdominal segment in which are a closely packed felt of

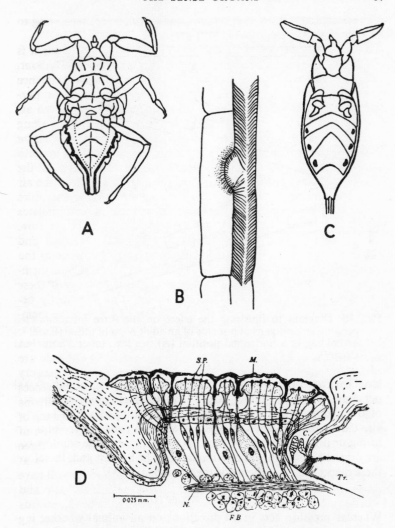

FIG. 9. Pressure sense organs in aquatic Hemiptera. A, ventral view of
nymph of *Nepa* showing respiratory furrow (solid black). B, detail
of similar furrow in nymph of *Ranatra*. C, ventral view of adult *Nepa*
showing the position of the pressure sense organs (solid black). D,
detail of one of these organs; C, closed spiracle; Tr, trachea; M, membrane of overlapping expanded margins of scale sensilla; SP, sensory
papillae; N, nerve. (after Wigglesworth, *Principles of Insect Physiology*
and Thorpe and Crisp[517]).

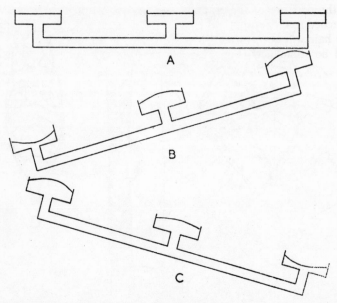

FIG. 10. Diagram to illustrate the effect on the three interconnected pressure sense organs of one side of an adult *Nepa* of tilting (B and C) or holding in a horizontal position (A), see text. (after Thorpe and Crisp[517]).

long backward-pointing hydrofuge hairs numbering about 60,000 per mm^2. These are rather larger than the hairs covering the rest of the abdomen and among which is also trapped a thin layer of air. Under the influence of pressure the film expands or contracts lifting or drawing down the hairs. Among those in the shallow pits are other hairs which will be stimulated by being bent and, therefore, these detect the movements of their companions.[517]

GRAVITY RECEPTORS

Whereas pressure acts in all directions on an animal whether it is in air or in water, gravity acts in one direction only. Therefore detectors for the pull of gravity can also be used to deduce the position of an animal with regard to gravity, in other words, whether it is upright or not. All these organs contain a mass of some substance which is denser than the surrounding tissues and will move when the animal moves its body axis out of the vertical. The mass is usually of calcium carbonate, either resting loosely as granules in a chamber lined with sensitive cells which will respond to the pressure of the granules on themselves, or as a concretion attached to the sensory cell by a hair so that on a change of position the hair will be bent over by the weight of the carbonate and the cell be stimulated (Fig. 11A, B). Yet there are no concretions in

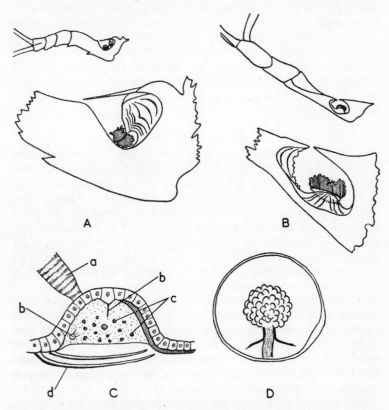

FIG. 11. Types of static organ, in crustacea, A and B. A, the position in the antennule and a detailed view of the statocyst of *Crangon vulgaris.* B, similar views of that of *Palaemonetes varians* (from Schöne[488]). In insects, C, the static organ of *Ephelia* larva (Limnobiidae); a, muscle; b, sensory hairs; c, statoliths; d, bristles closing sac from below (from Weber, *Lehrbuch der Entomologie*). In protozoa, D, a statocyst-like organelle from *Loxodes* (from Penard[427]).

the statocysts of some crustaceans, which may indicate that the hairs can be bent without the aid of weights on their tips (p. 205). Among Lepidoptera there are organs on the labial palps consisting of a central cavity lined with sensory cells on each of which there is

B

a chitinous club.[348] The movement of this club is believed to stimulate the cell, though their function has not been full investigated.[293]

Although possession of statocyst organs is almost a prerogative of crustacea (p. 202), there is an example among the insects. There are a pair of sacs in the last abdominal segment of the larvae of *Limnophila fuscipennis*[507] and of *Ephelia* which contain sensory hairs and scattered granules (Fig. 11c). The sacs are filled and emptied of water regularly so that the granules are disturbed. The direction of gravity is determined by the way in which the granules fall back into place stimulating the hairs as they do so. An organelle which may function as a statocyst has been described in the ciliate, *Loxodes*[427] (Fig. 11).

HEARING ORGANS

Hearing is a specialized and very sensitive type of pressure reception, since sound consists of a series of pressure peaks in the medium in which it is travelling. But associated with these peaks is displacement of the particles of the medium. Therefore the sound wave consists of a fluctuation of pressure and a displacement effect. Each of these characteristics can be detected in a different manner.[439] Theoretically the best type of pressure receptor is a solid-walled box one face of which is a stiff diaphragm (Fig. 12A). When a pressure change occurs outside the box the diaphragm will be pushed inwards by a pressure increase and drawn outwards by a decrease. This movement can be recorded by some arrangement of sensory cells. The ideal diaphragm is stiff enough not to be moved by the displacement effect of the wave, but to be moved only when there is a pressure difference between the inside and the outside of the box. Since pressure is a force which acts in all directions such a box-like organ cannot, by detection of pressure changes alone, be used as a sound direction finder.

On the other hand, displacement occurs along lines radiating from the source so that detectors of these changes can also be direction finders. Such detectors may consist of a box with a diaphragm as before, but in this case the diaphragm is more flexible and one other wall of the box is transparent to sound (Fig. 12B). Again the movement of the diaphragm is registered though now the movement occurs for a different reason. Displacement will be greatest when the diaphragm faces the sound source. Alternatively some kind of vane can be utilized so that it is deflected by the sound, (Fig. 12c) in the same way that the diaphragm is displaced. A hair, for example, may be bent over by the wave. Again this movement is registered by sense organs, usually at the base of the vane where it is pivoted.

It is doubtful if any actual sense organ functions in one of these two ways exclusively. Insect tympanic hearing organs function mainly on the displacement principle and their sensory hairs and the weighted hairs of the statocysts of other arthropods also fulfil the requirements as vanes to pick up the translational effect of the sound wave. On the other hand vertebrate ears function mainly as pressure receptors.[439]

Among the invertebrates only the insects have been shown to have a clearcut ability to detect sound. An ability to react to vibrations of frequencies within the human auditory range has been suspected in coelenterates, various worms, molluscs and echinoderms.

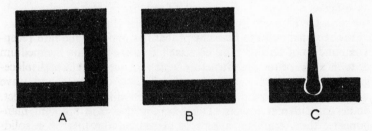

FIG. 12. To illustrate the basic plan of different organs for receiving airborne vibrations. A, a pressure receptor, B and C, displacement detectors (after Pumphrey[439]).

The ranges of sound received vary among the different species but the actual organs involved have not been determined for certain, except in insects. Not only is the structure of the receptors known, but also the structure of the sound-producing organs. It was at one time believed that the statocysts of crustacea were seats of hearing,[243] their original name of otocysts bearing witness to his belief. But though there is no doubt that the hairs in statocysts will vibrate under the influence of sound waves, as the hairs on the bodies of insects do, their primary function seems to be the perception of gravity.

The essential parts of an insect's hearing organ are a drum and a number of sensitive cells of special structure, the chordotonal organs. The drum head is usually a thin piece of cuticle lying between an enlarged tracheal tube and a chamber communicating directly with the exterior. Since the air within the tracheal tube will remain at approximately atmospheric pressure as it communicates with the exterior, there will be little difference in pressure when a sound strikes the drum. Also because the trachea opens to the air the other side of the theoretical box is transparent to sound. Sometimes the other side of the tube forms another drum lying in another chamber, so that the waves can pass through one drum, across the trachea, through the second drum, and out to the exterior again. In either case this type of insect tympanic organ is a displacement detector.

Vibrations of the drum head are perceived by chordotonal organs (or scolopidia) which are attached either onto the tympanum or onto a membrane connected in turn with the vibrating part, their other ends being fixed to a part of the integument or apparently lying free in the body cavity. Each contains a number of sensilla consisting of a nerve cell, through which runs a terminal filament, and a scolopale coupled to the filament and attached at its other end to the moving part of the organ. An accessory cell supports the elongated end of the nerve cell (Fig. 14b). Movement of the scolopale on the filament probably stimulates the nerve cell. The bundles of sensilla may be attached to the primary tympanum or to its edge, or to some structure which is connected in turn to the tympanum (Fig. 13).

Organs of this basic structure occur on different parts of the bodies of different insects. Thus, among the short-horned grass-hoppers, the Acrididae, a pair is placed on the first abdominal segment, while they are situated on the second abdominal segment of cicadas. The hearing organs of the long-horned grass-hoppers, the Tettigonidae, appear from the exterior as two slits on the front surface of the enlarged upper end of the front tibiae. Each slit opens into a chamber, one wall of which is formed by the drum. A number of Lepidoptera have structures very similar to those on the first abdominal segment of acridids, but it is not certain that they are used for picking up sound vibrations.

All these insects live in air; however, some aquatic bugs, such as *Nepa* and *Naucoris*, have similar organs but of a simpler form. Organs utilizing drums of this sort are not apparently the only sound receivers on an insect's body. Hairs will be moved by sound waves and, if the sense cells connected with them are sufficiently sensitive, they can be stimulated by the small movements of the hair when it is deflected by the displacement effect of a sound wave.

This appears to be true of the hairs on the ventral side of the cerci of cockroaches and crickets (*Periplaneta* and *Gryllus*). Stimulation of these hairs produces electrical responses in the cercal nerves, responses which are eliminated by vaselining the hairs thus preventing their movement. The reactions of these nerves are exceptions to the general rule that frequency of discharge in the nerve bears no relationship to the frequency of the stimulus. For pure

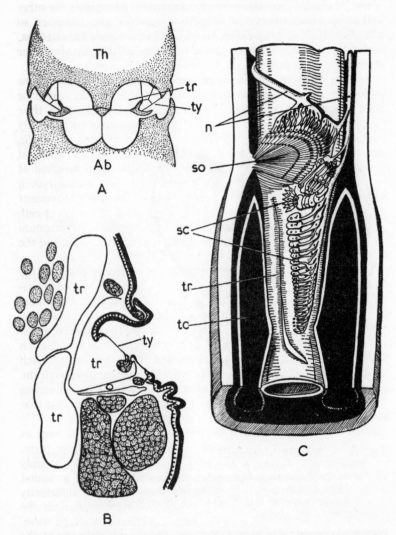

FIG. 13. Hearing organs of some insects. A, diagrammatic section through the thoracic tympanal organs of the moth, *Catocala*; tr, enlarged trachea; ty, tympanum; Th, metathorax; Ab, abdomen. B, section through abdominal tympanal organ of the orthopteran, *Oedipoda coerulescens*; tr, enlarged tracheae; ty, tympanum. C, the tibial organ of the orthopteran *Decticus verrucivorus* from the dorsal side; n, nerves; so, subgenual organ; sc, receptor cells of tympanal organ; tr, trachea; tc, tympanal cavity. (after Weber, *Lehrbuch der Entomologie*).

sound of from 50 to 400 cycles per second, the rhythm of discharge and stimulation are synchronous.[442] Responses are still given to sounds as high as 3,000 cycles per second but between 400 and 3,000 cycles the response is no longer a reflection of the rhythm of the stimulus.

Sensory hairs of this sort exist on the bodies of many insects, including some caterpillars which can react to sounds over the wide range of 32 to 1,024 cycles. Even those insects which have

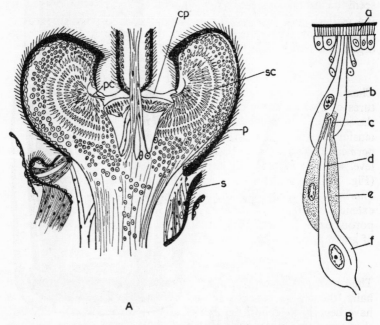

A

B

FIG. 14. A, Johnston's organ of *Chaoborus*; cp, conjunctival plate and process, pc; s, scape; p, pedicel; sc, scolopidia (from Weber, *Lehrbuch der Entomologie*). B, scolopidia from such an organ; a, cuticle; b, distal, or cap, cells; c, scolopale or sense rod; d, terminal filament; e, middle or sheath cell; f, sense cell (from Wigglesworth, *Principles of Insect Physiology*).

tympanal organs seem to be able to react to sounds after the organs have been put out of action. The residual sensitivity is slight compared with the normal and probably arises from sensitive hairs on the body.

Scolopidia may occur elsewhere without any evidence for activity in hearing. From their structure they can clearly react to stretching strains imposed on their bodies and, therefore, if connected between parts of the exoskeleton, can register stresses put on it. Thus, honey-bees have many scolopidia but there is only tenuous evidence that they can react to sounds. But placed in the joints of the legs, vibrations of the substrate may stimulate them (p. 235).

However, there is frequently a large concentration of these organs in the swollen second antennal segment of some insects. This is Johnston's organ (Fig. 14A). It is well developed in the male mosquito which finds the female by the sound of her wingbeats. The vibrations seem to cause movement of the flagellum of the male's antenna on the pedicel, and this movement is registered by the chordotonal organs strung across the joint between pedicel and flagellum. This organ also serves other functions (p. 232).

CHEMORECEPTORS

Chemicals are detected by receptors, which despite ancillary structures of various sorts, consist essentially of a naked extension of the sense cell in contact with the environment. In insects, these extensions connect to places where the cuticle is thinner and more permeable than it is over the rest of the body. These may be in pits, level with the surrounding cuticle, or raised to form a hollow hair (Fig. 15). Thus, the sensory hairs on the labellum of the blowfly, *Phormia regina*, contain three nerve cells at the base, two of which extend up one side of the two-chambered hair to connect with the porous tip[137] (Fig. 15). The tip of the sensory pegs on the antennae of grasshoppers is also porous.[495]

HUMIDITY RECEPTORS

The organs responsible in insects seem to be thin-walled truncated hairs, the pit-peg sensilla, so called because of their shape. They have been located in a number of other arthropods as well. Thus, they are placed in the anterior pit of Haller's organ on the tarsi of the forelegs of the tick, *Ixodes reduvius*,[329] (Fig. 16A) and in rather similar tarsal pits in spiders[50] (Fig. 16D), while the coxal sacs of *Scutigerella immaculata* seem to be responsible for the mediation of the centipede's reactions to water content of soil.[182] They are found on the antennae of mealworm beetles, *Tenebrio molitor*,[431] where they have been proved to function as humidity receptors, and they also occur on the maxillary palps. Removal of eight of the eleven antennal segments of these beetles eliminates the humidity reactions, although pit-peg organs occur on the remaining segments and on the maxillary palps. Since removal of the palps does not affect behaviour in a humidity gradient, it seems likely that the organs can only function properly when a certain minimum number are present, and that removal of the palps does not reduce the total enough to prevent their action; but since they occur in large numbers on the antennal segments the loss of the last eight segments brings the total below the minimum figure. That they are not the only humidity organs on the antennae is shown by the reduction in intensity of the reaction to a gradient after removal of the end

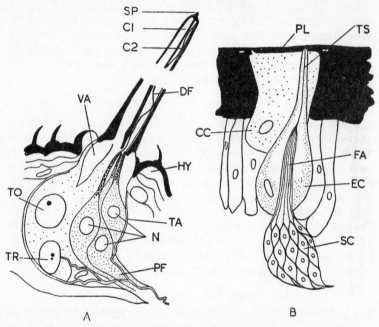

Fig. 15. A, typical chemosensory hair of *Phormia* (pigment cell layer omitted) HY, hypodermis; DF, distal nerve fibres; PF, proximal nerve fibres; N, neurones; TR, trichogen cell nucleus; TO, tormogen cell nucleus; Cl, thin walled cavity; C2, thick walled cavity; TA, tracheole; VA, vacuole (after Dethier[137]). B, Placoid sensillum from the antenna of the honeybee; PL, outer plate; TS, terminal strand; FA, fascicle of distal nerve fibres; EC, envelope cell; CC cap cell; SC, sense cells (after Snodgrass).

segment alone. This bears peg organs and bristles; either of these, probably the peg organs, mediate the humidity sense. There seems little doubt that the simple and branched peg organs found on segments seven to eleven of the antennae of *Tribolium confusum* (Fig. 16E) are sensitive to humidity[462]; only one or two are required for distinguishing between 0% and 100% R.H. Similar organs are present on the antennae of other species of *Tribolium* and have the

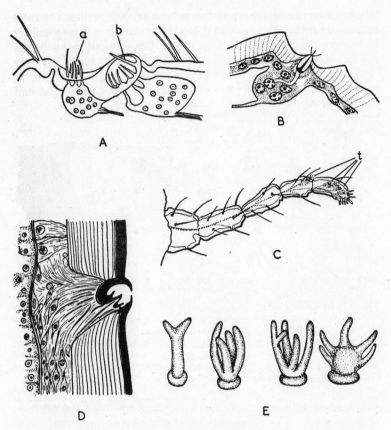

FIG. 16. Humidity receptors. A, Haller's organ of a tick, *Ixodes reduvius*; a, anterior pit; b, posterior pit (after Lees[329]). B, tuft organ from antenna of *Pediculus humanis* (from Wigglesworth[573]). C, antenna of *Pediculus* showing position of tuft organs,t. D, tarsal organ of spider (from Blumenthal[50]). E, typical receptive hairs, believed to be humidity receptors, from antennae of *Tribolium confusum* (from Roth and Willis[462]).

same function, though they are in all cases aided by basiconic sensillae on the terminal segments.of the maxillary palps (Fig. 17). A great variety of other trichoid and basiconic sensillae are candidates for the role of hygroreceptors on the antennae of other Coleoptera.[463]

Four tuft organs, each with four thin-walled hairs, are present on the antennae of *Pediculus* and seem to react to relative humidity (Fig. 16B). Receptors have been identified on the ventral side of the thorax of larvae of *Drosophila melanogaster*.[43] Covering them with vaseline reduces the sensitivity of the larvae but all sensitivity is lost when the hind end of the body is vaselined. It is likely that peg-like sense organs ('Fleischzapfenorgane') are the receptors there.

The identification of the organs on other insects has not been possible, though the areas in which they must lie is known. Loss of the antennae prevents adult flies, *Lucilia sericata* and *L. cuprina* from selecting one of two humidities, and 'Antennaless' mutants of *Drosophila* do not show the full humidity reaction of the normal

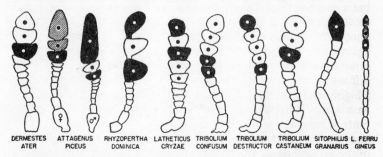

DERMESTES ATTAGENUS RHYZOPERTHA LATHETICUS TRIBOLIUM TRIBOLIUM TRIBOLIUM SITOPHILUS L. FERRU
ATER   PICEUS   DOMINICA   CRYZAE   CONFUSUM DESTRUCTOR CASTANEUM GRANARIUS GINEUS

FIG. 17. Diagrams of the antennae of adults of various species of Cole-optera, showing the segments on which hygroreceptors are located as demonstrated by olfactometer experiments. Solid black segments: hygroreceptors indicated. Diagonally hatched segments: receptors present on either one or the other or both the penultimate and terminal segments. Circles indicate segments that bear thin walled chemoreceptive types of sensilla (Roth and Willis[463]).

animals, suggesting that here again the receptors are on the antennae of the adult fly.[41] While earwigs, *Forficula auricularia*, seem to have the sensitivity localized on the underside of the abdomen.[568]

Reactions appear to be mediated without any sense organs in some animals, such as slugs and woodlice. Loss of water over the whole body surface would seem to cause physiological changes which in turn alter behaviour (p. 321).

EXPERIMENTING ON THE SENSORY CAPACITIES OF ANIMALS

Finally a few words must be said concerning the process of experimentation in order that the results of the investigations mentioned here may be discussed and evaluated more critically. The physical characteristics of the environment can be measured, often with great accuracy, so, too, can most of the chemical ones. Thus the strengths and directions of the various stimuli impinging on an animal can be clearly stated. But the capacity of an animal to react has to be measured in experiments in which ideally one of these factors can be varied independently of the others. The animal's behaviour in the altered conditions is noticed and interpreted by the experimenter as objectively as possible.

A first essential of such an approach is that the experimental situation should have a meaning for the animal, that is, that the conditions imposed should be those in which the animal is likely to react. A positive observation, in the form of an alteration in behaviour occurring after a change in conditions, has importance but a negative result, where there is no change in behaviour, may be meaningless for it does not necessarily imply that the animal is unable to perceive the stimuli, some factor in the situation may be against any reaction showing istelf. Evaluation of the experimental arrangements from the point of view of the animal is made doubly difficult by the fact that the experimenter, himself a vertebrate, and a highly evolved one at that, cannot by any stretch of his imagination have a trustworthy insight into the perceptual world of an invertebrate. There is no doubt that many of the situations devised for the testing of vertebrate capacities are based on the subjective opinions of the experimenter, and indeed this bias is not absent from invertebrate behaviour experiments, inevitably perhaps.

The diversity of form among invertebrates is greater than that of vertebrates and most important the plans and interconnections of the nervous systems and the sense organs are widely different. This diversity of structure calls for flexibility in the ways of approach to testing the sensory capacities of these animals.

Apart from the biological problems, there are the physical problems of making certain that one aspect of the physical stimuli is altered at a time, and indeed that all aspects have been taken into account. There is the notable case of the failure to recognize the ability of insects to react to polarized light, because that aspect of light stimulation was overlooked. Similarly, reactions to what appear to be pure tones may, in fact, be to harmonics which go undetected unless the 'pure' sound is carefully analysed.

On the other hand, careful investigation may reveal abilities which do not appear to have any function in the normal life of the animal. Thus the eye of the king crab, *Limulus*, discharges differently in polarized and unpolarized light, but whether the ability is called into action in the natural life of the animal remains to be discovered.[548] Such results can only be recorded, so that later perhaps they may be fitted into a larger concept of the animal's environment.

CHAPTER III

THE LIGHT SENSES

THE majority of the reactions of animals, both vertebrate and invertebrate, which have been studied arise from perception of light and it is not surprising, therefore, that most animals have been found to possess specialized structures to receive this form of radiant energy. The transmission of light energy is an electromagnetic phenomenon, though it can be treated abstractly as waves travelling in straight lines. This is a useful concept for it makes the explanation of the phenomena of colour and polarized light simpler to visualize. The eye of any animal is not sensitive to light of all wavelengths. Within the band of wavelengths perceived by ourselves, certain wavelengths produce subjective impressions distinguishable from those produced by other wavelengths and designated as colours. In the same way different wavelengths are often discriminated by animals, though not always in groups which correspond to our ideas of colour.

The minimum amount of light required to stimulate a receptor cell is one quantum—the smallest possible amount of light. One quantum will react with one molecule of the visual pigment giving rise to the series of chemical events which initiate the passage of impulses along the nerve fibre leaving the visual cell. According to the quantum theory, the quanta of light of short wavelengths have a greater energy content than those of long wavelengths. Hence, on physical grounds, the stimulating efficiency of light of all wavelengths is not the same, since greater amounts of energy can be transferred from short wavelength light of the same intensity as that of larger wavelength.

In white light, the waves are considered to be moving across the long axis of the ray at all angles within a plane at right angles to that axis (Fig. 18). If all waves except those vibrating in one direction are eliminated the light is plane polarized light. This can be done by using a Nicol prism, or a filter, such as Polaroid, which only permits the passage of waves moving in one plane (Fig. 18), or by reflecting unpolarized light when a considerable percentage becomes polarized. In nature, light from the sun is polarized when it is reflected off ionized particles in the atmosphere.

There are, then, various properties of light which can be considered as having behavioural significance in that they each represent different information: its brightness or intensity, the straightness of its rays, its wavelength and, possibly, its polarization. Animals usually react to not more than two of these properties at a time; different reactions may require the perception of different properties, for example, a honeybee finds a flower by reacting to the wavelength of the light reflected from it, but on its way back to the hive it orientates by means of the polarized light pattern in the sky.

It has already been pointed out (p. 5) that it is not always possible to recognize light receptors immediately on morphological grounds. But the essential part of any light receptor, whether part of a true eye or of a generalized dermal light sense, is a light sensitive screen consisting of one or more cells from which come nerve fibres.

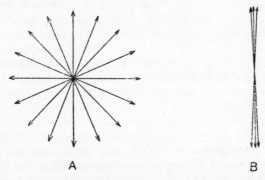

A   B

FIG. 18. Diagrams of A, the movement of waves across the axis of a ray of light and B, the effect of passing such a ray through a polarizing filter.

It would seem[234, 235] that the light impinging on a photosensitive substance S causes it to break down to form a substance P (a precursor of S) and an accessory substance A. This is followed by two reactions which can occur in the dark. In one, the photosensitive substance is reconstituted by a reversal of the 'light' reaction, thus:

$$S \underset{\text{light}}{\overset{\text{dark}}{\rightleftharpoons}} P + A$$

while the second reaction consists of the change of an inert substance L into an active substance T, which stimulates the sensory fibre, this reaction being catalysed by either P or A or both. This is the basic scheme upon which the changes in all stimulated light receptors are believed to be built.

Such a light-sensitive substance is rhodopsin, found in the rods of the vertebrate retina, but much of the work which led to the tentative analysis outlined above was performed on an invertebrate, the clam, *Mya*, whose siphon is sensitive to light, but in which the light-sensitive pigment is unknown.[234, 235] It suffices to say that, so far, there is a suggestive correlation between light-sensitive areas and the presence of carotenoids within them[377] for in the vertebrate eye all sensitive pigments contain carotenoids[542a]. The visual pigment of the eye of the lobster is known to be closely akin to vertebrate rhodopsin,[543] and it seems likely that this similarity extends to the visual pigments of other invertebrates. Indirect evidence supports this, in the insect's compound eye, for example, stimulation by various light intensities develops potentials in the optic nerve which bear a strong likeness to those produced in the vertebrate. This suggests that the intermediary chemical changes may be similar though biochemical analysis of the sensitive pigment has not been carried out.[586a].

However that may be, the chemical changes are dependent upon the intensity of the light stimulating them, the minimum being one quantum to one receptor cell. And indeed many of the simplest reactions to light consist of movement whose intensity is dependent on the brightness of the light, being greater either in bright light or in dim light. Among the Protozoa, this action of light is often directly upon the body processes without the intervention of a special receptor, the energy having an immediate effect on the physiology of the body.

Simple reactions to brightness and to changes of intensity do not require any auxiliary apparatus to concentrate or analyse the light. They may occur in animals which have a generalized light sensitivity over their whole body, not concentrated into any organ. Shading a light which shines on the radial nerve or superficial inter-ambulacral receptors of the sea urchin, *Diadema antillarum*, produces visible responses, the most striking of which are the jerking of the neighbouring spines.[375] The direction of the jerk is orientated to the light source, the result is that dark-adapted animals move out of the light and light-adapted ones move out of a shadow. In the gulf of Suakin (Sudan), *D. setosum* migrates under cover during the day[512] to emerge and feed at night; this behaviour is probably based on reactions similar to those described for the nearly related *D. antillarum* in the laboratory.

A more complex directed movement may result from illuminating a patch of the surface of another urchin, *Lytechinus variegatus*.[376] The tube feet on the illuminated area stretch out and pick up cover which is lifted and held over the stimulated area (a reaction which is intensified in dark-adapted animals) (Fig. 19). However, the way in which shells or stones are picked up or prised loose for this purpose is variable, though the final result is the same. Once suitable cover is located and the tube feet are stimulated by contact with the stone or shell, they no longer react to light by stretching out, for a clear glass coverslip may be picked up and lifted into place in shadow, and the tube feet still cling to it though they may subsequently be illuminated through it.

Though these movements of parts of urchins are directed, they are only directed because the light stimulation is restricted to a

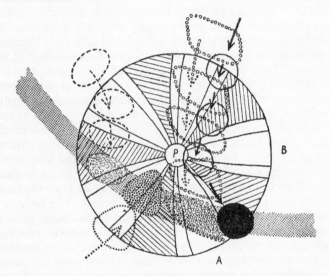

FIG. 19. Diagram showing the placing of cover over localized brightly lit areas of the surface of *Lytechinus*. Four stones are moved into a narrow band of sunlight (stippled) by the routes shown. P, periproct (Millott[376]).

small area. Movements of the whole animal directed according to the position of the light source are possible only if the sensitive surface is shaded in such a way that light can reach it from a limited direction. Such localization is possible because light travels in straight lines. And, therefore, a sensitive surface mainly surrounded by an opaque covering can alone be stimulated by a source which lies in front of the opening in the light-tight cover. Rays from any other direction are obstructed. Thus the direction of the source can be detected and the animal can move towards or away from it. Orientation in other ways is possible under these conditions for the animal can move while maintaining a definite angle between its course and the direction of the light rays (light compass reaction). Guided in this way an animal may move round and round a circle centred on the source so that at all points on its circuit the long axis of its body is at right angles to the rays. Such a path may also be followed by an animal which is not navigating in this way but simply reacting to intensity. As the intensity falls off as the square of the distance away from the source, points of equal light intensity will lie along circles concentric with the source, the intensity decreasing with increased radius of the circle. If an animal is moving round the light in its preferred intensity band the path it follows will be very similar to that traced out by a navigating animal. Thus, merely by observing the movement, it may be difficult to decide the type of behaviour causing the response, as will be seen later.

The wave form of light may be detected in two different ways, either by the length of the wave or by the direction of its movement across the ray of which it forms part. The first property is called colour by ourselves and we distinguish a spectrum grading from red to blue-violet. Light of wavelengths 760 mμ to 390 mμ is visible to the human eye but this may not coincide with the range which is visible to an insect, for example. The honey bee can certainly see light of wavelengths 650 mμ to 310 mμ and parts of this range are distinguished from each other as 'colours' but without the human subjective interpretation of colour as we know it. The bee's range extends its vision into the ultra-violet which is invisible to us.

Daylight is a mixture of waves of various lengths which are vibrating across the line of the ray in all directions. If, by means of a filter, all the component rays are eliminated apart from those vibrating in one particular direction this light becomes polarized (Fig. 18). This process occurs naturally when light is reflected, and when light from the sun is refracted by particles in the upper atmosphere. Few humans can detect the difference between this and unpolarized light. But it is now quite clear that a number of arthropods can do so.

Finally the light reflected from many objects, some wavelengths being absorbed by them, enables them to be identified. Their shapes can be picked out and recognized, that is, the animal may react differently to objects with different shapes and colours. This requires a light sensitive screen which is divided up into units each of which is screened from its neighbours and the neurones from each reach the central nervous system independently. The smaller the units the finer the details of the objects which are seen. The units may be individual receptor cells or groups of them. Many invertebrates, and particularly insects, have eyes which are capable of form vision in this way.

However, in this chapter we shall be concerned with the behavioural role of simple reactions to light as radiant energy travelling in straight lines, the other characteristics of light and the reactions to them will be dealt with in later chapters. Here the reactions to the presence or absence of light and to gradients of light intensity will be considered, to be followed by a discussion of the types of behaviour in which the direction of the light rays is utilized.

A GENERAL VIEW OF LIGHT REACTIONS

Generally an animal's activities lead it towards or away from light. A creature that moves away from light and rests in shade is photonegative and one that relinquishes the shadows for the light, photopositive. These terms merely describe the direction and end result of the movements, a closer analysis is necessary to find out why the particular movements lead the animal into the preferred place. They may be orientated with regard to the light, or they may move at random in such a way that they pass more time in either the shaded areas or the light.

But the sign of the light reaction is not, in every instance, fixed. It may alter during the animal's life, at the various stages in its life history or as a result of changes in its internal state. Young king crabs, *Limulus*, are photopositive to moderate intensities, becoming negative and finally indifferent to the same stimulus. On the other hand, the maggots of blow flies are negative to light, looping away from the source, while the adults are positive and move towards it. Varnishing the ocelli of the normally negatively phototactic queens of the ant, *Camponotus ligniperdus* causes them to become temporarily positive to light,[391] while wood ants (*Formica rufa*) leaving the nest are positively phototactic, but negatively phototactic when carrying pupae or food back to the nest.[284a] Feeding is one of the many ways in which the physiology of an animal may be changed, for example, such a change in the caterpillars of *Porthesia* is reflected in a change from the photopositive state before a meal to a photonegative one afterwards.[339]

THE INFLUENCE OF LIGHT ON THE AGGREGATION OF ANIMALS

Aggregation by alteration in speed

Light, in itself, is rarely of any direct consequence to an animal but indirectly as an indicator of other conditions it has great value.

Thus many animals will congregate either in the dark or in the light
and under normal conditions their optimal requirements for existence
are found coupled with one of the two alternatives. There are two
ways in which this can be brought about by undirected reaction to
light stimulation. They may move more quickly under adverse
stimulation and slow down or stop in favourable areas. This will
have the effect of collecting the animals into the favourable areas
in just the same way that alterations in the speed of a crowd walking
down a road makes the walkers clump together or string out. As
they walk on the flat they remain strung out but as soon as they
begin to climb a hill the speed of each individual goes down and the
crowd draws together only to spread out again as soon as they
reach the top. In much the same way animals moving about at
random may reach a favourable place and slow down. Should they
then pass out into the less favourable area again, their speed increases until by chance they pass back into the more favourable
area. They will spend more time where they move more slowly.
When the speed of undirected movement is correlated with the
strength of stimulation the behaviour is called ortho-kinesis.[177]

No highly developed and complicated sense organs are required
for reactions of this sort. Those which are responsible are probably
fairly widespread throughout invertebrates but it is somewhat
difficult to find direct measurements of the effect of light on the
speed of movement of animals. Some medusae (e.g. *Gonionemus
murbachi*) will gather in the more brilliantly lit parts of the tank in
which they are swimming, though after a time there they may cease
to show this preference.[587] An increase in the intensity of the light
causes an increase in the speed of swimming until they come into a
part of the tank where conditions are favourable and they slow down.
There are no figures for the rates of swimming but the time for
reaction to a light stimulus of various brightnesses has been measured. *Gonionemus* will react to weak daylight in 9·4 sec. after
the light is admitted into the tank, to daylight in 7·0 sec. and to
sunlight in 5·5 sec. Thus the strongest light has the greatest
stimulating effect.[588, 589]

An effect on movement has been claimed for fly larvae, such as
those of *Calliphora* and *Musca*. They are photonegative as already
mentioned. The speed with which they move away from lights of
various intensities may differ very little, as one worker claimed on
finding that with a light of 7 meter candles strength the maggots
moved at 0·321 cm./sec. and at 0·345 cm./sec. in a much brighter
light of 3,888 meter candles.[358] But the effect may be considerable,
other results obtained (*Lucilia caesar*) are 0·416 cm./sec. in 325 m.c.

and 0·469 cm./sec. in 1,057 m.c.[245] A heat filter was used in the experiments which produced the first set of figures but not in the second. Though warmth may have enhanced the higher speed at greater intensities of illumination, this does not appear to have been an important factor. On this basis the aggregation of these maggots could hardly be explained by an alteration of speed alone. Indeed, even when temperature variations are directly controlled, which is possible in studying an aquatic animal since the water reduces the temperature fluctuations, the differences in speed at different light intensities are slight.[102]

Similar considerations apply when the behaviour of planarian worms is investigated. These flatworms are typically photonegative at certain stages in their life and aggregate in the shaded parts of a dish lit from above. Yet there does not seem to be a great difference in their speed in light and dark. *Dugesia gonocephala* (= *Planaria gonocephala*), one of the freshwater species, was found to crawl at 0·50 mm./sec. in darkness and at 0·82 mm./sec. in light of 38 m.c.[545] Again the marine flatworm, *Plagiostomum* sp., crawled only 10–20% faster at about 15,000 m.c. than at 75 m.c.[565] Such differences in speed can hardly have any great effects in gathering animals into the shade. A very much greater difference would be necessary to produce the grouping which is observed. It will be seen later that other reactions are playing a larger part in drawing the animals together, particularly the increased number of turns which these worms make when moving in the light. But light does serve to stimulate stationary animals to move and absence of that stimulation helps to keep them in the dark once they are there.

A more important category is that of the animals which come to rest in darkness or in dim light. Clearly the difference between the speeds in light and in the dark will be at a maximum in these cases for the speed in darkness is nil. Thus, maggots of the flies mentioned above come to rest in dim light of less than 0·00007 m.c.[245] and planarian worms may stop when they come into shade. The whip tailed scorpion, *Mastigoproctus giganteus*, will only move in lights brighter than 0·16 m.c.[425]

The stimulating effect of light is affected by masking or removing the sense organs. After both eyes have been removed, planarians, e.g. *Dugesia tigrina* (= *Planaria maculata*) and marine turbellarians[356] are stimulated by an increase in light and become more active but they are no longer able to orientate away from the source as accurately as normal worms. Their eyes are, in fact, responsible for truly directional perception.[509] The speed at which they move is little altered by the operation, but removal of the whole head reduces the speed considerably (e.g. normal worms move at 1·18 mm. per sec., decapitated worms at 0·62 mm. per sec.). This may be due to the decrease in the area of the body which can be stimulated, in other words, the stimulating effect of light appears to be an additive one, resulting from stimulation not only of the eyes but also of light-sensitive cells widely distributed over the body. The total effective stimulation of the decapitated body will be less than that of a whole animal, including, as it does, the eyes which are more sensitive than the body receptors.

It has already been shown that blackening of the ocelli of an insect may lead to a reversal in its reaction to light (p. 35). The ocelli have been regarded for some time as stimulating organs, for varnishing of them may reduce the stimulating efficiency of a particular light intensity. If the ocelli of *Drosophila*,[59] or of a honey bee,[391] are covered the speed of the insects' reactions goes down. Placed between lamps of unequal brightness, an unoperated bee will turn towards the brighter lamp most often. If the median ocellus and that on one side are blackened, the bee will move towards the light on the unmasked side when it is placed equidistant between two lights of equal brightness.[391] If the lamps are of unequal brightness, and the dimmer one is on the unmasked side, the bee will turn towards this lamp, suggesting that the stimulating effect of the unvarnished ocellus causes the lamp on that side to appear brighter than the other.

Aggregation by increased rate of turning

If on entering an unfavourable zone an animal begins to turn more frequently the chance of it re-entering a favoured area will be greater. Then, once back in a more favourable area, it will turn less and move through the area to another boundary. On crossing the boundary, turning increases once more and the animal turns back again. This increased rate of turning is called 'high klinokinesis' as opposed to simple increase in speed or 'high orthokinesis'.[177] The two are usually combined so that when an animal shows high klinokinesis it also shows high orthokinesis, both kinetic effects reinforcing each other.

A classic example is the gathering of planarian worms in darkness. When *Dendrocoelum lacteum* is moving in uniform conditions with no stimulus acting on it to direct it in any way, for example, when the water is still and the lighting is diffuse so that the direction of light rays can have no effect, it turns only occasionally. Its rate of turning measured as number of degrees of turn to either right or left in one minute remains fairly constant. But when the intensity of the light is increased the rate of turning also increases for a time but gradually decreases to its original level[536] (Fig. 20). This decrease is due to adaption of the eyes to the new conditions. Perhaps the change in rate happens because the photochemical effect on the eyes increases when the light intensity increases stimulating the optic nerve and, by way of this, the rest of the nervous system. Adaptation occurs when a new equilibrium is set up.

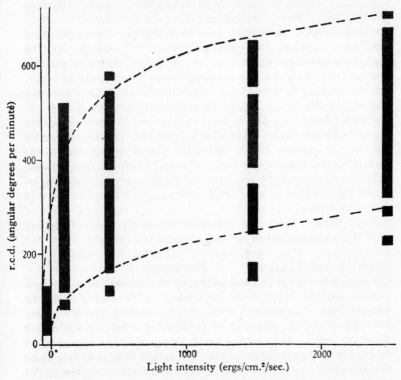

FIG. 20. Relationship between the intensity of light and the rate of change of direction of *Dendrocoelum lacteum* (Ullyott[536]).

Without adaptation the animals would perhaps become evenly distributed between light and dark, for on leaving the shade some might turn back into it by chance but, similarly, others will turn away. The latter will then follow a very tortuous track in the light and may be trapped there. But if, after a time, adaptation occurs and they begin to turn less often, their chances of returning into the dark will be increased. Though such a series of reactions gives the appearance of being directed towards the shade, in fact, the final course is based upon random movements each of which is undirected.

A special case of such klinokinetic behaviour is the shock reaction, or avoiding reaction, shown when an animal turns violently at the boundary between favourable and unfavourable areas. As such it has been observed in many invertebrates but in most it has not received such detailed analysis as that of the movements of *Dendrocoelum lacteum*. In general, an abrupt change of environmental conditions, such as a steep rise in light intensity, brings about an abrupt change in the rate of turning. When the advancing pseudopodium of an amoeba, for example, enters a brilliantly lit patch, say, the circle of light cast by a microscope mirror onto a slide, the animal stops.[286] New pseudopodia are put out near the base of the one which has halted and if one of these does not enter a lighted area the amoeba moves off in its direction. The abrupt halt is probably due to gelation of the tip of the pseudopodium which will prevent further extension in that direction.[363] This is a direct photochemical effect without the intervention of other mechanisms, as might be expected in an animal such as this without a complex system of organelles.

Some ciliates show this behaviour strikingly. As *Paramecium* sp.,[286] for example, swims forward rotating and gyrating on its long axis, it may pass over the border dividing the favourable area in which it travelled in straight lines into an unfavourable area, as, for example, when an individual swims from shadow into a patch of ultra-violet light. When it does so it turns violently usually heading into the dark once more. Should it still remain in the light it will halt and reverse the direction of its ciliary beat moving backwards a short distance. It halts once again, turns and moves forward once more. The new path followed after the retreat does not seem to be chosen in any way for the angle through which the animal turns and the direction in which it does so seems to be random. Though it does appear, that once a turn has been made in a particular direction, the subsequent turns will also be to the same side. This behaviour gives the appearance of an animal trying a particular direction and correcting its error if it is misled, thus it was called 'trial and error' behaviour, but probably the terms 'shock reaction' or 'avoiding reaction' are more in keeping with modern ideas upon objective terminology. Though it is often considered as a special case of klinokinesis, this behaviour is more complex as it involves a complete reversal of direction before the animal turns; it would not seem to be strictly comparable with the simpler increase in rate of turning.

Paramecium bursaria is the only species of *Paramecium* which shows such reaction to visible light, but all species react to ultraviolet rays.[246]

The strength of the stimulation determines the form of the evolutions which a ciliate performs. With milder stimulation it merely comes to a stop and turns in the way just described (Fig. 21). But if the stimulation is greatly increased the animal gyrates on its posterior end in an exaggerated form of the gyrations it performs as it moves forwards. As it turns it generally moves with its aboral side towards the outside of its revolution (Fig. 21). As the stimulating effect increases it tends to swerve more violently towards the aboral side until ultimately it is swinging round in a flat path with its hind end towards the centre.[286] (Fig. 21).

Stentor caeruleus is another ciliate with very similar reactions to light. As with *Paramecium*, it is the anterior oral side which is most sensitive and, in the same way, as the light intensity is increased, it swerves strongly to the aboral side increasing the diameter of its swing.[285, 355] Finally when the intensity is too great, it stops, backs and turns. Such a simple random behaviour can produce the appearance of a truly directed reaction under certain conditions. For example, if a *Stentor* is approaching a light beam, its normal rotation about its long axis will expose the oral and aboral sides to the light alternately as it enters the beam. Since exposure of the oral side causes increased swerving to the aboral, and, in this position, the 'downbeam' side, while the alternate exposure of the aboral surface produces no response, the animal will turn away from the light and move down the beam. The directive response towards the light of *Euglena* can be explained in this way also. In this case the sensitive part is restricted to a small nodule near the base of the flagellum (Fig. 1A). This appears to be sensitive to light from all directions. But on the so-called dorsal side of the animal is a small pigment spot which shields the eye-spot. Thus, the dorsal side is the blind side and the ventral side the seeing side. The test of the function of these structures is to allow the animal to swim towards a light and then to switch on another beam to strike it at right angles to the first, at the same time the original light is switched off. The animal moves towards the light rotating about its own long axis in a spiral, its dorsal surface on the outside of the spiral. When the second light is switched on its reaction depends upon the point in its spiral path at which it is illuminated. If it is a positively phototactic animal and if the light strikes the ventral side first, there is no

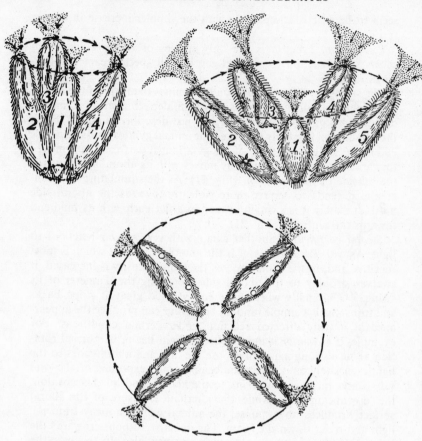

FIG. 21. Avoiding reactions of *Paramecium*. Above left, weak avoiding
reaction, the anterior end swinging round in a small circle. Above
right, more pronounced reaction. Below, strong reaction when
revolution about the longitudinal axis ceases completely. The anterior end swings about a circle of which the body forms a radius.
(Successive positions are numbered) (Jennings[286]).

change in its direction. But, as it turns, the pigmented cup is brought
round to shade the eye-spot. The result of the decrease in illumination
of the spot is a bend towards the dorsal side, i.e. towards the light
(Fig. 22). When *Euglena* is crawling, it also rotates but with its ventral side outermost, decrease in illumination causes a bend to the
ventral side; it is not easy to see how this bending away from the
light can result in a path curving round towards the light until

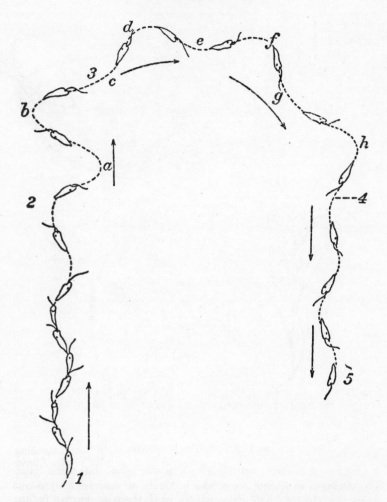

FIG. 22. Re-orientation of *Euglena* when swimming. From 1 to 2, light
from the top of the page; at 2, direction of light reversed. Each time
the receptor is shielded by the eyespot, the organism swerves to the
dorsal side. Consequently it becomes reorientated after a few turns
round the spiral (Jennings[286]).

ultimately the animal is moving directly up the beam (Fig. 23).
On the other hand, relatively little is known about the mechanics
of the crawling movement so that the effect of the bending cannot
be judged; there is no doubt that the path turns to the light.

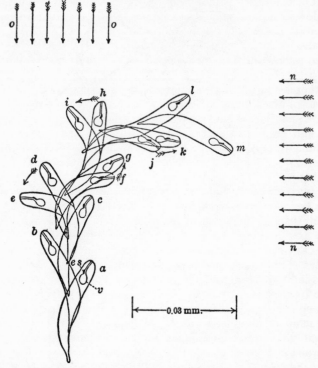

FIG. 23. Re-orientation of *Euglena* when crawling. When the organism is
at *c*, the light *o* is switched off and *n* is switched on (Mast[358]).

REACTIONS TO SHADOWS

A number of animals will react to shadows which fall upon them.
The decrease in illumination which occurs at successive moments
when the shadow boundary passes over them seems to be the
stimulus. Very often they retract themselves into their coverings or
contract up, extreme cases of avoidance. They do not expand
again until they are no longer stimulated by the flicker of passing
shadows. They behave in the same way when they are illuminated
less strongly but they often do not react to an increase in illumination.
They recover if they are left in the shadow after a lapse of time. So
that the rate of decrease in light intensity, rather than the lowered
intensity itself, seems to be responsible for the stimulation. Slow
decreases in brightness do not have the same effect. These reactions

should be contrasted with those in which the animal moves towards a shadow or a dark patch, the stimulus is then a spatial difference in intensity rather than a temporal one.

Bivalve molluscs such as the clams, *Mya arenaria*,[234] or the mussel, *Mytilus edulis*, withdraw their siphons or foot and close their shells when a shadow passes over them. Similarly barnacles will retract their thoracic cirri.[164] It is not necessary for a shadow to fall upon the eyes of a snail (*Helix pomatia*) to cause it to withdraw into its shell.[164] *Culex* larvae hanging from the surface film of a pond break away and swim downwards when a shadow passes over them. Sabellid and serpulid marine worms living in tubes projecting from the bottom spend much of their time with the tentacular crown extended to feed by ciliary currents. They withdraw into the tube if the intensity of the light is suddenly decreased, indeed, *Branchiomma vesiculosum* in weak light is sensitive to a decrease of only 0·3 metre candle. In this worm, the reaction to a decrease of intensity wanes as the animal becomes rapidly adapted. However, the reaction to shadows disappears less rapidly on repetition of the stimulus.[398] Shadows would seem in all these cases to be token stimuli of possible predators and the reaction to be a protective one of escape from potential danger. The importance of having a system which adapts rapidly to mere changes of intensity unaccompanied by the temporal and spatial components inherent in moving shadows is manifest for water movements and other events not potentially dangerous may cause changes in illumination. It may be that the extra components of the stimulus which are present in a moving shadow make each shadow unique, since each will not only cause a particular decrease of intensity, but this will occur over a definite period, either quickly or slowly, and at particular points on the tentacular crown. This renders the likelihood of becoming adapted to a shadow stimulus small as a particular shadow stimulus is unlikely to be repeated.

On the other hand shadows may arouse animals from inactivity. This is true of various parasites of aquatic animals which themselves live in water. Hungry leeches (e.g. *Theromyzon tessulatum* (= *Protoclepsis tesselata*))[249] lying at the bottom of a pond will swim upwards when the intensity of the light falling on them suddenly drops. Similarly, the larvae of some trematode worms rest on the bottom of ponds until they react to the onset of shadows by swimming upwards.[374] In all these cases the reactions are not directed with precision, that is the *Culex* larvae swim generally downwards but not exactly vertically downwards; again, the trematodes swim upwards but not in any exact direction. There does appear to be some evidence, however, that the leeches do swim towards the dark object causing the shadow.

The extent to which the intensity must be reduced varies with the species. *Pecten* will close after a drop of 0·3 %,[228] *Helix pomatia* 18 %[164] and *Mya* 60 %.[311] It does not seem that the sense organs involved are always the eyes. They are responsible in mosquitoes and scallops but the most sensitive part of the snail seems not to be its head or tail but the front edge of the mantle cavity roof; its foot is completely insensitive. The sensitivity varies with all these species according to the frequency with which the animal is stimulated. After two or three stimuli close together in time the reaction fades for a long period, indicating that adaptation is rapid.

MOVEMENT TOWARDS OR AWAY FROM LIGHT

In none of the responses which have been dealt with so far has the movement been directed towards or away from the source of light. Random movements have brought the animals into light conditions which are more favourable. Only in the case of leeches' movements towards shadows has there been any indication that the source of the stimulus acts as a beacon (a spatially arranged intensity difference). They are probably explicable as examples of simple form vision rather than negative phototaxis, as we shall see (p. 65). In all the other cases the animals have wandered until they have found themselves under those conditions which tend to alter their speed or rate of turning so that they are effectively trapped there. But many responses are to the direction of the rays of the light and animals showing them move more or less directly towards the light if they are positively phototactic, and away from it if they are negatively phototactic. Since these are directed movements they are known as taxes, as opposed to the undirected kineses.

While the random movements of ortho- and klino-kineses can be performed by animals with a generalized light sense receiving and perceiving light stimulation from all directions, movement towards a light source requires sense organs which receive the rays from one direction only, or over a narrow sector. Typically an eye has a pigmented backing which prevents the sensitive cells within the cup of pigment from being stimulated by any rays other than those entering the opening. But even organs sensitive to stimulation from all directions may function as a directional receiver if the body of the animal is opaque and shades the sensitive part at times. This will be less efficient and the path traced out a less direct one. An example is the case of an animal with a sensitive head end which moves away from light, it will move down the beam away from the source once it has reached a position parallel to the beam, for its head will then be shaded by the mass of its body behind it.

This type of receptor is often found in those animals which move along a zig-zag path as they orient themselves. The reactions of *Stentor* when it enters a horizontal beam of light have already been mentioned. As it turns about its long axis the sensitive side of the body is alternately stimulated by the light and shaded by the rest of the body. Whenever it is stimulated the whole animal turns towards the unstimulated side. The result of a number of these small avoidance turns is to guide the animal down the beam. In this position the sensitive areas are no longer stimulated as they are shaded by the hind end of the body. Similar considerations apply to the orientation of *Paramecium*.

And a very similar explanation can be applied to the negatively phototactic movement of the tadpole larvae of the ascidian, *Amaroucium pellucidum*.[361] Here again the sensitive area is set asymmetrically in the body so that as the animal swims forward the spot is alternately illuminated and shaded by the body, for it also turns upon its long axis as it swims.

The light sensitive cells in the head of Muscid larvae are borne in two pockets, one on either side of the condylar spine of pharyngeal skeleton. In this position the body and the skeleton occlude light which does not fall from directly in front.[54] (Fig. 24).

The behaviour of these grubs in moving away from light has many similarities to the activities of *Euglena* and *Amaroucium*. It is best shown by larvae which are in the fully fed condition awaiting pupation for at this time they are markedly negatively phototactic. The demonstration is even more effective if the larvae are left in the dark for some hours before being used, they will then be dark-adapted. When they are placed in a light beam they turn to head away from the source down the beam. When their movements are closely examined they can be seen to move by a wave of extension which passes up their bodies from the hind end after it has fixed itself down. This wave passes to the head which is lifted and stretched out to one side of the body before swinging back to the midline and attaching itself in turn, the rest of the body then being drawn up and the whole cycle repeated. The head extends to alternate sides and, between times, is withdrawn into the body, being tele-scoped into the thoracic segments, so that the movements are: extension to one side, withdrawal, and then extension to the other side and withdrawal again. The head waving is initiated by illuminating the maggot. The result is that the path which it follows down the beam is not straight but rather a zig-zag.

It is possible to analyse the orientation further by shining another beam horizontally at right angles to the original one. When the maggot enters the new beam and the other is switched off its ultimate path is at right angles to the one it had been following, crawling down the new beam. But the immediate reaction to the new stimulus depends upon which side the head is pointing when the light is switched on. If it is pointing towards the new light, and, therefore, is illuminated at once, the anterior end of the body is swung violently over to the opposite side away from the light. If, however, the head happens to be swinging away from the light and is sufficiently far

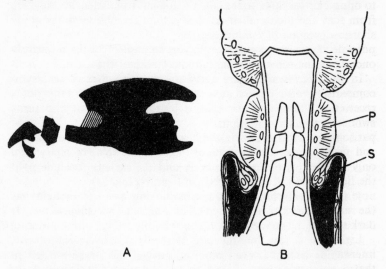

A   B

Fig. 24. A, the pharyngeal skeleton of *Musca*, the pocket in which the light-sensitive cells lie is shaded. B, horizontal section of the head and skeleton showing the light-sensitive cells, S, and the prismatic layer, P, (after Bolwig[54]).

over for the receptors to be completely shaded, no reaction occurs until it stretches to the light when the same violent swing back occurs. This is an avoidance reaction, very similar to the strong bending of *Euglena* to the dorsal side when the ventral side is illuminated. The result is that each time the head is stimulated as it swings out there will be a counterswing in the other direction until the maggot is turned down beam, the light receptors are then shaded by the rest of the body unless it deviates from the path down the beam again. Also in this position the receptors will be equally stimulated on both sides if they are swung far enough out to leave the body's shadow. That the body does shade the sensitive area is proved by the immediate counterswing when a strong light beam is shone from one side. Then, whatever position the head is occupying, it is turned away from the light immediately. This is because even if the body is shielding the head the light is strong enough to penetrate it and stimulate the sensitive areas. If a maggot is allowed to crawl on a surface illuminated by a dim light with a brighter light also arranged to shine on it when a switch is pressed, it will continue in a straight line until the bright light is flashed on. If the flashes are timed so that they occur whenever the head swings over to one particular side, the maggot will crawl in a circle turning away from that side. After a time, however, its head is moved through shorter distances and, therefore, faster and faster, so that it is not possible to continue synchronizing the flashes.[214] This demonstrates once again the role of the head movements in orientation.

In *Euglena*, *Amaroucium* and *Lucilia* alike, there is clearly a comparison being carried out between the amount of stimulation received on the sides of the body, all the way round in the spiralling swimmers and to left and right of the fly larvae. Since these comparisons are successive in time there must be some rudimentary and probably shortlived memory. It may be that this memory is only a matter of the persistence of chemical substances released in the light-sensitive cells by the light stimulus. But it is interesting to note that in between the comparison to one side and the other by the maggot there must be a time when its head is completely in the dark when it is withdrawn into the body.

Light beams can be arranged to point at each other and the intensity of each made to vary independently. A maggot so placed that it was equally illuminated on both sides would move forward along an approximately straight line. The two stimuli are apparently compared simultaneously in this case, perhaps because the intensities of light used were sufficient to affect the sense cells withdrawn into the pharyngeal skeleton, through the body wall. If the lights were of unequal intensity then it steered a course which deviated towards the weaker light by an angle proportional to the difference in strength of the two beams. So that when the ratio of the two lights was 3 : 4 the deflection was 8·86°, while when one was half as strong as the other, a ratio of 2 : 1, the deflection was 20·28°, both figures being an average of observations taken at five different absolute intensities of the stronger light.[424]

Orientation which involves pendular movements, testing the amount of stimulation coming from each side of the body, is called klinotaxis.[177] It is possible, however, that an animal's path towards the light may be fairly direct, at least, more so than would be that of an animal which is orientating by klinotaxis. Usually this type of path is found where the animal has two eyes. It may result from constant comparison of the strength of the stimulation received on both of the eyes. That both must play their part can be proved by blinding the animal unilaterally when, if both eyes are important for orientation, it may begin to move round in circles, towards the blinded side if it is negatively phototactic and to the seeing side if it is positively phototactic. When such proof that the two eyes are necessary is forthcoming, the behaviour is known as tropotaxis.[177] If, however, after blinding, the animal still goes towards or away from the light as directly as before, one eye being clearly sufficient and comparison unnecessary, the reaction is telotaxis.

It might be supposed that orientation by comparison of the stimulation of the two eyes arises from the different amount of stimulation passing to the muscles of the two sides so that compensatory movements are made until the two eyes are equally stimulated and the impulses leaving them are balanced. Almost certainly the background of such behaviour is not as simple as this. The action is not through simple increased or decreased tonus of the muscles, for the movements for correcting the position may be very variable, quite unlike the stereotyped ones to be expected on the simpler hypothesis.

To produce the best orientation the visual fields of the two eyes should overlap in front. If the eyes are set far round to the side so that the fields do not overlap, then the 'straight' course in the light beam will become wavy since the animal will be able to deviate quite considerably before an eye is stimulated to start a compensating reaction. When an uneven path of this sort is observed, it is necessary to apply other tests to determine whether the animal is performing a tropotaxis or a klinotaxis.

It has been claimed that unfed ticks would move towards the light when illuminated laterally from a window, or by artificial light. Under these conditions the tracks were wavy at first, the animal apparently performing klinokinetic movements; later the track straightened, until finally it became quite straight as they moved towards the light, a change from klinokinesis to klinotaxis and finally to tropotaxis.[528] But this has not been confirmed by later work. This has shown no positive reaction in young unfed ticks, a month after moulting, indeed, they are strongly repelled by light, as are also engorged ticks of any age (Fig. 25). Ticks one year after moulting are less sensitive and move up a beam of intense light (Fig. 25) but females also crawl across the beam so that the direction of the rays seems, in fact, not to play an essential part. Both unfed and engorged ticks move in a more direct manner than was originally stated and they seem to be moving tropotactically. However, the power of engorged ticks to compensate for turns from

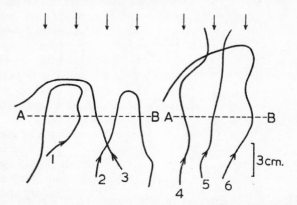

FIG. 25. Response of ticks to light. Tracks of unfed females walking on a flat horizontal surface dimly lit from above. On crossing the line AB the intense horizontal light is switched on. Nos. 1–3, females 1 month after moulting; nos. 4–6, unfed females 1 year after moulting (after Lees[329]).

the direct line away from the light was very poor, on occasion individuals diverged by as much as 160° before swerving back, but other individuals only deviated by 10°[329] (Fig. 26).

Gaps in the all-round coverage of the visual field by the eyes of *Ephestia kühniella* larvae are also responsible for deviation from accurate orientation. This flour moth caterpillar is negatively phototactic.[61] Its eyes are two groups of six ocelli, one on either side of its head. Light from behind the caterpillar in an area covered by an angle of 40° centred on the insect's axis is shaded from the eyes by the body. So the path which it follows when illuminated from behind is not always exactly downbeam (Fig. 27). When the variations of a number of individuals was measured it was found that about 40% of them were correct to within 5° of the line of the beam.

When one of these caterpillars is blinded on one side its behaviour depends upon the way in which it is illuminated. In a horizontal beam it crawls in a gradual curve towards the blind side, that is away from the stimulation as it is negatively phototactic, until the blinded eye is towards the light source when the uncovered eye will

c

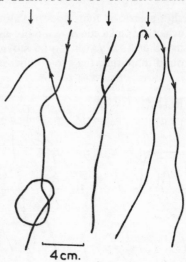

FIG. 26. Tracks of engorged nymphs orientating to a bright light (after Lees[329]).

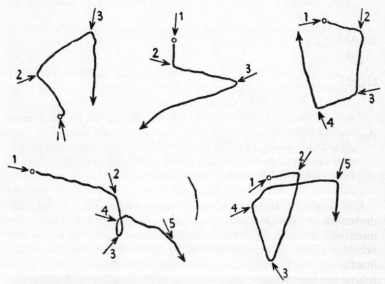

FIG. 27. Tracks of *Ephestia* larvae away from the light. Each track starts from a small circle, with a light from the direction shown by the arrow (1). When the animal reached a point on the track indicated by the arrow (2), the first light was switched off and the new light from the new direction (2) is switched on, and so forth (from Fraenkel and Gunn,[177] after Brandt[61]).

be shaded by the body and the light does not stimulate the animal any further. But when it is placed in an arena with white walls lit from above so that the illumination on all sides is approximately equal, it crawls round in circles, the typical circus movement (Fig. 28).

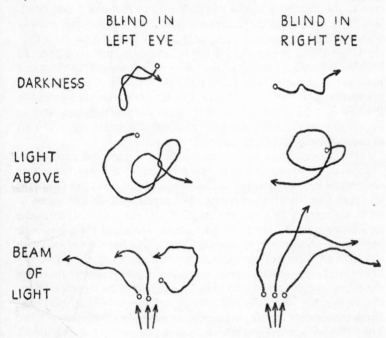

FIG. 28. Tracks of photo-negative *Ephestia* larvae blinded on one side, each track starting at the small circle and ending at the arrow head. The straight arrows below indicate the direction of the light for the adjacent tracks only (from Fraenkel and Gunn[177] and Brandt[61]).

If it is placed midway between two lights of equal intensity it moves away following a path between the two beams. But if the intensities differ, it turns towards the dimmer light so that its path becomes closer to the line of the stronger beam. Once again the inaccuracy due to the blind spot behind shows itself for only 55% follow the intermediate path between two equal lights to within an accuracy of $\pm 5°$.

We shall see later how the various reactions of the woodlouse, *Armadillidium*, serve to keep it in places where the conditions are most favourable for it (p. 321). One of these is its negative reaction to light, but on occasion, such as when it is starved or desiccated, the sign of the reaction is reversed so that temporarily at least it becomes positively phototactic.[238] When these positive individuals are blinded on one side they perform similar manoeuvres to those of *Ephestia* caterpillars. But, whereas in the arena the caterpillars turn to the blinded side, the woodlice turn to the seeing side. Similarly, in a horizontal beam striking them head on, they move away from the light across the beam, going to the left if their right eyes are blinded and to the right if the other eye is varnished over. In both cases they are turning to the seeing side as they do in the arena but this takes them away from the light.[390] In darkness both the caterpillars and the woodlice are disorientated whether one eye is covered or not, this confirms that the circling movements and so on are due to the light and not some disturbances in another part of their systems caused by the operation.

Circus movements of some animals, however, are not permanent. They occur immediately after being placed in a beam but wane, the circuits becoming wider and less frequent until they are following an approximately straight course. The explanation of this seems to lie in differences between the parts of the eye, certainly in some insects the ommatidia of one part cause turning to their own side and those of another to the opposite side. But combined with qualitative differences are quantitative differences in the sensitivity of the parts, apparently partly central and partly peripheral, from the effect of light adaptation. The backswimmer *Notonecta* demonstrates this for when blinded on one side an individual performs circus movements when crawling, out of water, in a horizontal beam. The path becomes straight after a number of turns[97] (Fig. 29) though this effect disappears if the insect is put in the dark. If the animal was completely dark-adapted, having been kept in the dark for a time, the circus movements did not disappear for some 48 minutes, after which the animal crawled towards the light along a fairly straight path. The time taken to eliminate the circles depended on the time that the animal had been in the light and not on having moved about, for if it was fixed down in the light immediately after being taken from the dark and then released to crawl, the time for the path to become straight depended on the length of time it had been exposed light so that the sum of the two times was about 50 minutes. For example, when held down for 10, 20, 30, 40 and 50 minutes, the times required subsequently for the disappearance of the circles was 34, 18, 18, 7 and 1 minute respectively.

The role this plays with regard to the quantitative differences in the turning movements called forth by different optical areas were

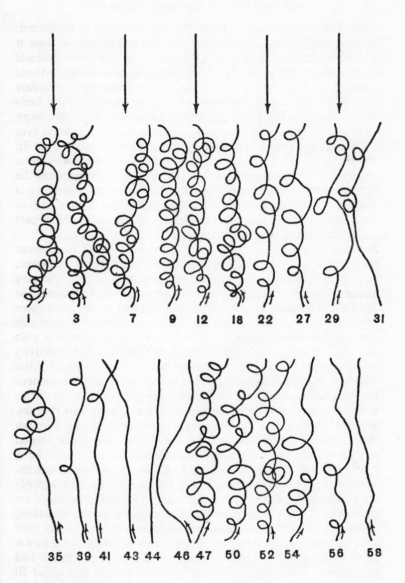

FIG. 29. Circus movements of a unilaterally blinded *Notonecta* in horizontal light. The track gradually straightened out in the course of successive trials 1–46, path 47 shows re-appearance of circus movements after a further period of 15 minutes in darkness, the tracks then straightened out once more (Clark[97]).

well shown in the whirligig beetle, *Dineutes assimilis*,[98] whose eye is divided into a dorsal and a ventral part. When a unilaterally blinded beetle is placed in a light beam it performs circus movements which carry it diagonally across the beam, unlike *Notonecta* which travels towards the light. But gradually its path becomes straighter until, after a few minutes, it travels straight across the beam turning towards the source when it reaches the further edge along the boundary. If the light intensity is increased as it is crawling straight, it turns away from the source and takes up a new direction. On a decrease, however, it turns towards the light. Both these reactions are unexpected in a photopositive insect. But they can be explained if the forward pointing ommatidia initiate turning to the opposite side and the lateral, posterior and ventral ommatidia initiate turns to their own side.[98] So that when the illumination is increased more of the posterior and ventral segments, hitherto dimly lit by reflection, are brought into action causing a turn to their own side, away from the light. When the light decreases, however, these are stimulated no longer and the forward pointing ommatidia take over control swinging the insect round towards the opposite side, that is, towards the light. The same effects are produced if the beetle crawls on a reflecting surface and crosses the boundary between one surface and another which is ten times more or less reflecting than the original. On a surface from which less light is reflected it turns towards the light, as it does when the light itself is diminished. And when the surface reflects more light its behaviour is the same as if the illumination intensity had been increased.

The elimination of the circus movements must arise from the adaptation of the posterior and ventral ommatidia in the light so that their sensitivity decreases and they no longer impose such strong turning movements. On a black non-reflecting surface the posterior ommatidia are not stimulated and the beetle can crawl directly towards the light. Here a balance will be struck between the forward ommatidia and those of the lateral ones which are stimulated. The sensitivity of the posterior ommatidia is shown by the occasional circus movements which the insect performs when a 2 cm. square piece of white card is held at right angles to the beam and 3 metres away behind the insect. At 10 cms. such a card causes continuous circling.[98]

If the beetle is allowed to crawl in a light beam over a glass plate illuminated from below, an increase in the beam intensity by a factor of ten, which is offset by a decrease in the illumination from below, causes no change in the beetle's path. Under these conditions the stimulation of the posterior and ventral ommatidia will remain constant despite the increased illumination in the beam. The sensitivity of the lower part of the eye is undoubtedly greater than that of the rest of the eye.

That this differentiation in sensitivity and resulting reaction of the ommatidia is not fixed was indicated by other experiments on *Notonecta*. It might be expected that an insect with one whole eye and the posterior part of the other covered would make circus movements to the totally blind side under the influence of the anterior ommatidia of the other side. Though this mainly occurs, it is not inevitable, some insects being able to make their way directly towards the light source. An explanation as rigid as that set out above is probably only a half-truth, there being, in fact, a far greater central plasticity, as work on other insects would also suggest (p. 58).

The effect on the sensitivity of the eye of exposure to light has been shown in planarians.[55] Lights were arranged around the dish in which the animal was so that its left side could be kept continuously illuminated by switching on the appropriate light and extinguishing the others. After this treatment, when the lights at the side were replaced by uniform illumination from above, the worm crawled in circles towards the left. The left eye had become light adapted and less sensitive than the right so that the right eye initiated a stronger turning movement when it was illuminated.

The eye of the drone fly, *Eristalis tenax*, is also divided in function and sensitivity.[152, 362] The posterior and lateral ommatidia cause turning to their own side while those lying in the anterior part of the eye against its anterior border turn the insect to the contrary side when they are stimulated. The anterior median elements cover an area which overlaps with that covered by similarly placed elements in the other eye while the lateral and posterior ones cover the visual field to the side. Between the two lie ommatidia which point straight forward. The behaviour of *Eristalis* is mixed, for, when it is blinded unilaterally, it may perform circus movements in an arena lit from above. Further it orientates itself between two lights provided that they are close enough to each other; both reactions could be described as tropotaxis. Yet it may go straight to a light after unilateral blinding which shows that at least on occasion orientation can occur by the use of one eye only. Now it is clear that if the ommatidia are qualitatively differentiated in the way that has been mentioned such behaviour could arise by the functioning of the one eye. For, while the lateral ommatidia controlled the reactions to light falling from the side, the medial anterior ones would observe the light on the other side of the insect. Orientation occurs by a balance between the stimulation of the two parts. There is also a quantitative difference for the amount of light required to stimulate the anterior ommatidia is fifty times as great as that required to stimulate the most posterior (Fig. 30). This means that at maximum deflection from the correct path, which will be when the light falls on the posterior ommatidia, there is maximum reaction to turn the insect into the light. This physiological differentiation is not, however, fixed, for if the fly's head is turned through

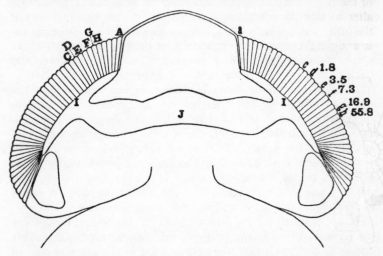

Fig. 30. Diagrammatic horizontal section through the head of *Eristalis*. Pairs of letters show which ommatidia are stimulated by two beams crossing at right-angles; thus C is stimulated by one light and c by the other. The numbers show the relative sensitivities as indicated by the experiments of Dolley and Wierda; thus h is 55·8 times as sensitive as H. I, retina; J, brain (after Dolley and Wierda[152]).

180° and fixed, its reactions in a light beam indicate that the fixation area now lies at the back of the eye (Fig. 31).[384] Also electrophysiological studies do not indicate that there are differences in sensitivity at points on the eye.[11] Thus the differentiation which has been postulated to account for the results of the experiments must be a central process.

Such behaviour in which there is a balance struck between the stimulation of the sense organs on the two sides is, as has been pointed out, tropotaxis, here we have, however, orientation in which one eye is sufficient. When there is apparently no necessity for a comparison of stimulation on the two sides the behaviour can be called telotaxis. It is marked by an ability to orientate to light with one eye only and by the animal going straight to one of the lights when presented with two lights.[177] Provided that the lights are near enough *Eristalis* does not ignore one of them but proceeds between them.[362] When the lights are far enough apart, however, for the light from one of them not to fall on the eye when the insect is orientated to move to the other light, the fly appears to be showing telotaxis. However, truly telotactic behaviour includes ignoring one of the two lights at any one time. The preference for one light may alter so that the animal goes first towards one and then towards the other but it is only orientating to one of them at once; its path is a zig-zag, not a resultant based on the relative strengths of the

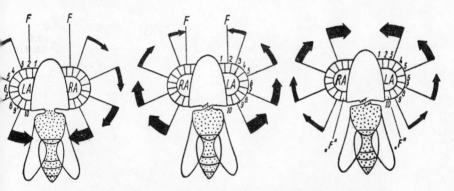

FIG. 31. Diagrams to demonstrate the effect of rotating the head of *Eristalis* through 180°. Left, the classical picture of the effect of stimulation of different ommatidia. Centre, the result of rotating the head if the classical picture still held. Right, the actual result of the operation. The arrows indicate the direction, and their thickness the relative strength, of the turning induced by stimulation of the particular part of the eye. F and 'F' are the fixation areas. LA and RA, left and right eye, respectively. (Mittelstaedt[384]).

lights. A honeybee moving towards one light continues to do so if another light is placed near it, though the second light must stimulate ommatidia in one of its eyes.[537]. Indeed while a crab is moving towards one light, its antennules may be beating in the direction of the second—an indication that the animal is perceiving the light though it is not moving towards it.[7] (Fig. 32).

Let us consider the behaviour of an animal which shows almost the theoretically expected behaviour. Set down before two lights in a dark room a bee will crawl towards one of them. Its initial direction may not be maintained for, though it may set off towards one, it

may turn later to the other. If the two lights are of equal intensity
it is as likely to crawl to one as to the other but when they are of
different strengths it crawls to the strongest. When the bees are
unilaterally blinded and placed in a horizontal light beam they
begin to circle towards the seeing side, but, after fifteen trials at ten
to twenty minute intervals with the same bee, it begins to go straight

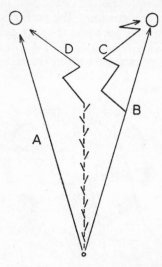

FIG. 32. Two-light experiment using a photopositive animal, *Eupagurus
bernhardus*. A and B, the crab ran to left and right lamp, respectively.
C, the crab went towards the right-hand lamp at first, but later changed
direction several times, heading towards the left lamp occasionally,
before reaching the right lamp. D, the crab followed a course towards
a point midway between the lamps but later followed a zig-zag path.
The short lines indicate the directions in which the antennules were
waved (from Alverdes[7]).

to the light[378] (Fig. 33). The initial turning is not that of a theoretical
telotaxis and is probably due to the great sensitivity of the dark-
adapted posterior ommatidia. It has been suggested that the conditions of the experiments were not ideal and that some light was
reflected into the hindermost ommatidia producing an imbalance
and hence circling as in *Dineutes*. For the same reasons as the beetle
the circling stops after a time.

A bee with one eye covered circles towards the seeing side when
put in a beam but soon becomes capable of moving directly up the
beam. This capability resides in one eye which, in fact, seems to be
differentiated in a manner similar to that already described for the

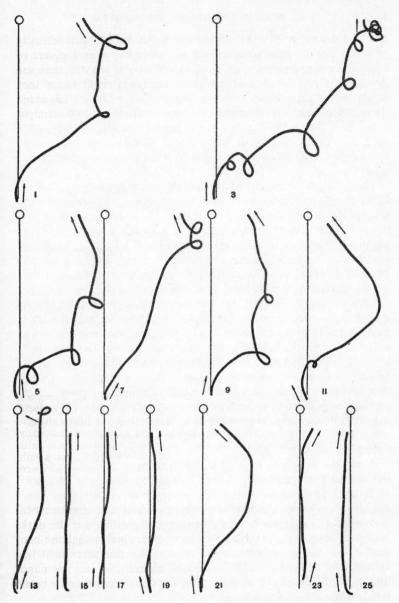

FIG. 33. Paths of a unilaterally blinded honeybee moving towards a light source (O) in a horizontal beam, selected from a series of trials. The circus movements to the right in the first few tracks are later gradually eliminated and the animal eventually walks directly towards the light (Minnich[378]).

eye of *Eristalis* (p. 57). As the bee can move straight with one eye
only, no balance of turning effects of the two eyes is apparently
necessary and a fixation area must exist. But the bee differs from
Eristalis for if it is confronted with two lights it may proceed towards one of them while *Eristalis* always takes the course between
them along which the illumination received from the two sources
is balanced. The behaviour of a bee is more efficient if it is telotactic
for then it can go to its goal, say, a flower instead of flying between
two neighbouring flowers as it might do if it behaved tropotactically
only.

There are other examples of animals which ignore one of two
lights. Peracarid crustaceans *Hemimysis lamornae*, will swim towards
a light shone into the side of their tank.[175] They swim along the
beam for about 10 cms. then turn the head away from the light for
about the same distance before turning to the light again. They
continue to shuttle backwards and forwards in the beam. If a second
beam is arranged to shine at right angles to the first, some of the
mysids change their beams and start moving along the new one. The
remainder stay in the original one but none of them take up an
intermediate course. So, in the rapid alternation of negative and
positive phototaxis, each individual ignores the light beam in which
it is not swimming. Since the two eyes must be stimulated by both
lights the inhibition must be a central process. Similarly, there must
be inhibition of the unwanted stimuli in the honey bee. Though the
disregarded light will stimulate ommatidia towards the posterior of
one eye only it seems likely that there is inhibition of all impulses
arising from that eye. This seems more likely than the inhibition of
the stimuli arising only from the posterior ommatidia which are
facing the unwanted light.

A number of species have been shown to have the ability to pick
out one of two lights and go only to that one. In many of them,
such as hermit crabs,[76] starfishes and gastropod molluscs, e.g.
Nassarius (= *Nassa*), individuals may start by taking a path midway between the lights but they usually swing off to one of them
sooner or later (Fig. 34). However, some individuals maintain their
middle way and pass between the lights. It is clear that the same
animal may behave tropotactically and telotactically but the conditions which decide upon the characteristics of its behaviour are
not known.

THE SELECTION OF BRIGHTNESS

Under normal conditions photonegative animals moving down a
beam away from the source are moving down a gradient of intensity

and following the direction of the light rays. Whether the gradient or the direction is the most important is, therefore, not immediately clear. But experimental conditions can be arranged so that following the beam leads into brighter conditions bringing about a conflict which is not normally present. A broad strip of wood placed horizontally across the middle of a window can be arranged to shade part of a table within the room so that the direct rays of sunlight fall only on the inner end of the table and diffuse light from the sky

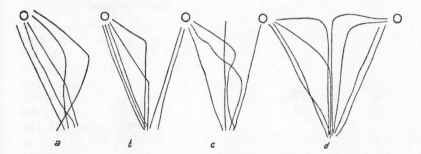

FIG. 34. Paths of a number of animals moving towards two lights of equal intensity. a, *Oerstadia dorsalis*; b, *Asterias rubens*; c, *Nassarius incrassatus*; d, *Armadillidium* (von Buddenbrock[80]).

illuminates the end nearest the window[337] (Fig. 35). A test tube containing fly maggots is placed on the table with the maggots at the window end lit by the diffuse light from the lower half of the window while the other end of the tube lies in direct sunlight. The maggots crawl away from the window, that is, they move down the gradient of light intensity, until they reach the shadow edge where a considerable increase in brightness occurs. At the boundary they hesitate swinging from side to side more violently than before. If their heads swing back into the shade they turn round and crawl back against the gradient. This only happens to comparatively few and the rest continue on and aggregate in the most brilliantly lit part, an unusual place for photonegative animals.

Another way of arranging the conflict is to use a convergent beam of light. Planktonic animals,[502] and termites,[456] have been tested in this way. In every case whether the animal was photopositive or negative they moved along the beam towards, or away from, the source, as appropriate, despite the apparently unfavourable light conditions into which such movements brought them (Fig. 36).

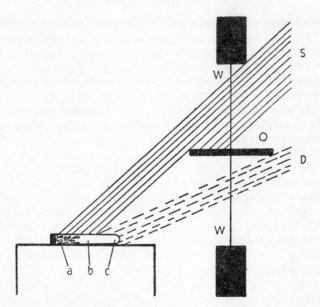

FIG. 35. Diagram to illustrate Loeb's classic experiments in which the direction of the light illuminating fly maggots was made to oppose the intensity gradient. The maggots moved from c to a away from the direction of the light rays, but collecting in the more brightly lit area at a. abc, tube containing the maggots; D, diffuse light from the sky; S, direct sunlight: O, opaque strip of wood (Fraenkel and Gunn[177]).

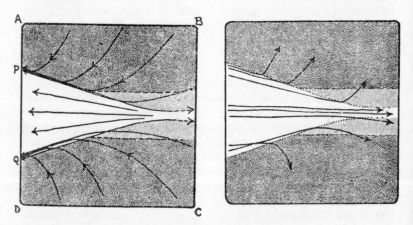

FIG. 36. Paths of planktonic organisms in convergent beams. Left, mean direction of those animals which move in the direction of the rays. ABCD, square dish; PQ, entrance of convergent beam. Right, paths of photonegative organism, *Nitocra typica* (after Spooner[502]).

However, it is not clear that the conditions for an animal moving in a beam are the same as those seen, synoptically, as it were, by an observer outside the beam. A photonegative animal moving away from the source with its eye shaded either by pigment or by its body (as with the copepods used in some of the experiments) will be stimulated by light from directly ahead. It would only appreciate that it was in a brighter area when it reached the convergence of the beams if it turned to face the light source. On the other hand, photopositive animals moving up the beam will be receiving a decreasing intensity of light on their retinae as they swim towards the source; but nevertheless at any moment the greatest intensity will be from the direction of the source and any deviation will produce a sharper drop in illumination than they will experience as they move up the beam. And, in the case of the photonegative animal, the downbeam direction is the one in which least stimulation will be experienced. It would seem, therefore, that the animals' behaviour in these conditions is not so enigmatic after all and that in taxes the directional quality of light rays is important while in kineses intensity is the stimulating factor.

Certain experiments involving a comparison of light intensities in space have been described as evidence for a positive choice of black screens by animals. Such reactions in which shadows and dark screens appear to take the places of light sources have been called skototaxis. It has been suggested that they should be explained as some form of negative phototaxis or as simple kinds of form vision. But there seems much evidence that they are a reaction separate from these. Periwinkles, *Littorina littorea*,[47] will move towards one or other of two black screens confronting them. Similar behaviour is found in ticks,[329] in the snail, *Helix aspersa*,[75] and in the marine worm, *Nereis diversicolor*,[8] among other invertebrates. One explanation could be that the animals ,are behaving negatively photo-tropotactically, for the screen to which the animal moves is reflecting little or no light and thus they are going to an area of decreased intensity. Though the behaviour of animals which move between two screens with which they are confronted suggests that the screens are efficient as sources of stimulus—as are twin lamps—this does not seem to be by any means the general rule for behaviour in these circumstances; indeed earlier work on *Littorina*[47] in which such results were claimed has not been confirmed.[396]

Some experiments on woodlice[147] show more about the mechanism of the reaction. In this case the woodlice were used while in their photonegative phase. Placed in the centre of a white-walled arena they ran in circles moving outwards. When a piece of black paper, 10 cms. by 7 cms., was placed on the wall, *Oniscus asellus* walked to it from 32 cms. away but ignored the paper if it was only half the width (5 cms. by 7 cms.). Ticks, *Ixodes reduvius*,[329] also ignored black stripes when they were reduced in size. It is clear that the reaction occurs only when the black area covers a considerable part of the visual field. Apparently, woodlice in a negatively phototactic state only will show the reaction. The behaviour could arise from lowered stimulation of the eye which faces the black areas compared with the stimulation of the other eye illuminated by light reflected from the arena's white wall. Though, since unilaterally blinded woodlice will still seek a black screen, it is unlikely that any comparison of intensities in the two eyes is essential, rather it would seem to be a telotactic movement to the screen. Other experiments do not show decisively whether animals are reacting to the screen as such. For example, *Porcellio scaber* was put down between a light and a screen. All the animals headed away from the light as would be expected since they were photonegative (Fig. 37). Of the 12 individuals used, 5 went to the screen while the remainder passed on each side of it. But such a proportion could arise by chance considering the width of the total track covered by the retreating woodlice and the width of the screen. When the screen was placed at right angles to the light beam (Fig. 37) only two animals went to the screen, three headed away from the light and three took up an intermediate course.[147] This again is hardly convincing proof of skototaxis, though it is significant that more than half of the animals were deflected from the track which would have been typical of woodlice moving away from a light. But crabs, *Carcinus maenas*, in a photonegative state will move towards, and between, two lights to reach a black screen[7]; while wood ants running from the light turn towards a black screen placed beside their path.[284a]

In another test, of chilopods and diplopods, the results again suggested positive reaction to black screens. Millipedes [*Schizophyllum sabulosum* (= *Julus sabulosus*)] were placed before two screens at equal distances from the animals and turned towards them.[301] The whole set-up was in an arena with white walls lit from above. The animals are photonegative and set off in various ways to the screens. Some took a zig-zag course reminiscent of telotaxis, others passed between the two screens but turned to one or the other when they were level with them, and the rest made their way directly to one or the other screen (Fig. 38). Once they had got to a screen many then went directly to the other and back again. An explanation of this could lie in a similar gradient of sensitivity over the eye,[177] as was suggested earlier for the eyes of various insects.

Thus, if, in Figure 39, the letters a, b, c, and d, represent the sensitivity and, thus, the turning effect of stimulation of the various ommatidia, those at the front being greatest and those at the back the least, we can suppose that when the eye is looking straight at a screen with another to its right, the total turning effect will arise

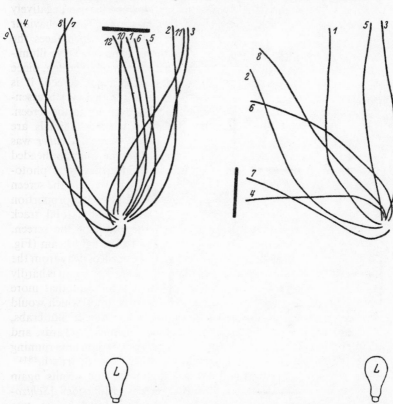

FIG. 37. Tracks of photonegative woodlice away from a light source. Left, when placed between a black screen and a light. Right, when the screen was placed at right-angles to the light beam (Dietrich[147]).

from the segments left white in the figure, for these will be stimulated by light from the arena walls. Therefore we have b + c + d turning the animal to the right, since our example is a photonegative individual, and B tending to turn it to the left. Cancelling out the segments whose action balances each other we have a final effect of turning to the right due to c + d. As the screen passes over the eye during the turn we arrive at the position shown in the second

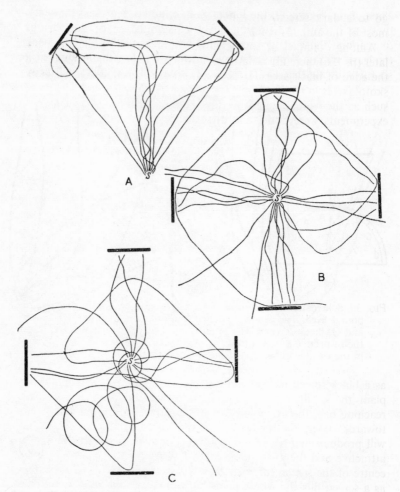

Fig. 38. Reactions to black screens. A, tracks of *Julus* to two screens. B, tracks of *Lithobius* to four screens. C, tracks of earwigs blinded on one side (Klein[301]).

part of the figure. Arguing as before, the turning effect is A to the left and c to the right. Since A is anterior and has a greater stimulating efficiency than c, the animal turns to the left. It will by this means oscillate about a line drawn to the boundary of the screen, and the behaviour involved would be no more than negative phototropotaxis, However, a one-eyed millipede or woodlouse will also go to a dark screen, moving telotactically, and it is striking that most of the animals reach the screens near the centre.

Among examples of simple form vision which we shall consider later (p. 126) there are a number in which the animals move towards the edge of black areas. It does not seem necessary to suggest that skototaxis is in reality simple form vision. In a uniform environment such as the white-painted, evenly illuminated arena in which these experiments were done, any disturbance in the homogeneity such

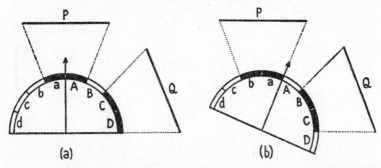

FIG. 39. Schematic representation of an arthropod head with paired compound eyes. The arrow indicates the animal's longitudinal axis. P and Q, black screens. The letters a to d represent the sensitivities of the respective groups of ommatidia in the left eye, and A to D those in the right eye. See text (Fraenkel and Gunn[177]).

as a black screen might be attractive to an animal. This might explain the oscillation of millipedes between two screens for, on reaching one, the other screen will be attractive; during movement towards either, the movement of the image of the screen's edges will produce changes in stimulation. These in themselves might be attractive and they will be greatest if the animal heads towards the centre of the screen for then they will occur in both eyes. As soon as a screen fills the whole field this will cease and only by moving to the other will such stimulation be recommenced. One would expect positively phototactic animals to be equally attracted to disturbances in the homogeneity of their surroundings but apart from crabs, *Carcinus maenas*,[7] they do not appear to be. But to a negatively phototactic animal in a well-lit arena, a dark area may represent an escape route, while a positively phototactic one is not under the same compulsion to flee. The positive reaction of *Schizophyllum* and *Cylindrojulus*[301] to grey screens strengthen the view that it is the darker area itself which is the stimulus, as it was also when a worm, *Nereis*[8], followed a spiral course to a black cylinder in the middle of a dish (Fig. 40). There is evidence too, that crabs remember the positions of black screens and revisit them after the screens have been removed, suggesting that the screens are treated as objects.[7] Thus skototaxis is a form of reaction in its own right, and not another name for a special case or form of phototaxis.

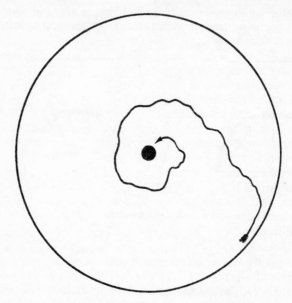

FIG. 40. Path followed by a worm, *Nereis diversicolor*, towards a black cylinder placed in the middle of the dish (Ameln[8]).

NAVIGATION BY MEANS OF LIGHT RAYS

In all the examples considered so far the animals have been moving either towards or away from the source of light. But there are many cases of animals which maintain a constant angle between the long axis of their body and the light rays. Since under natural conditions light from the sky is always present, though its direction varies in a constant way, the light rays from the sun form a useful beacon by which animals can find their way. It was the realization of the ability of ants to use this beacon that led to the discovery of this type of behaviour and to its name 'light compass reaction'.[70]

The streams of foraging ants returning to their nests have been noticed and commented upon for hundreds of years. At the beginning of this century it was shown that the light from the sky must play a part in the guidance of the ants back to their nests. For if a stream was shaded from surrounding objects by a cylindrical vertical screen they continued on their way yet if a horizontal screen was held over the upper end of the cylinder they became disorientated.[470] Such a horizontal screen would cut off the light from the sky. And further if the real sun was shaded from them and a mirror arranged on the opposite side of their track to reflect a false sun onto them they turned round and retraced their steps. Similar results have been found with many other ants and also with marching bands of young locusts, the 'hopper' stage, before they have fully developed wings,[297] as well as with *Talitrus saltator*,[575] *Littorina*[396] and other animals. Also if ants on their homeward march were transported either to one side of their track or to the other side of their nest they continued on their way maintaining their original direction until they had covered the distance which would in their original line of march have brought them to their nests.[105] Under these conditions no attention was being paid to the surface over which they were running or to scent trails but only to keeping constant their bearing on the sun's rays.

Very similar results are obtained when bees are transferred while they are feeding to some other place.[582] They take off and fly in the correct direction for the correct distance which would, if they had been left where they were, have carried them back to the hive. A bee will only do this if the place in which the experiment is carried out is featureless, like the open expanse of a disused aerodrome. Otherwise they can navigate by means of the natural features which are around them.[581, 582]

The disadvantage of the sun as a beacon is that it is not fixed but moves over the sky. This introduces an element of error into this form of navigation. When a garden ant, *Lasius niger*, is trapped under a light tight box on its homeward journey for a few hours its path when it is released deviates from the correct one by an angle equal to that through which the sun has travelled.[70] Such a result can only be obtained with young ants inexperienced in sun navigation, for later they learn to make allowance for the sun's movement, and move off in the correct direction on release from the box.[284a] Similar deviations are seen in bees when they are trapped and delayed at their feeding place, the course along which they fly back to the hive is 'out' by the same number of degrees as the sun's movement during their imprisonment, though they also can compensate for the sun's movement.

In Chapter IV we shall see that many of these reactions are probably not to light directly from the sun but to patterns of polarized light from the sky. These patterns move when the sun moves and so can also cause mistakes such as those just described.

The mechanism of such navigation must be that on the outward journey the sun's position is maintained at one point on the eye, somewhere, say, on the front part of the left eye. For the return the sun must now be held at a point on the back part of the right eye. There must be inversion of the position of the image for the return. With a compound eye of the sort that insects possess such localization is not difficult for the ommatidia will receive only that light which enters them more or less directly down the tube of pigment which surrounds the ommatidium. Since the ommatidium contains only a narrow angle, light will only come from a small part of the visual field.

The ability to fix a light source on a particular part of the eye is not a prerogative of the Hymenoptera. *Eristalis* maintains fairly accurate orientation to a light beam ahead of it when it is flying.[362] If the beam is raised or lowered it flies up or down so keeping the stimulation on the same group of ommatidia. Again the male firefly will turn towards the place where a female firefly has announced her presence by glowing. The male turns accurately even in the total darkness following the female's flash of light. He does not require the flash to be repeated.[359] And if the male glows near a female she turns her abdomen and raises it so that, when she flashes, her light-producing organs are pointed at the male. She can orientate herself without the continuous presence of the male flashes, one is sufficient and the remainder of her movements can take place in the dark. Here in both sexes the position of the flash is registered on the eye and then the insect turns through an angle equal to the angle between the stimulated part and the frontal ommatidia.

But light compass orientation seems to be responsible for the straight paths followed by most insects without necessarily being orientated for navigation to any particular spot. Thus, chrysomelid beetles, woodlice and millipedes[74] among others wander round and round in the dark. But when they are illuminated their paths are considerably straighter (Fig. 41). Any alteration in the position of the light causes the animal to turn so that the same part of the same eye is stimulated once again. This turn is the most economical possible, that is, the insect turns the quickest way round, through the smallest angle.

While this is true of insects which have fixed eyes, crabs with their mobile stalked eyes react differently. A movement of the light through 17° produces no change in their track for it is compensated by a movement of the eyes,[585] but if they are fixed in position, the

whole crab moves. Further movement of the light through 180°
which causes an insect to turn completely round, makes a crab turn
so that it faces the new position of the light but it continues to move
in the same direction as before (Fig. 42).

The width of the ommatidium of a compound eye determines the
angle through which the light must move before the insect alters its
course. If the angle of its ommatidium, that is, its angle of acceptance of light, is large, then the light must be moved a considerable
distance before it ceases to stimulate the original ommatidium and

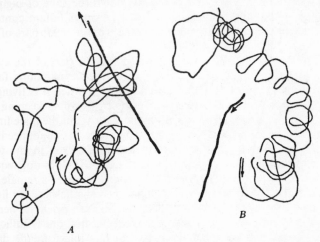

Fig. 41. Paths of (A) a chrysomelid beetle and (B) a woodlouse in the dark
(thin line) and in the light (thicker line) (von Buddenbrock[80]).

falls upon its neighbour instead. For compensatory alterations of
the track can only occur when stimulation is shifted from one element to the next. Thus an eye which consists of many closely packed
ommatidia will be able to detect smaller movements of the light
than an eye with fewer larger elements. There is a direct correlation
between these two angles[84] (Fig. 43).

The shape of the eye of other invertebrates also determines the
efficiency of the light compass reaction. The nudibranch, *Elysia
viridis*, will crawl in a horizontal beam maintaining a definite angle
to the beam.[170] The angle varies, the light may be kept at 90° to the
left or 45° to the right, for example (Fig. 44). But, if orientation
straight towards the light is taken as 0° and directly away as 180°,
it lies always between 45° and 135°. When the structure of the eye
is investigated it is found to be a cup-like retina containing a lens

at its opening (Fig. 45). The only light which can enter such an arrangement will come from between approximately 35° to 130° to its body axis which accounts for the absence of any observed orientation angles outside these limits.

When this mollusc is crawling along a track orientated to a light, switching on a second light does not disturb it provided that the

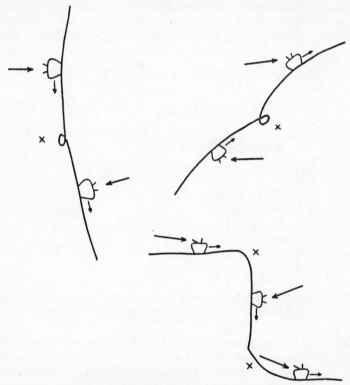

FIG. 42. Paths of crabs before and after altering the direction (at X) from which they were illuminated (represented by the larger arrows, the smaller indicating the direction of movement) (after Wolter[585]).

original one is left on. It is faithful to its first choice even though the new light may be considerably stronger. However, if the second light is on alone it will orientate itself by the new one moving along at the same angle as it had been maintaining to the first light. There appears to be central inhibition of one of the two as there is in most telotactic behaviour.

The natural source of light for orientation is the sun, the rays from which are parallel since the source is such a distant one. However,

under experimental conditions the source is often so near an animal
that its rays are divergent radiating from the source. An animal
performing a light compass reaction to these rays may be carried
towards the light along a spiral track because it will continue to
maintain its fixed angle to each of the rays[175] (Fig. 46). This is

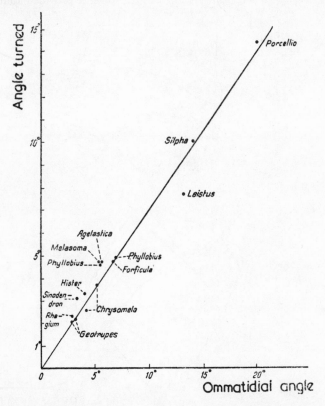

FIG. 43. Relationship between ommatidial angle and the angular movement of a light source required to produce a reaction, for a number
of arthropods (von Buddenbrock[50]).

probably part of the explanation for the suicidal flight of moths to
a candle flame.

This is corroborated by the tracks of *Lymantria* caterpillars when
they emerge into an arena lit by a movable lamp. In successive
trials with the lamp in different positions the caterpillar curves into
each place circling as it draws near to the lamp.[344] (Fig. 47).

(108)

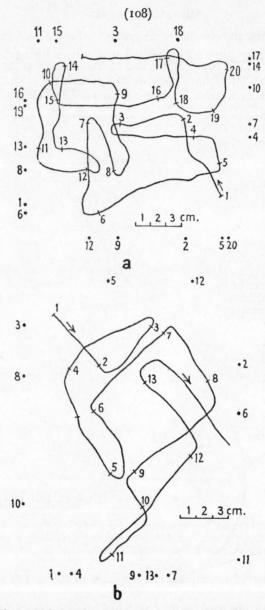

FIG. 44. *Elysia viridis* moving with an orientation angle of 90° to the left side of the animal (a) and of 45° to the right (b) to the incident light. The figures on the curves indicate the moments at which the light was placed at the places indicated by the same figures in the margin. The distance of the light sources from the animal are not to scale and were in fact greater (Fraenkel and Gunn[177]).

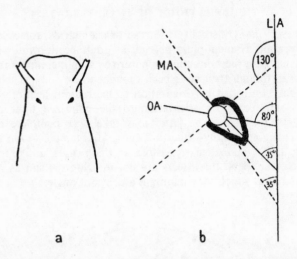

FIG. 45. Position of the eyes in the head of *Elysia*, showing that the only light entering the eye comes from an angle between 35° and 130° to the longitudinal axis of the animal (from Fraenkel and Gunn,[177] and Fraenkel[170]).

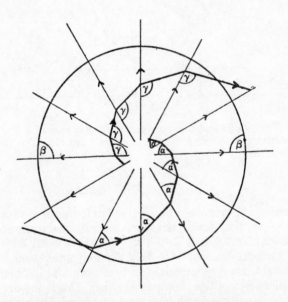

FIG. 46. To demonstrate that an animal maintaining a constant angle with regard to light radiating from a source may be led to the source (angles α and γ) or circle round it (β) (Fraenkel[175]).

However, many insects (e.g. larvae of geometrids, tortricids, etc. and diprionid Hymenoptera as well as adult beetles and sawflies) do not maintain their direction in nature by a light compass reaction to the sun though they have been thought to do so.[559] Their track is, in fact, controlled by orientation to the radiant heat of the sun, which is reinforced by orientation to the polarized light pattern of the sky (p. 117). The latter may take over complete control if it is changing rapidly—due to clouds, for example—even though the sun itself remains clearly visible. In these cases, unlike the ants and locust hoppers, the insects are not utilizing the sun as a small light source to which they maintain a constant angle.

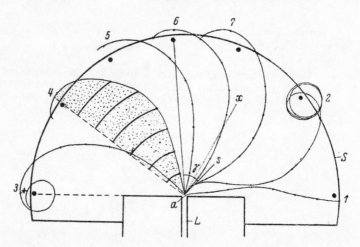

Fig. 47. Tracks of *Lymantria* caterpillars from *a* toward a lamp placed at different positions around a semi-circle centred on *a* (Ludwig[344]).

THE DORSAL LIGHT REACTION

Many animals both in water and on land or in the air always arrange themselves so that their backs are towards the main source of illumination. Since this is always the sun's rays under natural conditions, their posture will be to hold the body at right angles to the incident light, always maintaining this relationship, in other words, a particular form of light compass reaction. This is the dorsal light reaction. It usually plays an important role in reinforcing behaviour due to the gravity perception organs in maintaining normal posture in flight, or while walking or swimming. This is usually dorsal side up but in a few exceptional cases the animals may live ventral side uppermost when the dorsal light reaction is reversed.

A swimming animal is usually in an unstable or a metastable state for its centre of gravity is near the centre of its body and the upthrust of the water counteracts its weight, therefore it has to make active movements to maintain its position. Leeches such as *Hirudo medicinalis* swim with their back to a light shining on the tank from above but they turn over when the light is transferred to below them,[477] correcting their posture later. With their supra- and sub-oesophaeal ganglia removed, they still swim like normal animals

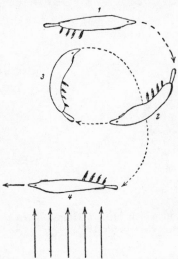

FIG. 48. *Argulus foliaceus*, the carp louse, turning over when illuminated from below (Herter[247]).

when lit from below, indicating that the dorsal light reflex is overridden by some gravity sense. But between two glass plates 3 mm. apart, an operated animal will remain with its dorsal side downwards towards the light, an intact animal would turn itself over. Co-ordination between the gravity sensitivity and the light reflex seems to break down under certain conditions when the ganglia are removed.

The fish louse, *Argulus*,[247] and the brine shrimp, *Artemia salina*,[491] both turn over when the light is placed beneath them. In this case, however, their normal position is ventral side up and so they then swim dorsal side up. They turn over in different ways, *Argulus* usually does a front somersault (Fig. 48), while *Artemia's* behaviour depends upon the individual's reaction to light. For a photopositive individual will turn a back somersault, a negative individual a front somersault and an indifferent individual will simply roll over (Fig. 49).

When unilaterally blinded an individual *Argulus* performs circus movements in the horizontal plane—it behaves phototropotactically and also makes spiral rolling movements in the vertical plane. This indicates that, in this animal at least, the dorsal light reaction depends upon balanced stimulation in the two eyes. This also seems to be so

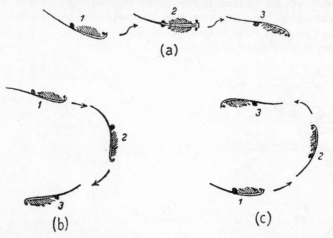

(a)

(b)   (c)

FIG. 49. Three ways in which brine shrimps, *Artemia salina*, may turn over when lit from below (Seifert[491]).

in the larvae of the aquatic beetles, *Acilius* and *Dytiscus*, which possess six ocelli on each side of the head (Fig. 50). Blackening the anterior three (1, 3 and 5) causes the insects to swim forwards in vertical dorsal loops, while blackening of the posterior eyes causes ventral loops, the insect turning downwards.[483] Normal posture seems to result from balanced stimulation of these two groups; while rolling is prevented by even stimulation of the two sides, for an insect which has all the ocelli of one side blackened rolls around its longitudinal axis towards the blind side as it swims forward. But balanced posture is restored within ten to twenty minutes of the ocelli being covered. A decrease in the light intensity after this causes rolling once again, but in the opposite direction. This suggests that the motor outflow from the central nervous system to the muscles of the two sides of the body becomes symmetrical at first. The outflow from the side to which the seeing eye is connected is

dependent upon stimulation of that eye, when this is reduced the
outflow also is reduced, producing an asymmetry. When rolling
first occurred after blinding, the reduced inflow was from the blind
side, now the reduction is on the seeing side so the rolling is in the
opposite direction.

In *Triops* the change of position seems to be initiated by the
median eye for this looks ventralwards as well as dorsalwards.[490]
But there must thereafter be balanced stimulation of the two compound eyes for blackening one of them makes the animal roll and
circle.

In Crustacea there is often a statocyst system which has ascen-
dancy in the control of righting and correct positioning. Removal of

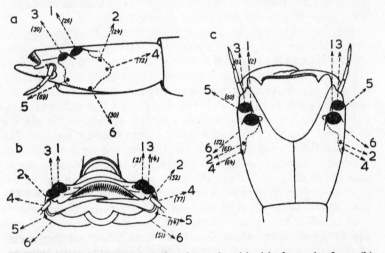

FIG. 50. Head of larva of *Acilius* from the side (a), from the front (b),
and from above (c) showing the arrangement of the eyes. The figures
in brackets represent the angle between the optical axis of the ocellus
and one of three main axes, in (a) that passing through the head
from side to side, vertical to the direction of movement, in (b), that
of the vertical axis of symmetry of the larva, in (c), the longitudinal
axis of the body (Schone[483]).

the statocysts often enables the light reaction to show its full possibilities. *Palaemon* (= *Leander*) *xiphias* possesses statocysts as well
as mobile stalked eyes. When a normal animal is turned on its side
the legs which are uppermost make kicking movements which will
right it again[5] (p. 206). In an intact animal these kicks appear even
when it is lit from the side so that its back is illuminated. But an
animal without its statocysts in this position remains docile for its

dorsal light reaction is satisfied. Also, when in the normal position but lit from one side, the operated animal makes kicking movements with its legs of the opposite side. When resting on the bottom and lit from the side the animal does not turn completely so that its back is perpendicular to the light but tilts through about 45°. This is probably because there is proprioceptive stimulation arising from the legs and their contact with the bottom. Once again it is obvious that the reaction depends upon a balance of stimulation in the two eyes for a unilaterally blinded animal without statoliths makes kicking movements on the seeing side. In fact it only becomes docile when it is tilted to about 45° with the seeing eye uppermost. This indicated that a third receptor must be coming into play to obtain this new position of equilibrium and, as we shall see in Chapter VII, it is in fact the remains of the statocyst.

This behaviour can be compared with that of *Processa canaliculata* which does not possess statocysts.[73] This animal always swims with its back to the light and is dependent solely upon a dorsal light reaction to keep upright, but one eye is sufficient for this. Though it might appear that the behaviour depends upon fixation of the light on a particular part of the eye, there being a variation in sensitivity among the ommatidia similar to that postulated for the eye of *Eristalis* (p. 57), closer investigation does not bear this out. The direction from which the light is coming seems to be transmitted to the central nervous system as a qualitatively specific position signal, thus the function of the eye in the dorsal light reaction can be explained best on the reafferentation principle since the reaction has been shown to be less rigid than the earlier experiments suggest.[487]

Dragonflies have a marked dorsal light reaction though they cannot fly upside down when illuminated from below but they do fly in upward or downward spirals so that they fulfil the ideal conditions as nearly as possible.[385] When they settle they turn their backs to the light whether it be coming from the side, below or above. Here again this insect also possesses a position sense based upon the twisting of the neck and this and the light reaction work together (see Chapter VII). Two mechanisms also function in the waterbugs, *Notonecta* and *Corixa*. Both have position sense organs (p. 212) but the action of these is normally reinforced by a ventral light reflex and a dorsal light reflex, respectively in the two animals.[445]

THE ROLE OF SIMPLE REACTIONS TO LIGHT IN THE LIFE OF
INVERTEBRATES

Light, as such, rarely has importance to an animal except those which have symbiotic photosynthetic organisms or, like *Euglena*, are capable of photosynthesis themselves. Its importance lies in what the presence or absence of light indicates. It thus takes the form of a token stimulus not reacted to for its own sake but for some secondary reason which is generally connected with it. Darkness and low light intensities are usually found in crevices and under stones for example. On land, higher humidities and lower temperatures are often found in such places. They are sought by those animals which have inadequate means of control of moisture loss for under these conditions evaporation is reduced (see also p. 321). Hence, the usefulness of kineses which aggregate animals in such places. No one particular place is necessary but any one which affords these conditions will do. The kinetic behaviour is unselective. Further, the dark places give protection against predators.

On the other hand, lighter places often contain the food and so we find reversal of the sign of an animal's phototactic responses when it is hungry. This brings it out into the open and into the vicinity of food. The movement of marine zoo-plankton to surface during the night may be a feeding movement but it certainly depends upon reduction of light intensity. The interaction of simple types of behaviour to light to produce complex total movements will be considered later (Chapter XIII).

The necessity to return to the nest is very great in the social insects for the foragers must not waste their efforts in collecting food by getting lost on the way home, so it is not surprising to find that the light compass reaction is well developed among bees and wasps. Even the inaccuracy due to the sun's normal movement is allowed for. The returning forager ant goes as far as it should and then begins searching in circles (Turner's turnings). While it was away from the nest the sun will have moved through a small angle and therefore it may not get back to the nest exactly. But on its automatic search it soon locates the nest entrance.

A spider, such as *Agelena labyrinthica*, returns to its lair on the edge of its web after dealing with prey that has landed on it. The decision as to the direction in which to set off is apparently made upon the direction of the light by means of a light compass reaction.[29] For if the light is moved the spider cannot find its way, nor can it if the light remains fixed but its web is turned through 180° (Fig. 51). In both cases it will go to the place it would expect its lair to be if the conditions had remained unchanged. Similarly turning of the web affects the spider's ability to find booty which it has left wrapped up on its web. After the turning it searches in the area relative to the light in which it would expect to find it.

The importance of the dorsal light reaction as another means of

D

keeping an animal's position has already been mentioned. But it also has a function in camouflage. Effective use of a pattern of countershading[464] requires that the light shall come from a particular direction with respect to the pattern. The colouring of the caterpillar of *Colias edusa* is such that it is countershaded if the light

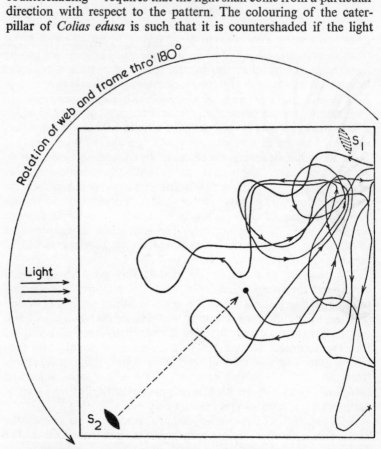

Fig. 51. Effect of rotating a spider's (*Agalena*) web through 180° with the light from one side. S_1, original position of place where spider rested; S_2, position after rotation. A fly was put down at •, picked up by spider which moved towards S_1, then wandered for 22 minutes until it sucked fly's juices at X (after Bartels and Baltzer[29]).

strikes it from above. This caterpillar shows a strong dorsal light reflex so that it crawls along the upper side of a leaf petiole for example.[508] Its pupa, on the other hand, is countershaded in the reverse direction, that is to say, as if the light were coming from

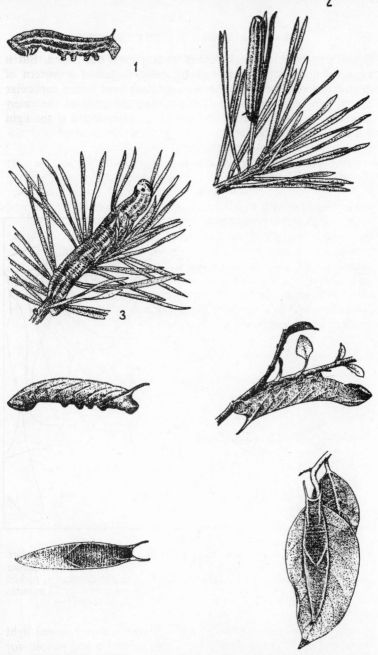

FIG. 52. Colour patterns, countershading and the positions taken up by caterpillars. Top, 1, pine hawk-moth, fourth instar, 2, same in natural position; 3, same, last instar in natural position. Centre, *Smerinthus ocellatus* in normal (right) and in reversed position (left). Below, *Apatura iris* in normal position (right) and in uniform light (left) (Tinbergen[521]).

below. The caterpillar hangs itself up to pupate with the morphologically underside uppermost. In *Apatura ilia* the caterpillar is darker at the head end and so arranges itself head to the light (Fig. 52); its pupa, however, has a darker tail end and arranges itself head downwards. All these reactions are to light and not due to some sense of gravity. The receptors are probably widespread over the skin and are not solely the eyes.

Other caterpillars, feeding on pine, arrange themselves so that the longitudinal stripes on their bodies are parallel with the needles.[521] Those with brown heads remain head downwards, their heads blending with the brown scales at the base of the needles, while others, with green heads, take up a reverse position. While the young caterpillars of the hawk moth, *Hyloicus pinastri*, lie parallel to the needles, in the last instar they cling parallel to the twig (Fig. 52). At this stage the colour pattern is changed from longitudinal to transverse markings, which in the new position mix with the bases of the needles springing from the twig. In all probability, though it has not been demonstrated, their behaviour is the result of light responses.

CHAPTER IV

THE PERCEPTION OF THE FREQUENCY AND PLANE OF VIBRATION OF LIGHT WAVES

COLOUR

Much of our aesthetic enjoyment of the world arises from our ability to detect colour related, physically, to the differences in wavelength of various lights. The spectrum which we can detect extends from wavelengths of 760 mμ to 390 mμ, though at both ends of this range the stimulating efficiency of the light is low. Beyond these two limits we do not react to light unless we use some device which will convert the rays into wavelengths of the visible spectrum. To us visible light appears as a series of colours grading from red (around 630 mμ) to blue-violet (around 400 mμ), as the wavelength diminishes. Though it is plain that other animals can also distinguish between parts of this same spectral range, we alone can attribute to the sensation produced by light of a certain wavelength the idea of colour referable to the human scale of colour and symbolized by our words which describe these sensations. So, proof that an animal can see and apparently may prefer, say, light of 630 mμ wavelength does not mean that it sees red in the human sense, but merely that it can distinguish this wavelength from others.

The ranges of wavelengths perceived by animals do not always coincide with those we see. Most insects are apparently blind to the red end of our spectrum, for example, and they may react to light of shorter wavelengths than those we can see. Not only may the spectrum detected by the animal differ from that of our own, but its range may be narrower.

Observation of the way of life of an animal will often give much evidence about its ability to perceive colour; it may spontaneously choose particular colours. More information can be obtained from experiments in which the animal is trained to perform some action involving the choice of a particular colour and is then confronted with the problem of picking out this colour from a set of mixed hues. Thus the bee-fly, *Bombylius fuliginosus*, can be seen to collect nectar only from the blue flowers of grape hyacinths. It will also visit pieces of blue paper placed in the neighbourhood of the flowers,[304] even picking out the blue pieces which most nearly match the flowers from sets of grey and blue papers of various shades. Another method of obtaining information is to use the optomotor reaction which most animals with good vision will show. This is movement of the head, or sometimes the whole body, when a pattern of vertical stripes is moved in front of the animal. If movement occurs, it is concluded that the stripes are distinguishably different from each other, if they are not, then no reaction is called forth. So if the stripes are of two colours not perceived by the animal as different, it will not react, but if they are differentiated by the animal, the optomotor movement will take place.

There are two major difficulties in testing an animal's appreciation of colour. First, every precaution must be taken to ensure that the animal is reacting to the differences in wavelength rather than to differences in brightness, and, second, the context in which the colour is presented must be one which has meaning for the animal.

Adequate control for the factor of brightness is particularly important when coloured artificial backgrounds are being used in a training situation. Thus, if an animal is being trained to come to food containers set out on coloured papers, food only being found on papers of one particular hue, it is most important that in the subsequent test, among the coloured papers should be placed grey papers of equivalent brightness. This is perfectly possible since various standard series of grey papers ranging between the extremes of black and white are available. Each of these greys reflects a known amount of light in daylight or artificial light. This sort of control has been applied in work on insects, notably, bees. Absence of this precaution in studies on other invertebrates has often rendered the experimenter's interpretation of his results suspect, as will be seen.

To be doubly certain that the animal is reacting to colour, the training situation can be altered so that the parts of a projected spectrum are used in place of coloured backgrounds. Under these conditions the animal will be stimulated by monochromatic light. Filters will give a similar result, but a less perfect one, for most filters, though transmitting light mainly of a narrow band of wavelengths also permit a small percentage of light outside this band to pass.

The second precaution is less easy to observe for it is necessary for behavioural reasons and not physical ones, it is, in other words, concerned with the animal's nervous system and not the physics of light. Certain colours have meaning (or valence) in certain situations and not in others. The butterfly, *Pieris brassicae*, feeds from flowers but lays its eggs on leaves. When choosing a site for egg-laying it performs characteristic 'drumming' behaviour, touching the background with its fore-legs.[281] Egg-laying females are attracted to and, apparently, are only able to 'see' green colour (Fig. 54). However, when the butterfly is feeding, yellow and blue are attractive while green is ignored, as experiments show. It would clearly be wrong to describe the butterfly as blind to green as one would be tempted to do on the basis of its feeding reactions alone. Only a considerable knowledge of the animal's whole life activities will show the complete repertoire of its abilities. It is useless to take an animal into the artificial conditions of the laboratory to test its potentialities without being certain of the background of its normal life.

THE INFLUENCE OF COLOUR IN THE BEHAVIOUR OF INVERTEBRATES

Among invertebrates, outside the arthropods and molluscs, there is no certain evidence for clearly defined attention to any particular wavelength, despite a large number of investigations. But apart from a preference for particular colours either as a background or as illuminating sources, the effects of various parts of the spectrum on the life activities of some of the lower invertebrates do seem to differ. Among protozoa, *Amoeba* spp. show a shock reaction to light. As has been mentioned in the previous chapter, this seems to be due to an increase in gelation at the tip of the advancing pseudopod so that the normally reversible sol-gel change is thrown towards gelation bringing the pseudopod to a halt. The intensity of this shock reaction is greater when the animal approaches an area lit by rays from the violet end of the spectrum.[227] On the other hand, in red light there is the greatest increase of movement. This is most probably a chemical effect on the sol-gel changeover.

This difference in reaction to different wavelengths when different behaviour patterns are considered is also present in *Amoeba proteus*. Here the shock reaction is greatest at 430–490 mμ,[357] nearly as great as that to white light, while other wavelengths appear to be only slightly active. Yet pseudopodia may be put out towards a vertical beam of white light when the animal is 65μ away. The stimulus which causes this has not been analysed.[472] However, when the pseudopodium enters the beam, movement ceases. Such a positive reaction is not invariable but may occur to all spectral colours, though red light seems slightly more attractive than blue and apparently the pseudopodium continues to move after entering the red light. On the other hand, *Euglena viridis* individuals will aggregate most efficiently in light of 470–490 mμ,[158] though some individuals select longer wavelengths,[118] and will orientate most efficiently over this range. If different patterns of behaviour have their maximum intensities at different parts of the spectrum, this may show an ability to react specifically to wavelength apart from brightness. It need hardly be pointed out that these experiments were carried out in lights of equivalent brightness to the human eye but it is impossible to be certain that they were not perceived by the organism as different in intensity. A grey paper series check is not possible for the animals apparently do not react to background colour but only to differences in the wave characteristics of the illuminating source. It is questionable whether there is evidence for true colour vision.

Experiments on coelenterates are similarly inconclusive because brightness has not been controlled. There seems some evidence for colour preference in *Pelmatohydra oligactis* (= *Hydra fusca*) and *Chlorohydra viridissima* (= *Hydra viridis*).[576] When coloured glass filters were placed against a tank containing some hundreds of individuals, there were gatherings on the walls over the area lit by blue light. Some control of brightness was achieved by doubling the lighter coloured glasses. But more convincing results were produced when a spectrum was used. The preference for blue remained with a smaller aggregation in the green area. Now this spectrum was from a gas light shone through a carbon-disulphide prism, under which conditions the greatest intensity is in the red region. Thus, the preference for blue seems to be a true choice of wavelength and not of brightness, though more control of brightness would be desirable for the animals may have been choosing an optimum intensity of light which may not have been the maximum in the spectrum.

Various sea-anemones have been tested with differing results. It appears as if *Cerianthus* and *Bunodes*[260] are colour blind but that *Cereactis aurantiaca* reacts differently to green and blue than to yellow and red.[478] But again adequate control of brightness was not employed.

In cases such as these it is difficult, if not impossible, to be certain that the observer is not confusing the greater stimulative efficiency of some wavelength with an actual preference for that spectral region.   Earthworms (*Lumbricus* sp.) are essentially photonegative animals. When they are free to move in a box illuminated by a spectrum they draw away from the blue colours passing along the series to move out of the light at the red end.[63] Similarly light passed through a red filter seems not to affect them, while blue light causes them to retreat into their burrows.[546] More detailed and careful experiments indicate that the range in the neighbourhood of 483 mμ produces the maximum effect, measured in this case by movement away from the light.[360] This seems to be independent of brightness. This greater stimulative effect of the shorter wavelengths seems to be the case with many other annelids, whether or not they possess eyes. But it is not clear that the earthworm or any other worm distinguishes the wavelength as such, apart from the increased stimulation from that light. Leeches (particularly *Helobdella* sp.) seem to have a preference for the longer wavelengths[128] even if these colours are of greater brightness than the alternative colours of shorter wavelength. This is quite in contrast to the normal choice by these leeches of a medium grey in preference to pale grey or black and, therefore, suggests that the reaction is, in fact, to colour. But lights, equal in intensity to the human eye, may have different physiological effects, by virtue of their wavelengths in some other animal's receptor.[476] This may be because of their effect on chemical changes in the light-sensitive cells. An extreme example is the effect of ultra-violet light on the speed of chemical reactions. Activity is increased when the animal is bathed in light of this sort.

One attempt has been made to apply a brightness test, using the grey paper series, to the effect of monochromatic light on the marine tube-dwelling polychaete *Serpula contortuplicata*.[263] These animals react strongly to a sudden decrease in illumination but not to a sudden increase. A board was erected beside the tank so that light was reflected into the tank from coloured or grey papers displayed on it. When a dark grey was substituted for a light grey, animals withdrew into their tubes, but they did not respond when light grey was substituted for dark grey. The replacement of green by red, or by a grey of the same brightness as the red, also produced active movement. From this it would appear that the worm's reactivity to a coloured light is very similar to that of a colour-blind human being. But *Branchiomma vesiculosum* contracts into its tube on decrease in the intensity of light of any wavelength within the visible spectrum, though it is most sensitive when the shorter wavelengths are employed.[398]

Lack of control of the brightness factor renders the investigations made on echinoderms inconclusive. The same is true of much of the work on molluscs. For example, *Limnaea stagnalis*, the pond snail, allowed to wander under various combinations of coloured lights, such as red and blue, shows an abhorrence for the red end of the spectrum.[331] The brightness of the lights used was carefully balanced but the subjective brightness to the animals was not investigated.

The animals considered thus far do not appear to distinguish colours in their life activities. They neither alter their colour for camouflage, nor are their sexes differentiated by coloured liveries for courtship, nor do they seek highly coloured prey. It is not surprising, therefore, that there is no clear evidence for colour preferences among these groups (except perhaps among leeches). But an

D*

exception occurs in the cephalopod molluscs, many of which can adapt their body colour to match the background by using their chromatophores. The range of this ability was indicated by study of the electrical discharge from the retina when an octopus' eye was

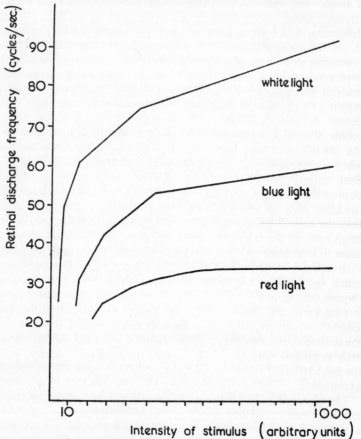

FIG. 53. Relation between frequency of discharge in the retina of *Eledon-moschata* and intensity of illumination for white light and two mono chromatic lights (after Frohlich[204]).

stimulated by various monochromatic lights. The discharge was correlated with the wavelength (Fig. 53).[204] This is not conclusive evidence, for these alterations in the discharge may not be inter-preted centrally and utilized behaviourally. However, octopuses have been trained to distinguish yellow pitchers, which during training contain food, from green ones,[320] and to associate a coloured light with punishment so that after a long period of training they avoid light of the same colour. It proved impossible to train an octopus to go to a red coloured disc, when food was given, rather than to a green disc, when an electric shock was given. But, as has been stressed earlier, a negative result of this sort may arise from a deficiency in the whole situation as the experimenter has arranged it, not from a deficiency in the animal's receptive apparatus. For it is possible to train an octopus to discriminate between green, yellow, blue, red and black discs, so that it avoids one or the other.[207] No attempt was made to eliminate the possibility that the animals were reacting to the relative brightness of the discs and, therefore, this cannot be considered as finally proving the existence of colour vision. But further suggestive evidence has come from a study of the behaviour of the chromatophores of both squids and octopus when the animals were placed on various coloured backgrounds.[321] Both animals possess black, yellow and orange-yellow chromatophores, the black being the largest and underlying the others. Below the black cells are iridocytes which reflect greenish light. It is clear that the overall colour of both animals will alter according to the brightness of the background which they find themselves, at the same time different colours produce different results irrespective of their relative brightness. The colour tone of the body remained much the same on white, black and various grey backgrounds, though the brightness of the animals' bodies matched these colourless backgrounds. On coloured grounds the tones varied very considerably to suit the conditions. On a green background, for example, the orange cells were contracted to pin points and the yellow moderately expanded while the black pigment spread slightly so that with the light reflected from the iridocytes, the body took on a greenish appearance.

The existence of colour vision among decapod crustacea has been inferred from the ability of some of them to alter their colours in a similar way. The common shrimp, *Crangon vulgaris*, possesses chromatophores containing sepia-brown, white, yellow and red pigments as well as other cells containing smaller combinations of these colours, or single pigments only. Whether present in the same cell or not the pigments are spread out or withdrawn independently. On red and yellow backgrounds the appropriate colours are always produced.

These results can be corroborated by testing the animal's optomotor reactions. But coloured objects may be avoided as, for example, when hermit crabs, *Eupagurus* sp., were offered coloured and grey shelters after having been made to leave their old shells, the grey ones were chosen whether they were lighter or darker than the yellow or blue ones offered them.[310] However, the crabs were not able to distinguish the grey shells from red and green ones. It must be admitted that under natural conditions there is no value in choosing shelters of particular colours, and hence the problem as set is completely artificial.

The objection has been made that experiments in which coloured papers, or pigments, are distinguished by arthropods are not conclusive and that only the use of monochromatic light can produce definite results. This criticism arises from the demonstration that many arthropods will react to ultra-violet rays outside the human spectrum. To judge colours, and even greys, on a human basis may lead to inaccurate conclusions unless the amount of ultra-violet absorbed by particular pigments is considered. Thus, the preference of *Eupagurus* for yellow rather than blue shelters and the inconclusive results in detection of red and green have been said to be due to the perception of light of this wavelength by the crabs.

Monochromatic light has, however, been used in the analysis of colour vision in *Daphnia magna*. These animals become photonegative when the intensity of the illumination increases and photopositive when it decreases. The result of this is that the animal will always tend to remain in the intensity of light to which it is accustomed. But if a blue filter is placed between the animals and the light source, they move away from the light despite the obvious reduction in intensity of the light. Again, when yellow light from another source is mixed with the white light already illuminating the animals, they move towards the combined source though the total intensity has increased.[203] But, when dark-adapted individuals were used, they were negative to all wavelengths and animals made positively phototactic by exposure to high carbon dioxide tensions reacted positively to all wavelengths even blue and ultra-violet.[308] Animals, however, adapted to medium lighting are positive to red, yellow and green, but negative to blue, blue-green and violet. The response of various cladocera of swimming downwards in light of wavelength 500 mμ or less has been called the 'blue response', and that of moving upwards in light of longer wavelengths, the 'yellow response'. In red light they tend to oscillate various distances in an upright position but with little horizontal movement. Since aggregations of phytoplankton will filter out short waves, these cladocera will tend to stay longer in the vicinity of plankton, their food, than elsewhere.[499]

INSECTS AND PLANT COLOURS

The insects are *par excellence* the animal group having most to do with plants and particularly with the coloured flowering plants. The visits of pollen and nectar collecting insects to brightly coloured flowers led to the natural inference that they are capable of perceiving the colour as such. Further, the larvae of some lepidoptera show a definite preference for a particular coloured background, thus *Pieris* caterpillars choose green though on pupation the preference is transferred to brown or black. Only a few insects, such as *Thrips* sp., *Ips typographus, Cetonia aurata, Attagenus pellio, Melasoma populi* and *Lasius niger*[386] seem to have no colour vision.

Observations of the reactions of nectar-feeding insects to imitation flowers and to pieces of coloured paper give a considerable insight into the colour preferences of those insects. Sometimes this preference is very narrow. The bee fly, *Bombylius fuliginosus,* can be seen feeding on the nectar of the blue grape hyacinth, *Muscara,* and when a set of coloured papers intermingled with grey papers of various brightnesses is placed among flowers, only the blue squares are visited.[304] Blue squares, both light and dark, are chosen when presented among grey squares of various shades. No food is placed on any of the squares, the visits are merely made by the fly while following its preference uninfluenced by the scent of food or any other attractant. From these observations it is deduced that the bee fly has only a very limited appreciation of colour though this conclusion is unjustified without further investigation of the fly's abilities in other situations. One could imagine that once 'set' in the food seeking drive, no other colour would have meaning. This does not exclude perception of other colours in other behavioural settings.

Some insects have been shown to have preferences for one colour during one activity and for another during another activity. In one situation one colour or set of colours draws the attention of the insect, in another, another colour. The cabbage white, *Pieris brassicae,* ignores both green paper squares and green imitation flowers when feeding, showing a definite preference for the yellow and blue ends of the spectrum[279] (Fig. 54). But when the female is searching for a place in which to lay eggs she performs her drumming manoeuvre mainly on green and blue-green backgrounds. This choice of yellow and yellow-green, and blue-violet and purple when feeding is typical of many butterflies (Fig 54), some, like *Vanessa polychloros,* the large tortoiseshell, preferring the yellow colours, others such as *Papilio machaon,* the swallowtail, the blue, while others still will choose colours in either part of the spectrum with almost equal frequency, e.g. *Vanessa urticae*, the small tortoiseshell.[279] One of the hawkmoths, *Macroglossa stellatarum* shows these two peaks in its preference curve also. Here the attraction is not only the colour but the saturation and brightness.[305] The same colour presented in

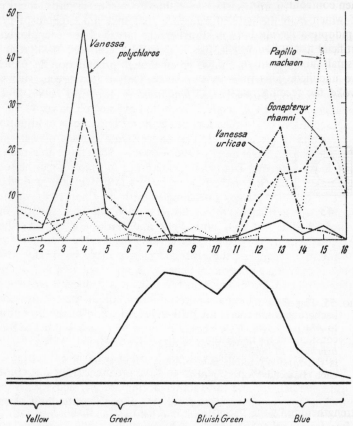

FIG. 54. Colour vision in butterflies. Above, spontaneous choices of colours by various butterflies. Spectrum: 1–3 red, 4–5 yellow, 6–7 yellow-green, 8–9 green, 10–11 blue-green, 12–13 blue, 14 violet, 15–16 purple (Ilse[279]). Below, drumming reactions of female *Pieris brassicae* to colours in the yellow-blue range (Ilse[281]).

different intensities against the same background is more attractive at its brightest, that is, when the contrast is greatest and it is most attractive when it is presented against the most contrasting background. Thus, the most attractive flower is that with the brightest colours presented against darker backgrounds (Fig. 55).

These are natural preferences and may not reveal the full range of the insect's colour appreciation which can be analysed more fully by the training method. The insects are permitted to visit coloured papers on which are placed dishes of sugar water or honey and are then confronted with a test set of coloured and grey papers on each of which is placed an empty dish. Sometimes, particularly with lepidoptera having long proboscides, it may be necessary to make artificial flowers on which they can alight, in the centre of which is a small tube containing the sugary food into which their proboscides are uncoiled. This may be necessary when colour alone will not evoke the feeding reaction in experimental situations but requires

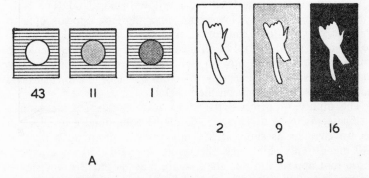

FIG. 55. The effect of contrast on the choice of colours by moths. A, the backgrounds are constant but the colours vary in brightness (offered to *Macroglossum stellatarum*), B, the colour of the flower shapes is constant but the backgrounds vary in brightness (offered to *Deilephila livornica*). In both cases the arrangement giving the greatest contrast is the most attractive as shown by the number of visits made to each (Baerends[20] after Knoll).

strengthening by the pattern of the artificial flower (see Chapter V). After training has occurred to a particular colour, empty food vessels are presented so that the situation is as like the training one as possible, but without food which might attract by its scent. The training colour is mixed with other colours and greys of various brightness. When the insect visits these papers it may or may not be able to pick out the colour to which it had been trained.[188]

This method was devised originally for testing the sensibility of the honeybee. By this means, and by presenting food vessels illuminated by monochromatic spectral light,[323] the colour spectrum of the bee was shown to be divided into four areas which were mutually distinguishable by the bee. These were 650–530 mμ (red, yellow), 510–480 mμ (blue-green), 470–400 mμ (blue and blue-green) and 400–300 mμ (ultra-violet),[188, 319] though shades of colour within the 650–530 mμ and 510–480 mμ bands might be distinguished.[322] The grey papers serve to distinguish brightness preferences from true colour distinction, and the use of spectral light eliminates the possible criticism that certain coloured and grey papers may be attractive by virtue of the ultra-violet reflected from them invisible to the human eye. The bee shows simultaneous contrast phenomena like those of the human being. When we view a grey on a coloured background we see the colour complementary to the background colour in place of the grey. Similarly bees trained to blue will visit a grey ring if it is presented on a yellow background. The complementary colour to yellow being blue, the ring appears blue to the bee.[319] Despite a contention that the bee sees colour like a colour-blind man, control of all the aspects of these experiments, so much criticized, seems now so rigid that there can be little doubt that the bees are reacting truly to colour as such, not to brightness nor to traces of scent left on the papers.

The ability to perceive the short wavelengths outside human vision seems to be a characteristic of the compound eye. Bees can see wavelengths as short as 297 mμ, noctuid moths to a limit of 240 mμ.[373] This ability has the result that so-called white papers, those that appear white to the human, may be interdistinguishable to the bee. Those papers that reflect much ultra-violet appear neutral, and those that absorb the longer wavelengths appear as blue-green. It is difficult to train bees to visit the first but easy to train them to visit the second.[258]

A further method of testing colour vision, but again not necessarily natural preferences, which avoids the necessity of training is that of the optomotor reaction (p. 134) using stripes of different colours. Green appears to have little attraction to the bee though it is apparently distinguished. The butterfly searching for food also shows little liking for this colour (which, of course, is not the colour of the insect pollinated flowers but rather of those that are wind pollinated and have insignificant inflorescences). Nor does testing by the optomotor method reveal any ability to distinguish green (Fig. 56) except in some leaf-eating insects.[475] Thus *Chrysomela fastuosa*, a leaf-eating beetle, will follow the movement of a set of alternate yellow and blue stripes of matched intensity, but is unaffected by yellow and grey, or blue and grey, stripes unless they are of different intensities (Fig. 56). It can however distinguish blue from grey or yellow.[475]

The majority of insects are red blind but though with the exception of bumble bees they seem unable to distinguish it as a colour, optomotor studies show that different species perceive the same standard red as very different subjective brightnesses. This is shown by moving a set of vertical stripes across the front of the insect using the standard red alternated with various shades of grey.[475] When no reaction is evinced it is reasonable to assume that the insect detects no difference in the stripes, thus that particular shade of grey and the red are equal in brightness—to the insect. By this means, it has been possible to show that part of the eye of *Notonecta glauca* is colour blind (Fig. 57).[459]

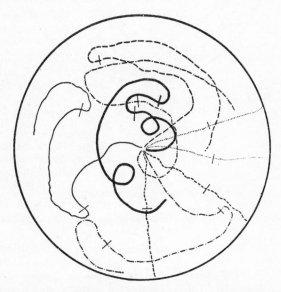

FIG. 56. A, tracks of *Chrysomela fastuosa* in an arena around which is rotated a striped cylinder: the direction of rotation was changed at points shown by a line across the track. Yellow was first matched to a grey (No. 3) (i.e. the combination which evinced no change of direction in the insect when the drum direction was changed), a blue (No. 2) was matched to the grey and the colours were tested together.

———————	when stripes were alternately yellow and grey No. 2				
··············	,,	,,	,,	,,	yellow and grey No. 3
—·——·——·	,,	,,	,,	,,	yellow and grey No. 4
·——·——·	,,	,,	,,	,,	grey No. 3 and blue No. 1
————————	,,	,,	,,	,,	grey No. 3 and blue No. 2
————————	,,	,,	,,	,,	grey No. 3 and blue No. 3
———————	,,	,,	,,	,,	yellow and blue No. 2

Thus *Chrysomela* can distinguish yellow from blue

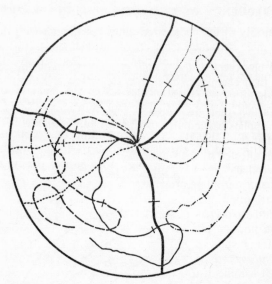

Fig 56. B, tracks of *Troilus luridus* under the same conditions as in A.
——————————— when stripes were alternately yellow and grey No. 2
···············   ,,   ,,   ,,   ,,   yellow and grey No. 3
—·—·—·—   ,,   ,,   ,,   ,,   yellow and grey No. 4
·——·——·   ,,   ,,   ,,   ,,   grey No. 3 and blue No. 2
——— ———   ,,   ,,   ,,   ,,   grey No. 3 and blue No. 3
———— ————   ,,   ,,   ,,   ,,   grey No. 3 and blue No. 4
         ,,   ,,   ,,   ,,   yellow and blue No. 3
Thus *Troilus* cannot distinguish between yellow and blue (Schlegtendal[475])

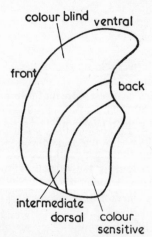

FIG. 57. Eye of an adult *Notonecta glauca* showing the distribution of colour sensitivity over its surface (after Rokohl[459]).

THE ROLE OF THESE REACTIONS

As would be expected, those animals that use matching coloration to escape their enemies or to hide while awaiting their prey seem to have the ability to detect the colour of their background. This ability goes no further than the range of colours covered by the pigment cells, this applies particularly to shrimps and cuttlefish. It has been claimed that the coloration of the caterpillars and pupae of *Pieris brassicae* is affected by the wavelength of the light illuminating them. Thus caterpillars emerging and growing in blue light tend to be greener than caterpillars growing in other lights.

The distribution of colour blindness among insects is not always what might be expected, *Cetonia aurata*, for example, a diurnal beetle feeding on flowers, possesses no colour vision, though it must be admitted that it shows a preference for white flowers, while the dung beetle, *Geotrupes* sp., is sensitive to colour but clearly finds its food by scent. It is difficult to explain why the one insect should possess the ability and not the other: this may be a further example of an inadequate testing method.

The world distribution of flower colours confirms the results of the various investigations performed on flower-visiting insects. The majority of flowers in the temperate zone are blue or yellow, purely red flowers are not frequent. The insects are there the main pollinators. There is no doubt, therefore, that these flowers, producing abundant nectar, as they do, are the most fruitful for the insects to visit, but in the tropics, red flowers are more abundant correlated with the major role as pollinators played by birds, who in these regions take ascendency over the insects as flower visitors carrying pollen.

The numerous patterns forming guides to the nectaries are ideally suited to the capabilities of the insect eye. When the flower visited by *Deilephila livornica* is presented to these moths under a glass plate, the marks left by their proboscides as they attempt to collect nectar from it can be seen to be grouped around the honey guides.[305] In fact, these conform to the most preferred experimental patterns, in being contrasted against their background. It is not only in the flower visitors that colour is the attracting stimulus, but also in various leaf insects. Here green is the attractive colour both in adult leaf chewers, such as *Chrysomela*, and in larvae, such as the caterpillars of *Vanessa* and *Pieris*.

Some red flowers like the poppy (*Papaver rhocas*) are visited by bees despite the general principle that insects are blind to red. The poppy itself has been shown to reflect ultra-violet light and it is by this and not by the red colour as perceived by man that the bees are attracted for they will distinguish between blooms placed under plain glass from those under dark glass permitting only ultra-violet rays to pass; if the plain glass is replaced by ultra-violet absorbing glass they prefer to visit the dark glass through which the ultra-violet can be perceived.[342] The shortest wavelengths also play a part in courtship, for the white and red spots on the wings of *Danaus gilippa,* the milk-weed butterfly, important distinguishing marks in the wing pattern, both reflect ultra-violet rays, the red spots particularly so.[69]

Colour in the visible range would be expected to play its part in distinguishing the sexes in many insects, particularly among those butterflies where the sexes are differentiated by colour patterns. Male silver-washed fritillaries (*Argynnis paphia*) are more frequently attracted to models of golden-yellow to orange coloured paper than they are attracted to actual wings of females. Here the artificial colour, despite the absence of dark markings, has a greater stimulating effect than the natural one with dark mottling.[349] The absence of the correct colours as releasers are no doubt one of the reasons why males are not attracted to females of another species even if their colours are close to those of their conspecific mates. The form *alcippus* of the butterfly, *Danaus chrysippus,* is mimicked by one form (*alcippoides*) of the female of *Hypolimnas misippus* (Fig. 58). Both these butterflies possess brown hind wings on each of which is a large white patch, unlike the other two female forms of *H. misippus.* Male *Hypolimnas* are not attracted to models with white or light-coloured hind wings and are not drawn to female *D. chrysippus,* or, indeed, to the rare *alcippoides* females. For a male to be attracted the hind wing must be largely coloured brown,[506] in fact, white has a positively inhibitory effect on male courtship behaviour. This prevents transspecific mating in these butterflies of closely similar appearance. On the other hand, colour may be only of minor importance, as in the grayling, *Eumenis* (= *Satyrus*) *semele,* males of which fly up to females recognized as potential mates mainly by the form of their flight (p. 134). No great differences are produced by differently coloured models, though the brighter ones are preferred to the darker,[523] and here again white inhibits courtship. (The spectral reflectance of the white patches in these two butterflies does not appear to have been measured, it would be interesting to know whether much ultra-violet is reflected from them.)

The insects are the group with the best developed vision apart from the birds and the primates. In both the flying groups it is interesting to note that colour vision is well developed. But among the

FIG. 58. Wing patterns of *Hypolimnas misippus* and *Danaus chrysippus*. a, *H. misippus* (typical female), ground colour of upper surface orange brown, borders and apex black with broken band of white. b, *H. misippus* (female form *inaria*) orange brown to golden yellow sometimes with pattern on apex resembling typical form. c, *H. misippus* (female form *alcippoides*), forewings rather similar to typical form, hind wing almost entirely white. d, *D. chrysippus*, typical female colour as for a. e, *D. chrysippus* (*form dorippus*) as for b. f, *D. chrysippus* (form *alcippus*), as for c. On right below, male of *H. misippus*, mainly black with large white patches and irridescent blue areas in centre of each wing (Stride[506]).

invertebrates outside the arthropods, there is practically no certain evidence of colour vision. The picture is confused by the various automatic behaviour patterns with regard to light of different intensities, and failure to allow for this has led to misleading observations. The less complex organisms, like the protozoa, may be more affected by light of some wavelengths than of others. This would be expected since it is well known that certain chemical processes are speeded up and others retarded by illumination of various wavelengths. That these biochemical effects may lead to physiological results which, in their turn, may lead to behaviour changes is no evidence for colour vision.

THE REACTIONS OF ORGANISMS TO POLARIZED LIGHT

Wave motion has another quality apart from the wavelength, that is, the direction of motion of the waves. It has already been explained that usually the light from the blue sky is composed mainly of waves in which the direction of motion is perpendicular to the axis of the light waves but at various angles to the vertical. If light consists of waves vibrating in one plane, this is plane polarized light.

It has been known for some time that light coming from the blue sky is partially polarized, the extent being dependent on the relative position of the patch of sky to the sun (Fig. 59). Also the angle of polarization is correlated with the position of the sun. Though some people can see this pattern of polarized light as a series of fringes or brushes (Haidinger's fringes), to the majority polarized light cannot be distinguished from any other. No ability to detect the wave plane of light was suspected among animals.

Work on bees, however, gave the first indication, and then the first proof, that such an ability does exist in the invertebrates. Thus far it has not been demonstrated in the vertebrates. Foraging bees returning to the hive after having successfully found food perform a dance which communicates the direction and distance of the food source to the other workers[196] (Fig. 60).* Either the true direction is given by dancing towards the food source, if the bee is moving on the horizontal alighting board, or the bearing relative to the position of the sun is given if the dance is performed on the vertical face of the comb within an observation hive. It was noticed that the direction was not given correctly if the sky was not visible to the performer, or if the sky was completely overcast. Yet only a small section of the blue sky needed to be visible for the dance to be

---

* Similar dances are performed by bees in a swarm which have found suitable places to which the swarm may go[334]; bees other than *Apis mellifera* by dances which are basically like those of the European honeybee.[335]

orientated correctly.[197] The direct rays of the sun apparently played no part in the organization of accurate communication under these conditions.

As would be expected, therefore, bees dancing on their return to a hive placed inside a tent were erratic and the pattern chaotic, for

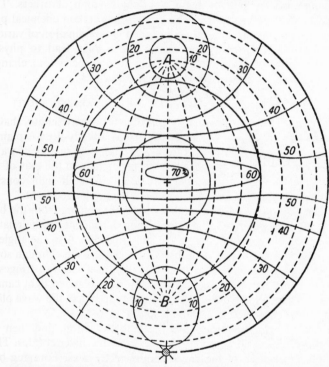

FIG. 59. Distribution of polarized light in the sky, when the sun is on the horizon. The solid lines indicate the points of equal percentage of polarization and the broken lines, points where the angle of polarization is the same. A and B are the two points where the light is unpolarized. The diagram represents the hemisphere of the sky, + being the highest point and the two rings concentric with + being the lines subtending angles of 30 deg. and 60 deg. with the horizontal. (After Müller-Pouillet, *Lehrbuch der Physik*).

all the sky was screened by the walls of the tent. But if a tube was arranged through the roof, its open lower end above the performers and its upper end open to the clear sky, the dance became correctly directed, the relative positions of food source and sun being accurately indicated. Only the polarized light pattern from the blue sky could give the position of the sun in this way. The possibility was corroborated by placing Polaroid sheet, which acts as an analyser, or filter, for polarized light, over the upper end of the tube. When this was rotated, the dances of the successful foragers moved round through the same angles, though with the analyser in certain positions the dances became chaotic again.[198]

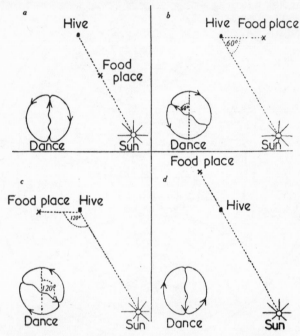

FIG. 60. Orientation of the dance performed by a succesful honeybee forager on the vertical face of the comb, see text (after von Frisch[196]).

Each ommatidium of the bee's eye contains eight retinulae, these light-sensitive cells being arranged around the rhabdome in an octagonal pattern when viewed in cross-section. A false eye was made of eight triangular pieces of Polaroid arranged in a pattern similar to that of the retinulae[199] (Fig. 61). The pattern of light from various parts of the sky gives different effects when viewed through this model so that some segments are dark, others brilliant and the remainder permitting light of intermediate intensities to pass through. The patterns which appeared when the Polaroid was put over the end of the cylinder were then investigated. When the direction of dancing was altered on turning the Polaroid, the pattern was found to be that of the piece of sky towards which the dance was not correctly orientated. Thus, if the pattern from the N.W. sky had been appearing, and now the pattern of the N.E. sky appeared, the dance would be moved through 90°, maintaining its correct relative orientation. Occasionally the new pattern presented to the dancers occurred nowhere in the sky, at these times good dancing was disrupted and the performers appeared lost.

These discoveries recalled earlier work on ants (*Tetramorium* sp.) in North Africa. It had been noticed that a horizontal screen

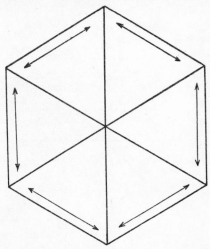

Fig. 61. Arrangement of Polaroid sheet to form a 'false eye'. The arrows indicate the direction of vibration of the light permitted to pass through each piece (after von Frisch[199]).

placed over foragers returning to the nest did not disturb them unless it was so close to the ground as to screen all view of the sky and the surroundings. Further, a cylindrical shield placed over the returning ants did not disorientate them, though all landmarks were obscured. Disturbance did occur, however, when the open top of the cylinder was closed, so that no view of the sky was obtained.[470] Clearly some beacon from the sky, not necessarily the sun itself, was being used. Patterned brightness over the sky was suggested but there seemed to be no such pattern in fact. Finally the suggestion was put forward that the ants could see the stars by day. Stars become visible if the sky be viewed from the bottom of a deep shaft; the sleeve of pigment around the ommatidium of the eye was said to have the same effect.

It has now been shown by a number of examples that ants are able to detect and utilize the direction of the plane of polarization of light.[284a] The experiments originally carried out on the North African ants were repeated on the red ant, *Myrmica rubra*, in an English meadow.[541] Comparable results were obtained. In the laboratory, when illuminated by polarized light, this same ant, which runs in a series of short rushes, was seen to alter its direction by an angle equivalent to the angle through which the analyser was turned (Fig. 62). The black garden ant (*Lasius niger*) was permitted to pick

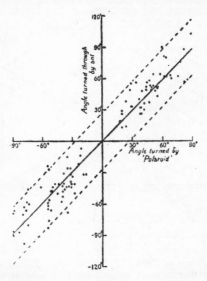

FIG. 62. Relationship between the angle through which the polarizing filter was turned and the angle by which the ants, *Myrmica rubra*, altered course. (Vowles[541]).

up larvae from the middle of an arena and carry these back to the nest.[94] After a time individuals would always leave by the shortest route. But if when the ant was running to and fro in polarized light the plane of polarization was changed while it was picking up a larva, its return was less efficient than before. The extent of this confusion was related to the angle through which the analyser was turned.

Behavioural responses are not the only recordable indications that an animal has received a stimulus. In fact they are sometimes false indications, for an animal may receive a stimulus and not react to it, either for some physiological reason, if, say, the strength of stimulation is too low, or for some psychological reason, if, say, the animal is not in the mood to react. Therefore a more direct method is to record the electrical impulses travelling in the nerve from the sense organ at the time of applying the stimulus. This sort of study has shown the existence of this analysing power in unexpected places as, for example, the king crab, *Limulus*, which lives in the sea. Its eyes are simple in structure consisting only of a retina and a lens. Because there are no ganglion cells within the eye itself it is possible to study the responses of an individual retinal cell.[548]

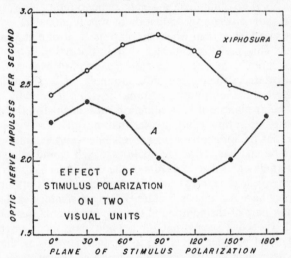

Fig. 63. Relationship between plane of polarized light and the discharge in the optic nerve for two different visual elements of the eye of *Limulus* (Waterman[548]).

In other eyes the individual sensitive cells are coupled together to nerve cells in the outer layer of the eye and when this occurs each one of the nerve fibres travelling in the optic stalk does not correspond to one sensitive cell but often to several. If this connecting ganglionic layer is absent, the electrical responses detected on one nerve fibre will correspond to the reaction of a single cell. By using a fine pencil of light the position of that cell on the retina can be localized.

When one of these eyes is illuminated with polarized light, the electrical response varies as the analyser is turned (Fig. 63). In other words maximum response of the single unit occurs to light polarized in one particular plane (see later, p. 111). With this animal, however, no behaviour response to polarized light has been discovered.

The way in which the eyes of these various animals are able to detect the plane of polarization is not entirely clear.[586a] Only the mechanism of the bee's eye has been investigated in detail and this too was an electro-physiological study of the responses of the eye when it is illuminated in various ways.[17] First the whole eye, that is the whole set of ommatidia which constitute the complete compound eye, was illuminated with polarized light. There was no change in the level of response as the plane of polarization was altered. Nor did a change in the plane cause any alteration when a fine pencil of light was used to illuminate a single ommatidium. However, the level of response when an ommatidium was illuminated by polarized light was higher than when unpolarized light of equal intensity was used. This perhaps indicates that in normal illumination the individual retinula does not react at its maximum. However, if polarized light produces the pattern on the retinulae cells which the false eye suggests, the two opposite retinulae reacting maximally to light of a particular plane will be responding supranormally, the general level of excitation thus being greater than normal. The implication of this is that the individual cells are in some way the analyser.

The rhabdome has refractive qualities which would enable it to act as an analyser.[372] The segments of the rhabdome have a complex ultra-microscopic structure, being arranged in pairs so that members of each pair have a similar structure.[162] No satisfactory explanation of how any part of the compound eye can act as analyser has been produced. Indeed it seems that for aquatic arthropods orientation to the plane of polarization is due to an analyser outside the body. Mysids, *Mysidium gracile*, orientate accurately when they are in water which is even slightly turbid while they do not do so to any significant extent when they are in ultra-filtrated water. When plane polarized light enters, the particles present in turbid water scatter the polarized light so that there is a greater intensity of light produced at right angles to the plane of polarization and points of lower intensity along the plane. Animals appearing to orientate across the plane are, in fact, simply performing a positively phototactic reaction.[21a]

Though there is considerably less turbidity in the atmosphere a further aspect of the properties of polarized light may be important in air. The light will be reflected anisotropically from the objects surrounding an animal and it might be able to orientate by this pattern of reflected light.[21a] However that may be, yet another effect of polarized light may explain the ability of some animals to detect the plane of polarization, again without postulating an analyser within the eye. Changes in the intensity of the light entering the eye will result from alterations in the plane of polarization. The amount of light entering is governed, among other factors, by the different refractive indices of the air and the lens material, by the plane of polarization of the incident light and by the angle at which it strikes the lens surface; this relationship arises from Fresnel's Laws. Table I below sets out the difference in the proportion of the light entering the lens for rays striking the surface at different angles of incidence, assuming the cuticular lens is homogeneous and has a refractive index of 1·55.[505]

TABLE I. The refraction of light passing from air into an homogeneous medium of refractive index 1·55, (from Stephens. Fingerman and Brown[505])

Angle of Incidence	Component of light vibrating parallel to refracting surface (% refracted)	Component of light vibrating parallel to refracting surface (% refracted)
0	95·35	95·35
10	95·16	95·53
20	94·55	96·08
30	93·36	97·00
40	91·23	98·25
50	87·46	99·54
60	80·65	99·88
70	68 01	96·00
80	44·26	76·66
90	0·00	0·00

Thus, at large angles of incidence, the amount of light entering the eye will be dependent not only on the angle of incidence but also on the plane of polarization, while the differences between rays of different planes is almost negligible at small angles of incidence. In fact the electrical responses in the optic nerve of Limulus show little variation when a single ommatidium is illuminated by rays at different planes of polarization parallel or close to the optical axis of the ommatidium, while at larger angles differences become apparent.[550]

The fruit fly, Drosophila, when illuminated vertically from above by plane polarized light will tend to move parallel to the plane when the intensity is optimum.[505] There is no evidence that the fly orientates itself by polarized light under normal conditions nor does it show light compass reactions; in this it resembles Limulus. It is very likely that the movement comes about because the frontal ommatidia of the two eyes will be equally and strongly illuminated in this position as the amount of light which will be refracted into the eye at the air/lens interface will then be greatest for the reasons set out above. The eyes of *Drosophila* are so placed on the side of the head that no incident rays from vertically overhead would impinge directly onto any ommatidium, that is, at an angle close enough to the vertical axis of the ommatidium for the light to travel down the ommatidium to the retinulae without reflection or refraction, but rays will strike at a large angle of incidence. If the fly is parallel to the plane of polarization maximum refraction of light into the eye will occur. The fly would, therefore, be orientating itself to light of higher intensity in each eye by a tropotactic response, such as this insect is known to have for it will take a middle path between two lights of equal intensity, maintaining equal illumination on each eye (see Chapter III).

This explanation may also apply to the ability of ants to orientate themselves when lit from above in the laboratory. For the artificial conditions of the experiment where ants are illuminated by a light source vertically above them, the light from which is almost completely polarized, are very different from natural conditions where the sky is showing a pattern of light polarized in different directions and to different degrees. On the other hand ants have been shown to be able to use this pattern when foraging in the open.[541,284a] Nevertheless the methods of orientation in the two situations may differ.

The sun forms a permanent navigational beacon but it suffers from the disadvantage that only small amounts of cloud need to appear for there to be a fairly high probability that the direct rays will be obscured. Therefore some method by which the position of this ideal beacon could be deduced in a very much greater range of conditions will be of great value, in the daytime, to any animal making numbers of movements which must be orientated between definite points.

This is well demonstrated by the use to which this ability is apparently put by the crustacean sand-hopper, *Talitrus saltator*. This animal moves down the shore following the retreating tide and keeping itself in the conditions of optimum humidity. Sand hoppers from the Tyrrhenean shore of Italy, near Pisa, where the sea lies to the west of the land, hop towards the west and continue to do so when they are transported to the Adriatic coast of Italy, where the sea lies to the east, though they are now hopping away from the optimal conditions.[417] When these animals were observed in glass bowls over which Polaroid filters were placed, the direction of their

movement was seen to change if the filters were rotated. The alteration was in the same direction as the change in the plane of polarization. They are apparently able to compensate for the sun's
movement. For this they are dependent upon some inner timing
mechanism which is controlled by the normal day–night sequence,
and is maintained despite transport to a different longitude.[413] For
example hoppers kept under artificial lighting conditions simulating
day and night but twelve hours out of phase with the real conditions, in fact orientated at about 180° away from the correct
direction[416] (Fig. 64) when brought out onto the open shore. If

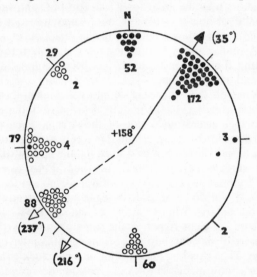

FIG. 64. Sand hoppers which had been kept in artificial 'day/night' conditions twelve hours out of phase with the actual conditions (●)
moved in a different direction to hoppers which had not been subjected to this treatment (O). The actual heading of the shortest
distance to the sea was 216 deg. The figures within the circle represent
the numbers of experimental animals and those outside of control
animals, each ● or O being equivalent to 5 observations (after
Pardi and Grassi[416]).

hoppers are screened from the sky and illuminated with skylight
reflected from a mirror, once again their orientation is disturbed.
That they are also able to perform the classical type of light compass reaction is shown by their ability to use the moon at night as
a beacon.[414] One is led to speculate upon the origin of the behavioural patterns of sand hoppers on either side of small bays, for

elsewhere it seems that each local population has a behaviour proper to the directions of the shore line in its particular area. If their behavioural reactions to polarized light patterns are instinctive, and therefore inherited, as seems most likely, two races with diametrically opposite responses would arise on the two sides. However, nothing seems to be known of the extent to which populations of hoppers are confined to one area and to what extent they intermingle. It is difficult to believe that the behaviour is inherited for it does not seem likely that populations of this sort would remain discrete. Further work would be of the greatest interest. The number of other factors must be great for it has also been shown that these hoppers make for breaks in the skyline[575] when moving up the shore and in a dark room they aggregate in the direction of an artificial breeze.[418] A similar ability to use the sun or the polarization pattern, compensating for their movement, has been demonstrated in the estuarine and river dwelling lycosid spider, *Arctosa perita*. This creature skates on the water surface and when taken from the river bank where it usually is to the middle of the stream, the spiders will go back to their accustomed side of the stream. Each population has its own direction of escape[412] but this seems to be acquired rather than innate as individuals can be trained to take up new directions.[415]

Another surface-skating animal, the bug, *Velia currens*, when placed on dry land always moves southwards, no matter what time of day it is. It will do so accurately if the sun is directly visible, or if part of the polarized light pattern of the sky is visible, or if an artificial source of light is put in the same azimuth as the sun. At different times of day the bug will orientate differently to the same light source. Thus this bug also has an internal clock compensating for the sun's movement. This clock runs in the reverse direction during the night when the bug will orientate to the moon.[49] The amplitude of the oscillation of the angle between the sun and the animal's path of movement is affected by the length of daylight to which the insect is exposed. It can be altered so that it remains regular even in periods of five hours light followed by five hours darkness. Shorter light/dark intervals cause breakdown of the regular fluctuations.[49a]

It is of the greatest importance that the social insects should have a means of accurate orientation, for their social life depends upon the return of foragers laden with food to the nest. It is interesting therefore that the ability to use the sky pattern has been demonstrated in two of the major groups of social insects that have eyes, the bees and the ants.

It is possible to explain the light compass reactions of ants on this basis (see Chapter III). The outgoing forager maintains one sky pattern in its eye on one side and on its return maintains the same pattern in the eye on the other side. During the period that the forager is away from the colony the sun, and consequently the sky pattern, will have moved through a small angle. An error is thus introduced so that the ant does not return exactly to the nest entrance. It does not, however, get lost for it runs the distance required to carry it back to the nest and then begins to run in a series of widening circles until it meets the nest entrance unless it previously encounters some familiar feature of the surroundings of the nest. If it does this, then it proceeds to the entrance directly, using its learned knowledge of the immediate area around the colony. The fact that it can run the correct distance is perhaps more puzzling, since on its return journey it does not necessarily follow the outward track, and runs the correct distance even over unfamiliar ground.

 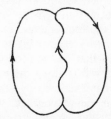

FIG. 65. The dances of successful honeybee foragers which have returned to the hive. Left, the round dance performed when the food source is less than 100 metres from the hive. Right, the waggle-tail figure-of-eight dance performed when the food lies farther from the hive. Intermediate patterns between these two extremes are shown at or around 100 metres distance (after von Frisch[196]).

It is not necessary to propose that an ant uses the sky pattern to detect the position of the sun but merely that it uses one pattern as a beacon. But the dance of any returned honey bee forager communicates the position of the food source with respect to one reference point, the sun. No such form of communication is suspected in any species of ant.

The successful forager's dance indicates not only direction but distance.[196] When the food source has been found less than 100 metres away, the bee moves in the round dance, which consists of two super-imposed circles (Fig. 65). Food sources found at about 100 metres give rise to a transitional dance between the round pattern and the figure-of-eight pattern of greater distances. It appears very much as if the two superimposed circles of the round dance move

E

apart after distances of 100 metres have been flown, the process
continuing until the two parts of the pattern lie side by side forming
a figure-of-eight. It is this dance that gives the indications of the
direction and distance of the food source, the round dance merely
implies that the food is within 100 metres without giving a direction
or an exact distance.

When the figure-of-eight dance is performed on the horizontal
alighting board, the bee when moving along the bar of the eight
gives the direction of the food source, that is, the food she has
found lies along the bar in the direction in which the bee is advancing.
But as she marks out the bar, the dancer 'waggles' her abdomen
from side to side. It appears that the time taken to perform this
part of the dance indicates the distance from hive to food source.[202]

More frequently the dance is performed on the vertical face of
the comb, which can be observed in an observation hive. When
the dance is performed vertically one alteration in the way of presenting the information is made. The waggle dance does not now point
directly at the food source, but the direction of the dance is at an
angle to gravity equivalent to the angle between the direction of
the sun and that of the food (Fig. 60). Thus, if the dancer moves
vertically upwards along the bar of the pattern, the food lies in the
direction of the sun; if downwards, in the opposite direction to the
sun; and at angles between, when the direction of the food is at
those particular angles to the sun's direction (Fig. 60). The
essential piece of information is, in this case, the direction of the sun;
the worker following the forager is not being informed of the polarized light pattern which should be received in her eyes. This is a
matter of what one would call in the human being, deduction. So
also is the central process by which the returning forager must determine the relative position of the sun from the polarized light
pattern received by her eyes. The further complexity of referring the
pattern to one reference point is not necessary unless the directional
information is to be passed on by imparting a minimum of information and, therefore, since there appears to be no means of communication of the direction between ants, it has no part in the ant's
use of the sky pattern. It is very difficult to imagine how a particular
pattern of polarized light in certain ommatidia would be communi-
cated; indicating solely the sun's position is the most economical and
at the same time the most exact way of rendering the information.
Honeybees, like sand hoppers, allow for the sun's movement, once
again dependent upon some inner timing mechanism. And, indeed,
in 425 years, bees originally from the Northern hemisphere have
acquired an inherited behaviour pattern suited to the reversed

movement of the sun which they encounter in the southern hemisphere.[291]

It is interesting to contrast this behaviour with the classic light compass reaction. In the latter, a direction is taken up at an angle to a small source of light and that angle is maintained for a period though the source may move, as when a trapped ant is released from a dark box (p. 71). But both sand hoppers and honeybees are maintaining their direction with respect, apparently, to a complex stimulus, the polarized light pattern, and constantly adjusting the angle. Thus these are in no way to be considered as light-compass reactions *sensu strictu*, but rather as akin to navigation by means of landmarks on the ground (pharotaxis) though even this is an unsatisfactory likeness for the landmarks are stationary but the light patterns are moving. Honeybees do perform true light-compass reactions to the ultra-violet rays (400–300 mμ) from the sun when the whole sky is obscured by cloud. Foragers can still perform accurately orientated dances under these conditions but cease to do so when a board is held between the sun's position (behind cloud) and the bees.[201]

A variety of insect larvae orientate themselves by means of polarized light from the sky when moving across open ground. The larvae of the sawfly, *Neodiprion banksianae*, for example, moves along a straight path in the open beneath a polaroid screen but as soon as the screen is rotated altering the polarized light pattern, the larvae turns through the same angle and crawls in the new direction.[560] Similarly when smoke or clouds made up of ice crystals drift across the sky new polarized light patterns are set up and larvae orientate themselves to these (Fig. 66). Tortricid moth caterpillars (e.g. *Choristoneura fumiferana*) will also utilize the polarized light pattern but if the sun itself is visible they orientate with respect to that whatever changes may be produced in the light pattern by turning the polaroid filter. It seems likely that the larvae are primarily orientated with respect to radiant heat from the sun,[559] and that polarized light navigation acts to maintain this orientation when the sun, and its radiant stimuli, are hidden (p. 78).

It has been found that a number of Cladocera, various species of *Daphnia* among them, also respond to changes in the plane of polarized light illuminating them[37] (these are probably phototactic reactions to light analysed for the reasons set out above in considering *Limulus* and *Drosophila* (p. 111)). This behaviour may permit these fresh-water invertebrates to home on shafts of light in the water, where their food, algae and diatoms, will be more plentiful. It is notable that, in general, only arthropods have been found to be able to orientate themselves according to the plane of polarization of the incident light. There is, however, one exception since it is claimed that the nut winkle, *Littorina littoralis,* orientates itself in this way[86a] (*Littorina littorea* does not possess this ability[396]). Such observations could be explained by the Fresnel effect and probably no analyser within the eye need be sought.

It has been observed that there is a constant pattern of polarized light under the sea,[549] as constant as that in the sky, and this may

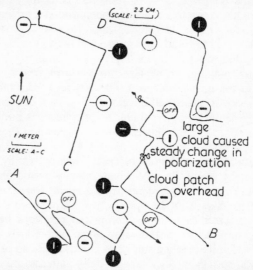

FIG. 66. Effects of rotation of the axis of a sheet of Polaroid on the direction of travel of *Sarcophaga* and of a *Neodiprion* larva crawling on the ground. Circles show the points at which the sheet of Polaroid was placed over a moving insect, or rotated, or withdrawn. The bars inside the circles show the orientation of the axis with respect to the sun, and the colour of the circle indicates whether or not the sky was appreciably darkened when viewed through the Polaroid with the axis set as shown. Track A, a fly with all its eyes functional; B, a fly with only its compound eyes uncovered; C, a fly with only its ocelli uncovered; D, a fourth-instar larva of *Neodiprion setifer* (Wellington[558]).

help to explain some of the diurnal movements of planktonic organisms (p. 319). In clear water off Bermuda, when the surface is viewed from beneath the water the sky pattern was seen unchanged within a cone of 96° centred on the zenith but outside this at all angles down to the horizontal there was a different pattern (Fig. 67). This pattern and that seen by looking down at any angle between the

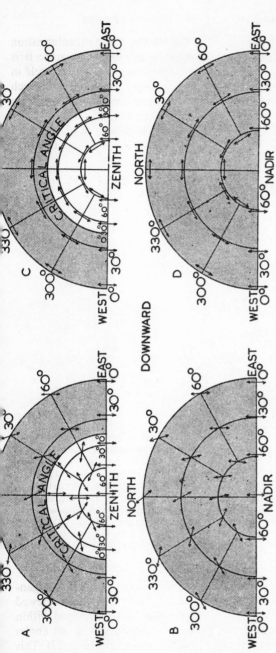

FIG. 67. Polarization patterns of submarine illumination as seen from a point a few metres under water at two different times of a clear cloudless day (diagrammatic). In A and B the pattern shown is that observed at sunrise with the sun on the horizon directly east. In C and D the pattern is that observed at noon with the sun directly overhead in the zenith. The diagrams are plotted on polar co-ordinates with azimuths represented by radii, and elevation or depression of the observer's line of sight as concentric circles. The outermost circle (0°) in each case is the underwater horizontal—that is, the edge of a plane passing through the observer and normal to the vertical. Diagrams A and C show polarization planes seen when the line of sight is raised upwards toward the zenith; B and D show polarization planes seen when it is depressed downward to the nadir. In looking upward, when the critical angle (about 42°) is reached, the sky and its polarization are seen, as they are at all greater elevations. The areas showing sky polarization as seen under water are unshaded; those where the polarization is produced by sunlight in the water itself are stippled. The numbers labelling angles between the critical angle and the zenith are altitudes in the sky measured from the water-level horizon (0° inside the semicircles). These are distorted by refraction, as the plot shows. In all cases the polarization planes are represented by vectors whose angular relationship to the azimuthal radius that they intersect is the same as that between the *e* vector of the polarized light and the vertical at the point plotted. The pattern of light polarization in the observer's other visual hemisphere would be a mirror image of that in the hemisphere shown. Intensities of polarization are not represented in this figure but vary markedly (Waterman [444]).

horizontal and nadir was caused by the scattering of light by particles in the water, the light being polarized nearly everywhere at right angles to the direction of its rays. The percentage polarization also varied. As in the sky, changes of this pattern resulting from the sun's movement occurred, even on cloudy days. These changes might control the diurnal migration of planktonic organisms,[546] no work has been done to prove or disprove this.

CHAPTER V

THE PERCEPTION OF FORM AND MOVEMENT

AN object is identified by eye by the pattern of lights of different intensities and colour which are reflected from its surface when it is illuminated. Some parts reflect more light than others, so that the light from them will be more intense, appearing more brilliant, than from other parts. As well, one part may reflect red light, for example, another blue according to which wavelengths are absorbed by the surface and which are reflected. Thus the light which illuminates the object causes it to assume a pattern of different wavelengths and different intensities which, on reflection, enables an eye to register the 'appearance' of the object, subjectively apprehended as its shape and the distribution of colour, light and shade on it.

The amount of detail in an object will vary. The white walls of an arena painted with vertical black stripes will produce a simpler pattern than, say, the appearance of a tree with all its leaves. Though one is simpler than the other the sharpness of the pattern will be the same in both cases. Different animals may perceive them with different degrees of clarity, but the stripes will have no fine detail while the tree will be full of fine detail.

It is not possible to classify what an animal sees by the amount of detail there is in the object seen, for there is no way of measuring the difference in amount of detail between the stripes on a wall and the leaves of a tree. An objective scale of complexity of this sort does not exist. Most natural objects have complex details while experimental situations are often simplified. Experiments suggest that natural objects are often seen as simple shapes—abstracts from the complexity—thus caterpillars which climb up trees react to black rods or black stripes on a white wall as they do to trees.[277] So that it is not possible to judge the influence of the details of an object on an animal by what a human sees of it. It is, however, proposed here to attempt an arbitrary division on a basis of the complexity of the observed reactions of the animals to shapes.

Clearly the finer the detail, the finer the visual screen upon which its image is received must be if the detail is to be seen. Two points, for example, whose images both fall on one sensitive cell of a retina would not be expected to be distinguished from each other and, indeed, they are not. But if one image falls on one cell and the other on its neighbour they may be perceived as distinct. A similar argument applies to the ommatidia of a compound eye, for each ommatidium, though theoretically capable of receiving an image, seems to act as a single visual element. Therefore, the finer the 'grain' of the retinal screen, or the grid of the ommatidia, that is, the greater the number of visual elements in a unit area, the more detail can be perceived (Fig. 68). The number of elements may be less than the number of ommatidia for often these are coupled together into visual units, e.g. of 7 ommatidia in honeybees.[84] The visual field angle of an ommatidium of an eye of a locust (*Locusta*

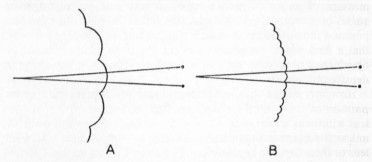

Fig. 68. The effect of numbers of ommatidia on acuity. A, eye with few ommatidia does not resolve the two spots the images of which both fall on one ommatidium. B, more, and smaller, ommatidia increase acuity for the image of each spot falls on a separate ommatidium and they are resolved.

migratoria migratorioides) is larger than the angle between the axes of adjacent ommatidia. Because of this overlapping of the fields, movements of only 0·16° angular displacement cause discharges in the ventral nerve cord, indicating that the movements are received, though the angle between the ommatidial axes is larger than this (2·4° in the horizontal meridian).[88] Thus calculations based on the histology of the eye may not agree with the result of physiological investigations.

This power of distinguishing detail can be measured as the acuity of an eye. It is estimated by finding out how close together two spots may be before they become indistinguishable. The reciprocal of the angle which these spots subtend at the eye when they are in this critical position may be used as the measure of acuity. Thus the acuity of the human eye is from 0·5′ to 1′, that is, two points 8 mm. apart will be seen as separate when they are 5 metres from the eye, but they will not be distinguished from each other when they are further away for the angle they subtend will be smaller. The acuity of a honeybee's eye is 59′ and of the fruit fly, *Drosophila*, about 10°. Acuity varies with the intensity of illumination[236] and, often, in insects, for example, with the part of the eye being tested.

But acuity is not only the result of the fineness of the retina but also of the efficiency of the optical apparatus. Detail cannot be perceived if the image is not properly focused on the retina. However, in the compound eye each ommatidium has a fixed focus and though capable of forming one does not react to an image of an object but only to the amount of light entering it. Here acuity is simply a measure of how closely packed are the ommatidia and of their angles of acceptance. And only those which have their optical axes pointing roughly in the direction of the object will be stimulated, so that a flattened eye may have more elements in action viewing an object than a strongly curved one, even if the latter has the same density of ommatidia.

However, an eye with a lens must have some way of altering the position of the plane at which the image is focused for the same lens will focus a near object behind the retina and a far one in front, unless the optical system can compensate for this. To do this the lens or the retina can be moved or the shape of the lens can be altered to change its focal length. Among invertebrates whose powers of accommodation, as this is called, have been studied, no example has been found of an eye in which the shape of the lens can be altered; this method of accommodation seems to be exclusive to vertebrates. There are various other mechanisms for accommodation found, for example, in the eyes of Alciopid polychaete worms and Heteropod and Cephalopod molluscs.

The Cephalopod eye has a band of cartilage running round its equator, the back is enclosed by separate pieces of cartilage and the whole lies in a cup of the cartilaginous capsule which also surrounds the brain (Fig. 4B). Muscles connect the cartilages together. The contraction of some of these has the effect of forcing the retina forward, decreasing the distance between lens and sensitive screen. Also, a ring of muscle around the lens forces the lens forwards when it contracts, for the pressure of the fluid within the eye is increased pushing the lens outwards. This is another method of increasing the lens/retina distance.[259] A muscle in the eye of Heteropods acts similarly.[260]

In the worm *Alciopa* on the other hand it seems that the lens/retina distance is altered by increased secretion of material into the front part of the vitreous humour which is divided into two parts each filled with a substance of different consistency (Fig. 4A). This is not absolutely certain for it may be that the shape of the eye is, in

E*

fact, altered by contraction of a muscle running round the whole eye ball, or by a combination of both methods.[261]

Acuity may not be the same in every direction across a compound eye, for the vertical width of an ommatidium may not be the same as the horizontal. In the honeybee's eye the horizontal measurement is two or three times that of the vertical. The facet of the eye is broader than it is tall. The eye's resolving power is greater, therefore, vertically than horizontally. Also a compound eye may be divided into areas in which the facet size differs considerably. Thus, in whirligig beetles, the eye is divided into two quite separated parts in which the facet size differs while the eye of a male Bibionid fly has two contiguous areas of larger and smaller facets. Since facet size determines the angle of the field of vision and, therefore, the acuity, these different parts must have different resolving properties, indeed the lower part of the gyrinid eye seems to be for vision through water, and its structure differs accordingly from that of the upper which is for vision in air.

The apposition eye gives greater acuity than the superposition eye. If the pigment sleeve covers the whole ommatidium it will function as a unit, but if the sleeve is withdrawn then the light affects several ommatidia instead of one only and the number of effective light-sensitive units, the grain of the screen, is reduced. Thus night-flying moths which can utilize light of low intensity because of their superposition eyes in which light is used economically will surrender acuity for their ability to see in little light. Some mutant strains of *Drosophila* have no pigment in their eyes, they cannot distinguish the stripes in a pattern which the wild strain can appreciate.[290] Some doubt is thrown upon this evaluation of the importance of the pigment in increasing acuity by measurements made of the acuity of the eye of *Eupagurus bernhardus*, both with the pigment extended and withdrawn. The acuity remained unaltered by a change of position of the pigment. However, this crab's eye has no tapetal layer at the base of the ommatidia. In those crustacea which have, e.g. *Leander serratus* and *Pandalus montagui*, extension of the proximal pigment to cover the tapetal layer (thus reducing internal reflection) and to surround the rhabdomes, did increase acuity, while the movement of the distal pigment had no effect.[69a]

Often the part of a compound eye having the greatest acuity is that which covers the part of the visual field which is covered by the other eye as well. When an overlap of this sort occurs binocular vision is possible. The eyes of *Notonecta*, for example, cover a field of 246° horizontally and of this 94° is viewed by both eyes[343] (Fig. 69). There is all-round vision in a vertical plane of which a segment of

120° dorsally and one of 80° ventrally are covered by both eyes. A similar overlap of visual fields occurs in the eyes of the two sides of the head of salticid spiders (Fig. 70).[271] Such binocular vision usually carries with it an ability to judge distance, it is most important to predacious insects which stalk their prey and finally leap on it or grasp it in their mandibles. The nymphs of the dragonfly genus, *Aeschna*, turn towards their prey so that they are facing directly

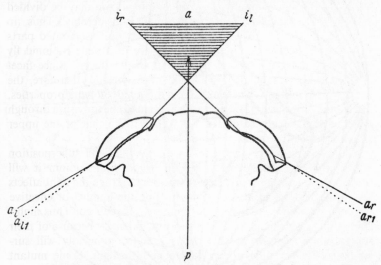

FIG. 69. Diagram of the visual field (in the horizontal plane) of *Notonecta glauca*. The area covered by both eyes is shaded. a–p, longitudinal axis of body; a, i, morphological axis of the outer and inner ommatidia; al_1, ar_1, line of last detectable ray (Ludtke[343]).

towards it. As they approach it the image moves on the inner parts of their two eyes onto the areas of binocular vision. As they approach closer the ommatidial angle of the part of eye upon which the image falls becomes smaller until it is at its limit of 1° 12′. The optical axes of these inner ommatidia intersect at the point where the extended labium will lie when it is shot out to grasp the prey (Fig. 71) so that as soon as its image falls on these elements the prey can be securely grasped. Thus the resolving power of the eye increases as the nymph approaches.[22] The mechanism of distance perception seems to be that the measurement of distance depends upon the stimulation in both eyes of certain ommatidia whose optical axes intersect at a particular distance from the eye. Background has no effect on the accuracy of this judgement so that the

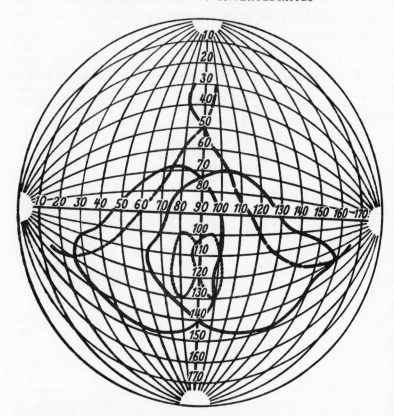

FIG. 70. The visual field of *Salticus* from the front. That of the anterior pair of eyes, dotted; the median pair, continuous line; and the posterior pair, dashed line. The visual field of the posterior eyes also stretches round to the side (Homann[271]).

perception is an absolute one and not relative to other objects. This suggests very strongly that the perception is unlearned unlike the long process, in ourselves, of learning during our upbringing to coordinate distance perceived by stretching out the hands to touch objects and distance as perceived by sight.

THE PERCEPTION OF SIMPLE FORMS

It has already been explained that some of the reactions attributed to movement towards shadows, or skototaxis, may be due to negative phototaxis (p. 67). At the same time it was stressed that some of

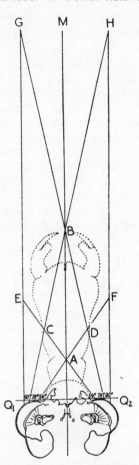

FIG. 71. Visual field of the larva of *Aeschna*, showing position of extended
    labial mask. The lines indicate the visual axes of various ommatidia,
    the intersections determining how far away an object is (Baldus[22]).

these reactions did show features which did not fit in with negative
phototaxis theoretically. Such behaviour as a millipede (*Schizophyllum sabulosum*) shows when it oscillates between two screens
after having reached one of them is not compatible with a phototactic explanation but suggests that the screens are appreciated as
dark objects. This belief is strengthened when the reactions of crabs
and hermit crabs are examined. Individuals of both *Carcinus
maenas* and *Eupagurus bernhardus* confronted by two black screens

will move between them. But before moving they beat their antennae in the direction of each of the screens which suggests that they perceive them as objects rather than as patches of different light intensity. After they have started to move forward their antennae continue to beat up and down but now in the direction in which they are travelling. They do this whether they are travelling backwards, forwards or sideways.[7]

A more striking choice of black stripes is made by caterpillars of the black arches moth, *Lymantria monacha*. These will go towards a man standing near them, to black sticks stuck in the ground, or to black stripes painted on the white walls of an arena. If four stripes are equally spaced out around the wall, caterpillars put in the middle of a circular arena will go in approximately equal numbers to all of the stripes (Fig. 72). When the stripes are of different widths more caterpillars go to the widest, making for the edge of the stripe wide enough to subtend an angle of 60° at the eye. If such a wide stripe

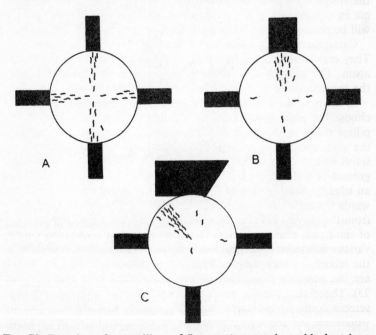

FIG. 72. Reaction of caterpillars of *Lymantria monacha* to black stripes. A, all stripes equal in size. B, one stripe wider than the other three, most caterpillars crawl towards the largest one. C, one wide stripe, one side vertical and the opposite slanting, most caterpillars go towards the vertical edge (after Hundertmark[277]).

is made so that its sides are not parallel but that one is vertical and the other slanting outwards more caterpillars make for the vertical edge (Fig. 72). Similarly if one edge is taller they make their way to that.[277]

The eyes of these caterpillars are groups of six ocelli on either side of its head. Though the lens of one of these ocelli will form an inverted image focused onto the retina, the cells of the retina are so constructed that the form of the image is not perceived. Thus an ocellus reacts simply to the amount of light entering it. This means that on each side of the head the grouped ocelli form an 'eye' with a very coarse visual screen which so long as the 'eye', or the image, is stationary will be too coarse to perceive form detail. But as the caterpillar moves it weaves its head from side to side. This causes the image of a stationary object to move back and forth over the group of ocelli. This is a form of scanning. As the image moves across the ocelli the amount of light falling on each one will alter so that the rough outline of the object will be perceived when all the ocelli act in concert. As the head is moved horizontally vertical objects will be perceived more accurately than horizontal ones.[130]

Caterpillars of this moth feed in trees but often fall to the ground. They crawl back to a tree, up its trunk and back to the food once again. The appreciation of verticals seems to be connected with the recognition of trees and hence of their food places.

In many of these reactions to relatively simple shapes the animals choose the edge of black figures on light backgrounds. The caterpillars move to the edge of wide stripes.[277] First stage nymphs of the stick insect, *Carausius* (= *Dixippus*) *morosus*, will place themselves so that their bodies are parallel with black stripes on a white ground beneath them. If the stripes are wide they stand parallel to an edge.[289] Sand hoppers (*Talitrus saltator*) move up the beach towards the high water region by means of the polarized light pattern from the sky (p. 112) but they also are guided by the configuration of the beach utilizing their ability to perceive simple forms. When various silhouettes are projected onto a screen in front of them in the laboratory they move towards those parts of the patterns which are the bottoms of inclines or to vertical dark-light edges[575] (Fig. 73). Theoretical consideration (p. 67) of how a track between two screens could be explained as negative tropotaxis showed that the woodlouse, or centipede, might be expected to go to the edge of one screen also. Such an edge may be most attractive for another reason for it is the place at which greatest change in light intensity occurs. The way in which crickets (*Dociostaurus maroccanus*) find a hole in any obstacle and proceed straight for it as they march across

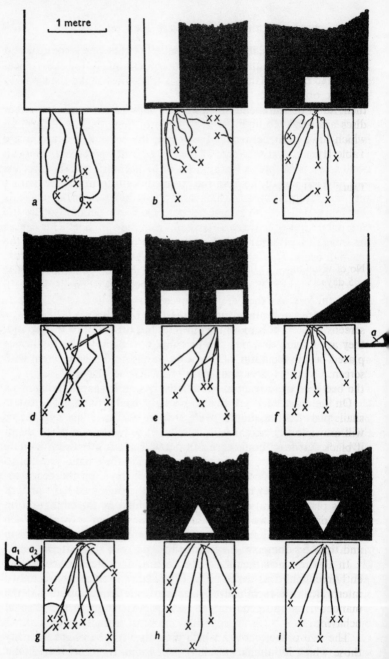

FIG. 73. Visual orientation in *Talitrus saltator*. The upper part of each figure shows projection on a vertical screen; the lower part shows the tracks of hoppers released at X on the horizontal board in front of the screen (Williamson[575]).

country is probably through the recognition of the patch of light of greater intensity against the darker background, for the sky seems to have to be visible through the hole before it is recognized as such.[95]

Dark objects are picked out by humming-bird hawk moths in their autumn search for crevices in which to overwinter. If black discs are scattered about where they are searching they visit those which have radii between 1·5 and 3·2 cms. most frequently[304] (see Table II).

TABLE II. The number of visits made in a five-day period by humming-bird hawk moths to black discs of various sizes.[304]

					Radius of disc in millimetres						
90	64	45	32	22	15	10	7	5	3	2	1·4
96	120	139	255	295	256	187	139	102	55	22	1

No of visits in 5 days (values in row above)

The carabid beetle, *Notiophilus* sp., is attracted by small dark screens. These beetles usually behave phototactically but if while they are moving towards a light a black screen, 4 cms. by 4 cms., is placed beside their track they turn away from the light towards the screen. Other larger screens placed near the small one do not deflect the beetle from moving to the smaller one.[569]

On the other hand animals may avoid black screens. For example, snails placed in the middle of an area covered by a large glass dome will crawl to the edge. They usually will travel in straight lines but if black screens are placed in their path but outside the glass dome they turn aside even when they are some distance from the glass and head for the edge of the screen (Fig. 74). Since the screens are outside the glass dome they must be seen and not sensed in some other way. Snails placed in an arena around which are arranged black screens will move to the edge avoiding the screens. They avoid the dark patches despite the fact that they are negatively phototactic animals and that, by doing so, they are moving into brighter areas.[75]

In all these instances the black objects, or the screens, are apparently recognized as shapes. The behaviour towards them cannot be interpreted as a form of tropo- or telo-taxis for the animals may be manoeuvring quite contrary to the current sign of their phototactic behaviour.

The size of objects is important. If they are of about the size of those which an animal normally encounters then they will evoke a reaction. If they are larger or very much smaller they will be ignored,

This is particularly true of predatory insects, dragon fly larvae, water beetles and so forth, which will turn towards and follow objects of much the same size as their normal prey, though they ignore larger things. Small black balls of paper pulled through the air on cotton with sufficient speed attract male flies if the paper pellets are of about

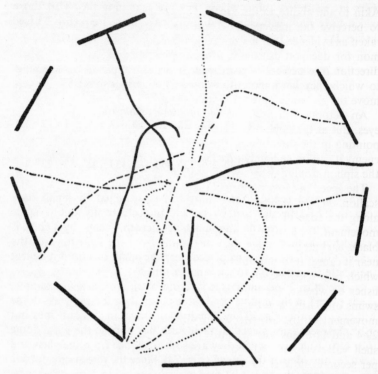

FIG. 74. Tracks of snails placed in the centre of an area covered by a glass dome outside of which are arranged black screens (von Budden-brock[75]).

the same size as females. The males fly after and grasp them as if they mistake them for females.[80]

Such examples as these and the caterpillars of the black arches moth show that an insect's appreciation of the shape of objects which appear to have many details to the human eye is very different from the shape we see. What has meaning for the insect is the essential basic shape, like the vertical darkness of a tree trunk, not the details of the bark. This also applies to more complex patterns of behaviour and we shall see how the shapes of many objects have been investigated to discover what characteristics they have which are important to insects.

PERCEPTION OF MOVEMENT

Akin to the ability to discern black screens or stripes is the ability to perceive the movement of objects. Various indications can be taken as evidence that an animal can see such movement. It is common for decapod crustacea to point their second antennae in the direction in which they are moving. They also point them at objects to which they are apparently paying attention, and as the objects move the antennae move to follow them.[150]

An octopus will follow a moving object in its vicinity with its eyes. But at the same time it turns its body so that its siphon is also pointing in the direction of the object. If the shape proves to be an enemy it can immediately expel water from its mantle cavity through the siphon driving it backwards and away from the danger.

The speed of movement may influence the animal's reactions. The scallop, *Pecten jacobeus*, has a row of eyes of complex structure along the edge of its mantle (see frontispiece). These can perceive movement, for a scallop will react to a pattern of white stripes on a black background which is rotated in front of it. Slow movement near it causes it to put out the tentacles which fringe the mantle and which bear chemosensory cells. If these detect the presence of starfishes or whelks, the main predators of these shellfish, the scallop swims off. Using a pattern of stripes the effect of different speeds of movement can be investigated. If the stripes are moving at between 29·4 and 11·6 cms. per second, the tentacles are withdrawn and the shell valves closed. At slower speeds, between 7·7 and 4·96 cms. per second, the shell is not closed completely and the tentacles are left out. When the speed is slower still, the tentacles are thrust out but the shell remains open. This reaction occurs even at speeds of 1·7 mms. per second but the animal does not react to movement at 0·66 mm/sec.[83] The reactions are produced, in other words, in the range of the speeds of movement of their natural enemies. The effect of moving shadows on the polychaete worm, *Branchiomma*, has already been mentioned (p. 45).

But movement is not only an attribute of an enemy but also of prey and of the opposite sex. Dragonfly larvae will snap only at moving objects. A false sense of movement is given when the objects are offered against a background of moving stripes, when, though the object may be stationary, the nymph will snap at it apparently deceived into perceiving it as moving.[205]

Male butterflies often recognize the female by the way in which she is flying as well as by colour and shape. They may not react to females when they are resting on the ground. The form of the flight track of female graylings, *Eumenis semele*, is important in making the male fly up from his watching post on the ground, for it is by this characteristic that he recognizes the other butterfly as a female of his own species. He will fly up to a small disc pulled through the air at the right speed but greater success is achieved in evoking the male's reaction if the disc is made to loop as it goes along and slightly greater still if it flutters unevenly as it moves[523] (Fig. 75).

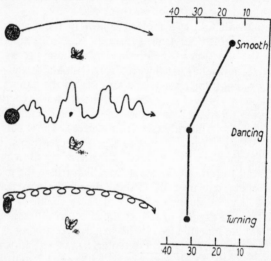

FIG. 75. The way in which a disc is moved influences the number of male graylings which are induced to fly up to it (from Tinbergen,[521] after Tinbergen, Meeuse, Boerema and Varossieau[523]).

THE OPTOMOTOR REACTION

When we watch the passing countryside through a train window our eyes may follow trees, houses, and so forth, quite involuntarily, until they pass out of sight past the back edge of the window. These eye movements keep the images still on the retina, a reflex tendency only subdued by fixation on a particular object. Similar optomotor movements occur in invertebrates, especially insects. Where the animals' eyes are fixed either their heads or the whole of their bodies must move to keep pace with the moving pattern. So these movements are evidence of the perception of the moving object.

The optomotor reaction is usually tested by moving a series of stripes in front of the animal. When this is done, many invertebrates, such as insects, crabs, cephalopods and spiders, follow the moving pattern. The fly, *Pollenia rudis*, for example, will move its head to follow black stripes passing from in front to behind beneath it, tilting its body down at the same time (Fig. 76). If the stripes are travelling in the opposite direction, its head goes up and its front legs extend raising the front of its thorax and its head so that its body tilts upwards.[205] However, the eyes of animals with statocysts,

FIG. 76. Posture of flies, *Pollenia rudis*, when a striped background is moved either forwards (a) or backwards (b) beneath them (Gaffron[205])

e.g. the fresh-water crab, *Eriocheir sinensis*, do not follow the movement of stripes coming from above or below, apparently because eye stalk movement is rigidly controlled by the statocysts in this plane, though the eyes do move to follow in the horizontal direction.[80]

A stroboscopic effect may be observed when stripes of particular width are moved past the eye of the beetle, *Chlorophanus viridis*, for the beetle may tend to move in a direction opposite to the movement of the stripes rather than with the stripes' movement. Movement seems to be perceived as a vector without spatial connotations when two stimulated ommatidia are separated by an unstimulated one.[233a]

That the head movement in response to the stripes causes the body movement which follows is well shown by investigation of the effect of such a pattern moving round a dragonfly standing on a support. As the pattern of horizontal stripes moves from above downwards, the insect sidles round the support in the same direction. If it is suspended so that it can still fly and orientate itself freely, the moving stripes make it roll in the direction of their movement. Proof that it is movement of its mobile head in following the stripes which causes its change of posture comes from the behaviour of a dragonfly when its head is twisted to the left and fixed in position. It rolls in this direction and continues to do so until its head is freed again. Also when a small piece of iron attached to one side of its head is attracted by a magnet so that the head is twisted out of position, it starts to roll in the same direction[385] (Fig. 77).

Libellulid dragonfly larvae can be attached to a moving arm so that they can swim round in a circular tank, the arm being pivoted at its centre. When vertical stripes are moved horizontally past the wall of the tank the nymph reacts differently according to the speed

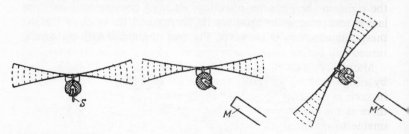

FIG. 77. A small piece of metal, S, is attached to the head of a dragonfly flying in a harness. A magnet, M, is brought up to it twisting the head. As a result the pattern of wingbeat is changed so that the whole body is tilted (Mittelstaedt[385]).

and direction of their movement. If they are moving in the opposite direction to the insect, it bends its body sideways so that its head and abdomen are pointing away from the centre (Fig. 78). At the same time its legs on the side towards the centre are extended and kick vigorously while its outer legs are drawn up in their position of rest. If the stripes follow the insect at about the same speed at which it

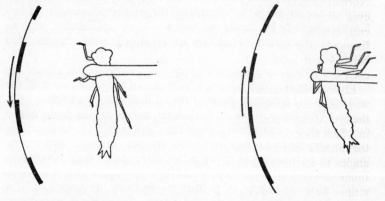

FIG. 78. Movements of a dragonfly larva attached to a support but otherwise swimming freely when stripes are drawn past it (from photograph in Tonner[525]).

is swimming they produce no reaction, but, if they move faster, the nymph bends in the opposite direction to that just described. Clearly these reactions are attempts to maintain a fixed position with regard to the stripes; as they pass from front to back the nymph bends and kicks in such a way that, were it not fixed, it would turn to follow the stripes.[525] Movement to the insect's left is perceived through the right eye, and movement to the right by the left eye. Only the lateral and posterior ommatidia are effective, however, in producing these compensatory movements. The first reaction is that the head is turned and flexing of the body follows.

Many stream dwelling animals hold their position in the current by using visual marks rather than a current sense, i.e. by swimming in such a way that the visual background appears stationary and there is no movement of images over their eyes. So *Notonecta* is unable to maintain its position if its eyes are blackened or if it is swimming in the dark. The absence of any visual beacons when it is in a tank with white sides also causes it to be carried downstream.[489] Movement of images across the eye from behind forwards has the greater stimulating value causing it to swim strongly in an attempt to keep up with the stripes. The eye can be divided according to the reaction evoked by the movement of images over it. There is a medial part which causes turning to the same side, a middle part stimulation of which produces turning in the same direction as the movement of the images and a lateral part which evokes swimming straight forward if the images move from behind forwards, or turning to the opposite side if the movement is in the reverse direction. Normal station keeping in a current seems to depend upon both eyes being used.[343] *Dytiscus marginalis* with one eye covered apparently ignores the movement of stripes unless they pass from behind forwards, the way in which they would move if the insect were being swept backwards by the current (like the dragonfly larva, each eye perceives movement in one horizontal direction only.)[387]

Flying insects also keep their position in air currents in a similar way; they are intolerant of image movement from back to front of the eye. Mosquitoes, *Aedes aegypti*, were put into a small wind tunnel in which they could fly freely. The speed of the air current through the tunnel could be adjusted and the floor was patterned at right angles to its length with stripes which could be moved along the tunnel at various speeds. When there was no air current and the floor stripes were stationary the mosquitoes flew in any direction but as soon as a gentle current of air was made to flow along the tunnel they orientated themselves so that they were flying into the wind. They appeared to adjust the speed of flying so that their ground speed was about 17 cm./sec. They were able to do this in winds of up to 33 cm./sec. when their air speed must have been 50 cm./sec. But as the wind speed increased their ability to maintain forward movement decreased and at a wind speed of 100 cm./sec. they were not able to make any headway. At this point they alighted on the floor. Now, at all times when the mosquitoes were able to fly into the wind, the images of the stripes on the floor must have been passing over their eyes from front to back. At the point at which they ceased to fly forwards and alighted the images would either be stationary or would have begun to move from back to front as they were swept backwards by the air stream. That the movement of these images did in fact have this effect was proved by watching the effect of moving the stripes under mosquitoes flying in still air. When the stripes moved they aligned themselves so that they flew with the stripes moving in the direction in which they were going. As the speed of the stripes increased, more and more mosquitoes flew in this direction until all the mosquitoes under observation had taken up a course parallel to the movement when the stripes were moving at between 13 and 17 cm./sec. It is perhaps difficult to see why the insects which were originally flying against the movement of the stripes turned to follow them. The most probable explanation seems to be that the speed at which the images crossed the eye was higher than some preferred velocity, and, in order to decrease the speed, the mosquito would then turn to follow the stripes. Obviously if in the new position the insect flew more slowly than the stripes were moving, the images would pass from behind forwards over its eye, a situation which seemed to be avoided. And, in fact, when they turned to follow they always flew as fast as the stripes were moving and often travelled faster. It might be expected from the observations in moving air that the insects would settle but they did this only when the images began to move from back to front. In the present conditions, provided that they travelled as fast as the stripes or faster, the images would always travel in the preferred direction.[296] The preference for the upwind direction shown when the air is moving is probably reinforced by the stimulation of some receptors when they are heading into the wind (see p. 254). There are often two combined influences at work, firstly, a preference for image movement over the eye from front to back and, secondly, a preference for a particular speed of movement. The last is well shown in the mosquito's reaction to moving stripes and also when it turns to fly into the wind, as the speed of a following wind increases so much that the speed of image movement exceeds the preferred speed, which can only be counteracted by flying upwind.

Image movement in other directions across the eyes causes an insect to turn so that they once more pass from front to back. This happens when a cross-wind strikes the insect and the images begin to move across the eye transversely, for example, from left to right in a wind coming from the right. It then turns to the right following the direction of the image movement and heading into the wind. This restores front to back movement. This is a further mechanism to ensure upwind orientation which reinforces any mechano-receptor stimulated by the air stream.

It is very probable that the direction and speed of flight of locusts is controlled to some extent by a similar mechanism. Experiments to prove this have not been carried out but there is every indication from observations on locust swarms under natural conditions that it is so. For example, low-flying locusts prefer to fly upwind but, if the head wind is so strong that they cannot maintain any forward speed, they settle. The importance of the movement of the images of objects observed on the ground is clear when a swarm is flying over water. When an increase of wind speed occurs such a swarm may be swept backwards. However, they make no attempt to compensate for the increased headwind maintaining their upwind direction and being carried backwards over the uniform surface which lies below them. On occasion a swarm has been observed in which part has already reached land while the end is still over the water. In such a swarm its members overland turn and settle when the wind speed increases while the tail is swept backwards. Here the effects of the two different backgrounds, the featureless sheet of water and the tree-studded farm land, is clearly contrasted.

It would also be expected that a high-flying insect would be less able to respond to image movement because it would not be able to distinguish the objects on the ground and also their apparent movement would be slower than if it were flying lower down and nearer to them. It has been observed that high-flying locusts are in fact less consistent in their upwind heading and are not so responsive to changes in the wind velocity as insects flying at lower levels.[298]

THE PERCEPTION OF PATTERN

The beginnings of an ability to perceive the whole pattern of the surroundings can be seen in the fly, *Eristalis tenax*. Individuals, deprived of their wings, were allowed to walk along an alley between vertical walls illuminated by dim diffuse light (Fig. 79). If one wall was painted with a pattern of vertical stripes while the other was plain black or white, the fly would not walk straight through the alley but would be deflected towards the striped wall, walking towards it until it reaches it[78] (Fig. 79). The opposite wall might be uniformly white, grey or black, but, in each case, the patterned wall was preferred. This demonstrated that it was not the intensity of the light reflected from the patterned wall which attracted the fly, for white reflected more light and black less than the pattern. Provided the wall bore a pattern it did not matter in what direction the stripes ran, for, if one wall had vertical and the other horizontal stripes, the fly showed no preference for either and went straight through the passage between them. So it was not reacting to the

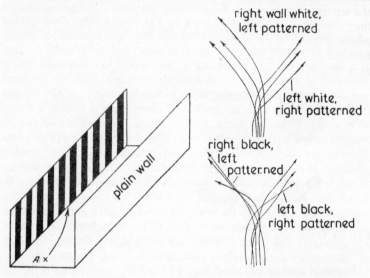

FIG. 79. Flies, *Eristalis tenax*, walking down an alleyway tend to turn towards a striped wall and away from a plain one (von Buddenbrock[80])

changes of intensity, or flickering, of the light reflected from the vertical pattern as it passes by, but was truly perceiving pattern.

A honeybee can distinguish simple shapes one from another. Clearly if it is possible to train bees to go to certain colours for food (see p. 97) it may also be possible to train them in the same way to go to certain symbols or shapes. This is in fact so. Yet when trained to go to a black disc the bee is unable to distinguish it from a square or a triangle when these are offered as alternatives[253] (Fig. 80). Though it can easily distinguish between the disc and a cross or a hollow diamond. Such learning is unaffected if the size of the figure is altered, the only essential is that the figure should contrast strongly with its background.

It is of interest to know not only what the bee can distinguish but also what shapes it prefers. This can be done by training the bee to come to a particular spot for food and then presenting it with various shapes usually two at a time, between which it can choose. Its preference is shown by which of the two it alights on. Training can then be continued to the preferred shape if necessary. Thus a bee will visit a cross rather than a disc. If the learning is then continued the disc becomes the one avoided. By altering the shape to which the bee is negatively trained in this way, some idea can be gained of the way in which the cross is perceived. If the cross is constructed of four straight pieces and the disc is replaced by four exactly similar pieces arranged as a square or laid side by side, the bee's choice becomes confused (Fig. 80). It appears that the cross is not perceived as a whole but that the bee reacts to part of it only, one single

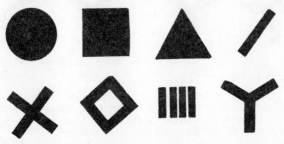

FIG. 80. Honeybees could be taught to distinguish the figures in the top row from each other only with great difficulty, they could, however, distinguish any of them from those in the bottom row with comparative ease (from Hertz[253]).

straight bar unit, in this case. The cross can be replaced by a Y-shaped figure without disturbance of the training for the bee visits it in place of the cross. But replacement by some Y-shaped figure made up of three triangles causes disturbance once again, while other figures formed from the same triangles do not (Fig. 81).

The more outline there is on a figure, the more attractive it is. For example, a figure with a toothed edge becomes more attractive as the number of teeth are increased. In fact, if a bee has been trained to a cog-wheel pattern as opposed to a disc, it will transfer its attention from the cog-wheel if the disc is replaced by another cog-wheel with more teeth than the first. There is a preference, in other words, for those shapes which have the longest outline with respect to their surface area ('Kontourreichtum'). Similarly when a checker board pattern is presented this is preferred, and of several such patterns the one with the greatest number of sub-divisions in a unit area is the most attractive, provided always that the small squares are not so small as to be indistinguishable to the bee's eye. When a series of broken patterns are presented and the bee allowed to make its own spontaneous choice, there is a direct relationship between the number of choices and the length of the outline of the shape[591] (Fig. 82). In nature this means that the more complicated flower shapes will be more attractive and that dark patterns on the petals, such as the honey guides, will enhance their attractiveness for these increase the unevenness of the pattern. In the experiments changes in the colour of the shapes make no difference to the reactions to them.

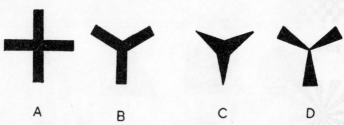

A   B   C   D

FIG. 81. In training experiments A was found to be interchangeable with B without confusing the honeybees. Replacing either one by C caused confusion, however, though the same triangular pieces in a different arrangement, D, did not cause confusion (after Hertz[253]).

Such uneven outlines will lead to numerous changes of stimulation of the ommatidia as the bee passes over them. As the outline increases in length so the unevenness of the outline increases if the figures used are all of the same overall size. Therefore, the number of changes of stimulation per unit time also goes up. As the field of view of any one ommatidium passes over the point of a star or cog of a wheel, the ommatidium will be stimulated by the light background, cease to be stimulated as it passes over the boundary of the dark figure, and be stimulated again when it passes over the further boundary onto the background. Repeated frequently this produces a flicker on the eye. The attractiveness of a figure would seem to depend upon its 'flicker-value'. In a dark room bees permitted to choose between two patches of flickering light both of the same intensity but of different frequencies, will move to the one with the higher frequency.[583] The numbers of choices will be in direct proportion to the speed of flicker. More bees settle on flowers on windy days than on still ones, and it is probably the movement of the flowers in the wind which causes them to attract bees in the first place, their attractiveness when the bee flies closer being dependent upon other factors, such as colour and scent. When half of a bed of artificial flowers were moved while the remainder were stationary, the moving half attracted twice as many bees.[584]

Experiments were also carried out on the influence of three-dimensional figures on the bee's choice. It appeared that when

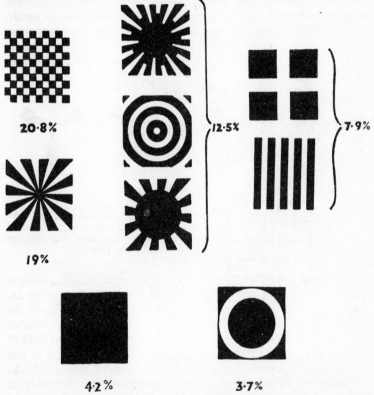

FIG. 82. When presented with these patterns among others without previous training, honeybees showed a spontaneous preference for some of them. The percentage of choices made to each one in 226 tests are shown (from Zerrahn[591]).

models of white paper on a white background were offered the bees visited those with the greatest amount of shadow. Strongly shadowed objects were preferred to uniform ones. Here transfer of learning could not be effected for another object similar in shape to that which had been learned but made of a different material was not visited. It was also clear that bees preferred raised objects, for, when the relative attractiveness of a chessboard pattern and a number of marbles arranged on a white background spaced at similar distances to the squares of the chessboard was observed, more bees chose the marbles.[255]

In view of the suspicion, raised by the experiment described with the four pieces arranged as a cross, that the bees might be reacting only to parts of the pattern and not to the whole, or the Gestalt, it was interesting to find out whether the arrangement of a number of

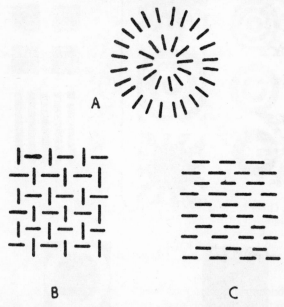

FIG. 83. The bees show a preference for the small pieces arranged as in A rather than B or C. If A is removed, the bees then show no clear preference for either B or C (after Hertz[254]).

similar parts made any difference to their attractiveness. In one experiment 36 short black lines were arranged in a criss-cross patterned square and 36 similar ones as radiating spokes in two concentric circles (Fig. 83). The circular arrangement was visited more frequently so that it was apparent that the bees were not reacting to the 36 similar lines which were in both patterns but to the arrangements themselves.[255] The square pattern probably lost its attractiveness because of the number of parallel lines in it, the total pattern not having so high a flicker-value as the radiating lines.

But though much evidence points to the importance of the flicker effect in the recognition of pattern it is not the only characteristic of importance. For though pattern discrimination is not always accurate—the patterns shown in Figure 80 were confused, for example —bees are still attracted to certain patterns to which they have been trained when they are offered others. Thus, of the patterns shown in Figure 84, bees trained to the sets of small discs would not visit the

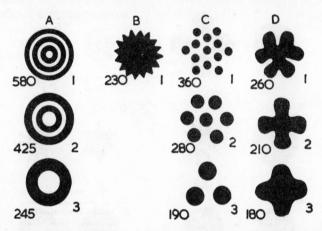

FIG. 84. Other patterns used to test the effect of length of outline on a bee's recognition of patterns (the figures give an index of the length of outline). Bees trained to A1 went equally to C1, to A2 equally to B1 and C2. But bees trained to C1 or 2 would not visit A1 and one trained to D2 ignored A2 (Hertz[256]).

three concentric circles, nor would ones trained to the cross-like figure go to the two concentric circles. Yet the patterns to which they remained faithful had a shorter length of outline than those offered as alternatives.[256] The refusal to transfer training also acted in the opposite direction, as would be expected from the results of the other experiments for the bees would have been deserting figures with longer outlines for those with shorter. It seems that there must be a true appreciation for the pattern and, indeed, alternative patterns with similarly arranged shapes can draw attention from the learned one. Also bees can be trained to go to either of the patterns though they are constructed of different elements, thus, a bee can be trained to go to either a set of three black discs or a set of seven smaller ones[257] (Fig. 84). Here the elements of the pattern are similar and seem to influence the choice.

A similar series of preferences for broken patterns is found in bumble-bees. Here again (Fig. 85) length of outline is important.[316] In addition when a hollow cone mounted on a stalk is offered and with it a black disc of the same area as the base of the cone, the three-dimensional object is preferred to the flat disc. Again we shall note very similar preferences in the hunting wasp, *Philanthus triangulum* (p. 166).

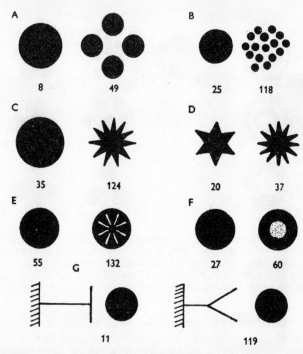

FIG. 85. Nos. of spontaneous choices made by bumble bees between members of pairs of patterns offered to them. In G, a disc on a stalk and an inverted cone on a stalk were offered (from Baerends,[20] after Kugler[316]).

Further proof that bees can learn a whole pattern was produced when they were trained to pick out patterns erected around the entrances to their hives. A disc, coloured blue on its left half and yellow on its right, was put up with the hive entrance at its centre. Other discs, coloured yellow and blue on their left and right sides respectively, were offered as alternatives. After training to the first discs, the second were ignored.[188] It is unlikely that the bees simply learned to fly to the pattern which stimulated the left eye with blue light and the right with yellow, for, before making their choice, they circled in front of the patterns so that the whole pattern must have frequently stimulated one eye only. They must, therefore, have appreciated the spatial relationships of the two colours.

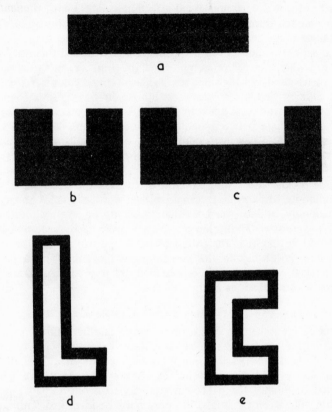

FIG. 86. Shapes used in test of visual discrimination by *Octopus*, see text (after Boycott and Young[58]).

The degree of complexity of structure found in the eye of *Octopus vulgaris* suggests that the animal has efficient vision. In fact, an octopus has considerable ability to distinguish shapes as has been demonstrated by training experiments. These required octopus to make a discrimination between two shapes, being rewarded with food when they attacked the one to which positive training was being set up and punished with a light electric shock when they attacked the

F

other.[58] In all cases the shapes had to be kept moving gently otherwise the octopus only attacked infrequently. They could distinguish between two squares of different sizes at whatever distance they were presented. The area, or the length of outline, did not appear to be the crucial characteristic for they could learn to approach a square of side 5 cms. and avoid a rectangle 8 × 3 cms. though the area and the outline of the two figures are almost the same. The rectangle (Fig. 86a) could be distinguished from the shape of the same area (Fig. 86b), even if the shape was presented the other way up. But when a larger version of the shape (Fig. 86c) was used opposite the rectangle of the same size as before (Fig. 86a), discriminaton was difficult and often unsuccessful. Again an octopus found it difficult to distinguish between Figure 86d and Figure 86e and could not discriminate between smaller versions of these shapes. Also a square of side 6 cms. was confused by one octopus with a disc of 6·8 cms. diameter, though this sort of discrimination appeared to be slightly easier to another octopus when confronted with a square of side 5 cms. and a disc 6·0 cms. across. On the other hand, discrimination between a rectangle placed vertically and one lying horizontally, and between a square standing on one side and one of the same size standing on one corner, were easily accomplished. It would appear that the extent of the shape in various directions and its relationship to the vertical were recognized by a neural mechanism which can be represented by a model scanning the figure in two directions at right angles.[149]

THE USE OF FORM VISION IN LIFE ACTIVITIES

Accurate identification of an object or of another animal is often essential for what might be called efficient behaviour. The recognition of the sexual partner must be confined to an animal of the same species and the opposite sex. A predator may have a very limited preference for particular prey so, to avoid wasted time in hunting the wrong animals, the prey must be identified with some certainty. Again once a route or a neighbourhood has been learned so that an animal can recognize it, accurate identification must often depend on seeing the details of the trees and houses, for example, which give the area its unique character. It cannot be pretended that this identification is always visual but very frequently, at least in the first place, and, particularly in flying insects, the animal's attention is drawn to the objects by their shape. Final identification may be by scent or touch which reinforce or destroy the first impressions.

Since we are dealing here with complex behaviour patterns, for

courtship or food getting are not necessarily simple pieces of behaviour and they often involve many different movements, it is
not always possible to point to the exact role of vision in these
activities for, in most cases, they have not been analysed in great
detail. But the behaviour of a few animals has been studied sufficiently to show the abilities for form vision which they have and how
those abilities are applied. The most usual approach is to determine
the animal's reaction to models. These are designed to present one
element of the visual situation at one time so that the perception of
each can be judged. Since these are models, other forms of stimulation which arise from the natural objects can be eliminated. In other
words, this is a crucial experiment and can be compared with the
animal's reaction to the natural object, as a control.

VISION AND MATING

Display plays a most important part in courtship for by it the two
sexes often recognize each other and are brought together. In birds
it has the additional function of rousing the female, and even the
male sometimes, to the necessary pitch for mating. Among invertebrates this does not seem to be so, the partners being roused in
other ways, the display acting merely as attractive signalling.

Outside the insects examples of visual courtship display are rare
among invertebrates. They would only be expected in animals
equipped with eyes capable of seeing a display and among these the
arthropods are well represented.

The fiddler crabs (genus *Uca*) live on flat shores. Each male makes
a burrow at the entrance of which he stands and entices a female
into the hole where copulation takes place below the ground. The
male has characteristically one chela very much enlarged; the movements of this, the major chela, gives the impression of bowing a
violin hence the crabs' common name. The other, smaller, minor
chela is also waved though it is less obvious (Fig. 87). The movements in *Uca pugnax* will serve as an example of the pattern of
display which also applies to all the species with modifications.
The male raises its body so that it is clear of the ground. At the
start the chelae are flexed in front of the mouth. When the male
starts to signal it raises its major chela, unflexing it so that it moves
obliquely upwards; the minor one moves up as well. When it has
reached the top of its stroke the chela may open and some of the
other legs may be kicked outwards. The major arm is then brought
down again in a series of jerks 'as if let down in worn notches so
that it slides down with the least hint of "braking" '.[108] At the end
of a series of waves the male makes a number of 'curtsies' which are

quick slight movements. He lowers his body with chelae stationary in front of his face and drums on the ground with his other legs. Such behaviour, which in tropical species is combined with striking coloration of the major chela, certainly attract the females to the holes. But no further analysis has been carried out. It is not clear, for example, how the males recognize the females of their own species, for the females do not apparently display in answer to the

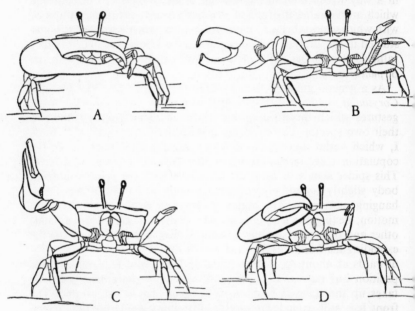

FIG. 87. Display in *Uca*. A–D, *U. lactea*, showing maximum development of the lateral circular wave, in which the cheliped starting from the flexed position (A) is unflexed outwards (B), then raised (C), and finally returned (D) to the starting point. This wave is best developed in displays of moderate intensity; at low intensity or high intensity during advanced display, the wave may be of a vertical or lateral single plane type (Crane[111]).

male. It may be that the ultimate decision to draw the female down into the burrow depends upon scent but she is certainly attracted to the male by his display in the first place.[108]

More is known of the function of the display of salticid spiders. These spiders spin no web, catching their prey by springing upon it. Anyone who has watched any of our native salticids and seen the way in which they will stalk a fly on a window sill will have no doubts that they are endowed with good vision. This is in contrast with the epeirid spiders which use scent as the main stimulus for courtship. These are the web builders and have relatively poor vision. But the bright colours and energetic movements of courting salticids immediately suggest visual stimulation. In fact the ornamentation of the appendages seems always to have a connection with display for any appendage which is used in the display is enlarged or coloured in a way which is visible to human eyes. The palps, for example, which are vibrated in front of the face are very frequently covered with white scales; this is true not only of the South American species, studied in the analysis to be described, but also of some of our native salticids [e.g. males of *Salticus scenicus* or *Sitticus truncorum* (= *S. pubescens*)].

As a general guide to the courtship movements the behaviour of *Corythalia xanthopa*, a South American species, indicates the main gestures which the male spiders make on identifying a female of their own species. The courtship divides itself into two parts, stage I, which varies among the different species, and stage II, a precopulation stage, which is much the same for any species.[109, 110] This spider stands in front of the female with the fore-part of his body slightly raised, his abdomen slightly lowered and his palps hanging motionless. He begins to move in a side to side rocking motion, flexing his legs on one side while extending them on the other and then reversing the movement (Fig. 88). He follows this by extending his front legs forward, parallel to each other but pointing upwards at about 45° to the horizontal. He does not pose in this position but moves. If he has attracted the female's attention he takes up the stage II position in front of and facing her with his front legs still extended forwards, his stance being similar to the second part of stage I.

A male will not court a female until he is adult and even then males differ in their excitability. The factor of different excitability affects the results of tests for they must be made on a number of different males to eliminate any differences in their sexual level. There is no doubt that the courtship is evoked by the sight of females for, if the eyes of a male are blacked over, it will not court a female. Of the three pairs of eyes the antero-median pair is the most important in courtship since blackening of these two alone will prevent the male recognizing the female. Recognition in the reverse direction, that is, of male by female, is also visual. A temporarily blinded young female, though in reproductive condition, would not react to a courting male, but five minutes after the varnish has been removed from her eyes she accepted him and they mated. There is, however,

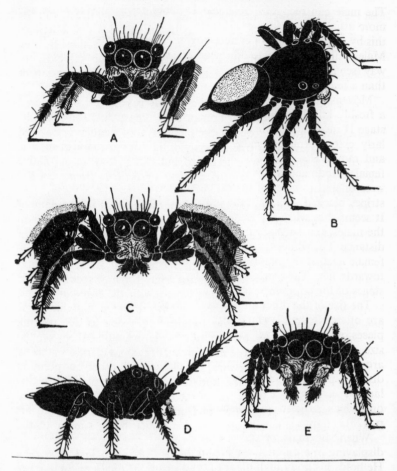

FIG. 88. Display in male *Corythalia xanthopa*. A. frontal view of rocking preface to threat and courtship displays; B, dorsal view of same; C, threat display; D, courtship, Stage I, lateral view; E, same, frontal view. Yellow areas stippled (redrawn from Crane[109]).

definite evidence that chemical stimuli also reinforce the recognition for a long dead female will not rouse a male. But as it is not possible to measure the differences in chemical stimuli these have had to be ignored for the moment.

Having established that vision is important, it is possible to proceed to analyse the factors which cause the recognition and thus to obtain some idea of the capabilities of the eyes for form vision.

The male can recognize a female at about ten inches distance but more usually he sees her at six inches. In both cases he demonstrates this by turning towards her and moving up to his courtship position. Males will also display to other males, threatening them in a different way (see later). They seem to recognize a male at a shorter distance than a female.[110]

Movement of the female is essential. While a male will not court a freshly killed female held quite still he will at least perform the stage II movements when the dead specimen is jerked about. Similarly chloroformed females evoke no response until they awake and move. Here the function of the two white stripes down the female's abdomen shows itself. For when two chloroformed females were offered to a set of males, one of the females having the white stripes blacked out, only the untouched female attracted attention. It seems that when the immobile females were twitched in front of the males, the normal one was most easily detected at the greatest distance. The white stripes may enable the male to pick out a moving female against the natural background so that he directs his search towards her. The stripes appear to have no function in the later stages of the courtship.

The size of the other animal exercises some influence. When males are offered females whose size has been enlarged by sticking on pieces of gauze they will court only animals up to twice the normal size. At the other end of the scale they will react only to models which are one half of the natural size or bigger. From a point of view of distance perception it is interesting to note that they react to the larger specimens at a greater distance than they would to a normal one which suggests that distance is perceived by relative size (cf. p. 125).

When the male perceives another male he will threaten it by displaying in a different way from that in which he greets a female. He holds his body high off the ground with his palps flexed in front of his face so that the yellow scales on them continue the band of yellow which crosses his clypeus (Fig. 88). His abdomen is lowered. His front legs are on the ground, but his other legs are raised off the ground, each pair progressively higher than the ones in front of them. He poses motionless in this position.

When a male reacts in this way to another spider or to a model we can say that the other is being perceived as a male. By altering various features we can find out the characteristics which distinguish the male from the female. We are helped by the fact that the male will notice its own reflection in a mirror. In fact it threatens itself. But if a male has its palps removed and its clypeus shaved to remove the yellow scales it courts its reflection, recognizing its changed appearance as that of a female.

A number of models can be offered to it as well. These vary from simple bars to crude representations of the shape of a threatening male when viewed head on. A selection of these are shown in Fig. 89; some of these were successful in evoking threatening and others

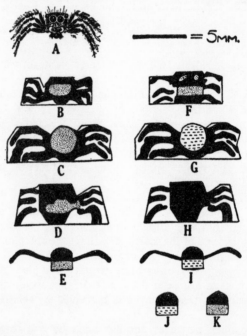

FIG. 89. Models used in tests to determine the stimuli responsible for evoking courtship from male *Corythalia*. Those in the left-hand column were successful, those on the right unsuccessful. Yellow areas, stippled; white areas, dashed; backgrounds of all, light green. Note that some unsuccessful patterns only differ from successful ones in colour (Crane[110]).

were not. When the patterns are examined it will be seen that the most successful always consisted of a square or rounded centre section which was black with a yellow patch on it. The 'body' of the model had to have lateral extensions to ensure its success. This agrees with the experiments on legless dried specimens of males which did not evoke threat. Similarly legless female bodies did not produce the complete courtship response for the male broke off his display before he had reached stage II and often before he had completed stage I. As soon as two legs were laid on the dead legless female the male courted her though he had refused to do so when only one leg was put on the specimen. Thus the legs of the other animal are clearly seen. The importance of legs on the female model has also been demonstrated in *Salticus scenicus* (= *Epiblemum scenicum*), the stripes on the female abdomen are important here as well.[153]

This sort of evidence goes further than simple observation of the courtship for from it we can say that the eyes, and particularly the antero-median eyes, of these salticids are capable of perceiving detail in the shape of another spider, only about 5 mm. across, at a distance of six inches, a very reasonable power of acuity (binocular vision may well aid in this).[271]

A rather similar analysis has been made of the courtship of grayling butterflies (*Eumenis semele*).[523] When they are in reproductive condition the male butterflies rest on the ground until a female flies by, when they fly up and follow her. If she is in the right physiological condition she alights on the ground where the male joins her. Then, facing her, he performs the courtship bowing and other movements, finally mating with her. Vision plays its part in the first recognition of the female as it flies past the male. It also plays a less important role in the courtship movements which are performed on the ground, for here scent plays the major part.

By the use of models we can investigate the recognition of the female. The shape of the model seems to have little influence nor does its colours, but the way in which it moves does influence the male. When a disc which is drawn through the air near waiting males, some will be stimulated to fly up; more of them will react when the disc is moved irregularly through the air, either rising and falling or looping, than when it is drawn along smoothly (Fig. 75). A male silver washed fritillary is attracted to the female by the flashing of the pattern on the upperside of her wings as they open and close in flight.[349] The importance of the form of the flight path has not been specifically investigated in either this butterfly or in *Hypolimnas misippus*,[506] (p. 102) but it would appear that with both these insects colour and colour pattern are the dominant features attracting the males to the females.

The way in which the female moves also attracts male flies. Small black balls of the same size as a female fly were covered with glue. They were pulled through the air on the end of a thread at roughly the same speed as a flying insect. Males flew to one and grasped the ball sticking to it themselves. The number of times

F*

that a male was caught showed how realistic the rough models were. Slower moving balls caught no males.[80] Since they only mimicked a fly in size and movement these must be the characteristics by which the male recognizes the female.

VISION AND PREY CATCHING

Relatively little work has been done on the identification of prey. It has long been known that many animals will not attack prey unless it is moving. The salticid spiders, for example, will not attack dead prey unless it is jerked about. It is movement which attracts dragonfly nymphs to their food.[22] These nymphs can be made to attack motionless prey if a striped screen is moved horizontally behind the prey.[205] This produces an impression of movement in stationary objects even to our eyes. An adult dragonfly notices moving objects in the air and it will turn towards pellets thrown into the air. But the reaction goes no further for, as soon as the image of the pellet is fixated so that the pellets are seen clearly, the dragonfly turns away.

But many animals and particularly insects have very restricted preferences for particular prey, which is often recognized, at least at a distance, by sight alone. But the factors upon which recognition depends have not been analysed in many species.

The hunting wasp, *Philanthus triangulum*, hunts honeybees and uses them exclusively for storage as food for the developing larvae. Its attention is drawn by any flying insect which looks like a honeybee so it flies towards hover-flies as well as to bees themselves. This recognition is entirely by vision and the wasp is not deflected from its flight to the prospective prey by the scent of a honeybee. This can be proved by offering the wasp a tube in which bees have been shaken and which will, therefore, be strongly scented with their smell. The wasp shows no interest in the tube. However, as it nears the prey it identifies it more certainly by scent, for a hover-fly is ignored when the wasp draws close but a bee is seized. Yet a hover-fly will also be grasped if it has been shaken with some bees; the wasp is then deceived by the bee scent adhering to the fly's body. After grasping the bee the final decision whether to sting it depends apparently upon the 'feel' of the bee since they discard other insects disguised with bee scent. It seems probable that the first recognition of the bee depends upon perception of the bee shape for the way in which hover-flies and bees fly are very different, they are only alike in their appearance.[520]

Spiders of the salticid species *Salticus scenicus* were kept in a cage, two walls of which could slide back and forth horizontally.

They could be induced to stalk and jump at black figures on a white wall, provided that, in most cases, the figures were moved[153] (Fig. 90). Plasticine balls evoked more attacks than flat shapes, and the optimum speed of movement was lower for them than for the flat figures. If objects were small, i.e. less than 0·6–0·8 cms. across, or too large, they were not attacked, though hungry spiders might attack larger shapes than satiated ones would (compare with the importance of correct size in courtship, p. 153). Figures with long outlines were preferred to ones with shorter; thus, solid figures of flies were preferred to similar sized black shapes without wings, head and legs. The spiders confronted with a black shape from which

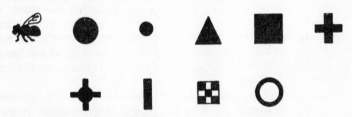

FIG. 90. Shapes releasing attack from spiders, *Salticus*, when moved in front of them (from Drees[153]).

they got a mild electric shock if they attacked it, learned not to attack. This learning was generalized to some extent to similar shapes, as was shown when other shapes were substituted for the one to which negative learning had been set up. Those releasing attack were ones which differed from the ones which they had learned to avoid (Table III).

Octopus can be trained to accept either fish or crabs as food. There is no clear evidence whether the recognition of food organisms is innate in *Octopus vulgaris*.[57] Since all slowly moving objects below a certain size are attacked by octopus in tanks, provided that the objects are presented for a long enough period,[58] it may be that the young octopus attacks almost anything moving, obtaining reward and, therefore, reinforcement when the objects are crabs or fish. The behaviour of young *Sepia* on the other hand immediately after emergence from the egg seems to indicate that at first they discriminate rather rigorously, attacking only objects which have a similar appearance to mysid crustacea, but that later their attack reaction becomes more generalized.[562] Later still, probably as the result of learning, they restrict their attacks to food objects only.

This is contrary to the more usual progression from generalized response to a more specific and ultimately, perhaps, a highly specific response found in most animals.

TABLE III. Numbers of attacks made by spiders (*Salticus scenicus*) on different shapes after negative training to the shapes in the left-hand column.[153]

Figure to be avoided	№	№ of attacks in 6 tests						
		▼	▲	▲	◣	◣	△	●
▲	1	0	0	3	2	6	4	6
	2	1	1	4	3	5	4	6
		✖	✚	+	✚	T	■	●
✚	3	1	2	5	3	5	6	5
	4	0	1	4	2	4	6	6

THE RECOGNITION OF FLOWERS AND FOOD PLACES

In much the same way that predatory insects may prefer certain prey so also insects which are nectar feeders prefer certain flowers because they give a good supply of nectar. The range of preference is quite wide, in effect most of the insect pollinated flowers will be visually attractive to insects. All these flowers have certain common characteristics. They are, for example, frequently coloured blue or reflect much ultra-violet and this end of the spectrum is most attractive to bees, moths and butterflies (see Chapter IV).

It is known that, after having picked out a patch of flowers which are yielding a good supply of nectar, bees will revisit the blooms until the nectar flow ceases when they will move on to others[91] though they may move on before the supply is exhausted.[453] Here there are two problems involved, first, the flowers must be found and second, their position must be learned.

The attraction of the colour of flowers is enhanced for a honeybee by their movement (p. 142). Dark stripes on petals which form honey guides contrast with the lighter background of the rest of the petal and increase the flicker value. It is unlikely that the bee actually follows the line of one of these stripes inwards to the centre of the flower, but it is more probable that it goes to the centre of the flower because the radiating lines of the guides come to a focus there and close to that point the flicker value will be greatest. The attraction of the colour of flowers is enhanced for a honeybee if they are moving. Dark stripes on petals which form honey guides contrast with the lighter background of the rest of the petal and would be expected to increase the flicker effect to which the whole pattern gives rise. It might be thought that this would make the flowers more attractive, but work on bumblebees suggests that this is not so and that the guides are only effective close to, when the bee has already approached the flower, though such a pattern may cause them to hover longer than a plain colour. Bumblebees approach the edge of an artificial flower pattern first and, if there are honey guides on it, on subsequent approaches, more get to the centre of the 'flower' immediately. It is the edge, where contrast between the flower colour and the background is most obvious, that is the major attraction. Often flowers with visual honey guides have coincident scent guides which enhance the guiding effect of the pattern.[352]

Though flower patterns with and without honey guides were not apparently distinguished by bumblebees, honeybees could learn to select patterns with guides from those without (Fig. 91a). These patterns were arranged with their centre formed by a hole into a box containing food. The essential part of the pattern which was learned by the bees was that part lying on the flight path and a few millimetres to either side of it. Single line guides were tested (Fig. 91b) and it was found that to be effective they must have a minimum width and also occupy a critical part of the 'petal'.[34]

Such radiating honey guides also attract moths. Model flowers with and without honey guides were offered to humming-bird hawk moths. They visited and attempted to suck at the circles which had lines radiating from them but they did not go to the plain circles with any great accuracy. The spot of orange on the lower lip of the toad flax flower also directs a visiting moth which protrudes its proboscis in the direction of the spot. This again is a contrasting pattern, albeit a simple one, of the dark orange spot against the paler yellow corolla.[304]

Both bees and bumblebees are attracted to fly towards disrupted patterns and certain colours. They do not alight, however, unless the scent they perceive is appropriate, thus they do not often visit artificial flowers which are unscented and have no food in them.

The way in which a bee learns the appearance and position of its food place has been investigated. Bees were trained to come to dishes of sugar water which were set out on glass plates beneath

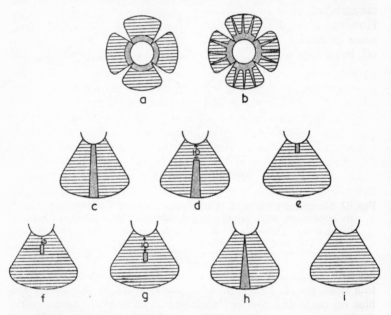

Fig. 91. Honeybees could learn to distinguish the right-hand (b) from the left-hand (a) pattern. Tests with various stripes on petalloid figures show that clearly marked honey-guides like the stripe on c (2–6 mms. in width) is most effective, thus, results of tests were:- i and h almost indistinguishable, i and c distinguished, d and i almost indistinguishable, i and e distinguished, i and f barely distinguished, i and g indistinguishable (after Baumgartner[34]).

which various coloured papers were put. These were arranged one above the other, for example, a blue piece above a red one which rested in turn on a white piece (Fig. 92). The topmost blue piece was left in place until the bee alighted and started feeding. Then the top piece was pulled away so that it fed on a background of red. As

soon as it stopped feeding and before it took off preparatory to returning to the hive, the next piece of paper was removed revealing
the last colour. On its return the bee was offered all three colours
from which to choose before alighting; whatever colour it had
learnt during its first visit would influence its choice. It was clear
from the choices made that the colour displayed while the bee approached the food was the one that was learned.[404]

Flat shapes and three-dimensional objects were also put out at the
three different stages of approach, drinking and departure. Again
the shape, say, a cross, which the bee saw as it approached was
remembered, while the square seen as it departed was not remembered.
However, if no distinctive shape was visible as they approached,
some individuals would learn the shape they saw when they flew
off, but if they did so, the choices they made as a result were more

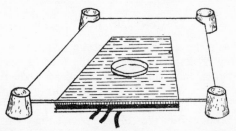

FIG. 92. Method of presenting different coloured or patterned backgrounds
to honeybees while approaching a food source, feeding there or
flying away. Three papers are arranged under a dish of sugar water
so that they may be withdrawn one after another to expose different
patterns or colours (after Opfinger[404]).

hesitant and less accurate than before. They would also learn to go
to a small box, $5 \times 5 \times 9$ cms., painted black on the outside and
blue on the inside, if it was displayed to them as they approached
the food.

Sometimes the food on its glass plate was put under a small roof
on a table. The roof was removed before the bee flew away. Again,
to judge from its subsequent preference for roofed rather than un-
roofed food places, the bee learned that food was present under a
roof on its approach flight. In addition a bee seems to learn the
appearance of the surroundings of the food over a radius of some
10–35 cms. round the food dish. These experiments suggest that a
bee learns the look of a bed of flowers as it flies towards them.

When a bee leaves such a food dish which it has visited for the
first time, it circles in the air before flying away to its hive. For a
long time it was believed that the bee was then learning the position

and appearance of the food dish. But it is now quite clear that the appearance of the dish is learned as it approaches and other experiments have proved that, as it circles on leaving, it learns the more distant surroundings of the dish, so that it can navigate on its return to the general position of the dish and then, finally, pick it out by the information it has gathered on a previous approach. Throughout the experiments which have been described the bees only performed these orientation flights when they left a dish which had been put into a new place and which they had visited for the first time, despite any changes in the coloured backgrounds while they visited the dish in that place. This was to be expected as the distant landmarks would need to be learned only once, and changes in the immediate surroundings of the food would not affect the learning of these distant objects.

VISION AND HOMING

Once a bee has collected its load of nectar or pollen it must be able to find its way back to the hive for the food is destined for the growing larvae. In fact, social insects depend upon the ability of the foragers which search for food to return to the colony. And this homing must be accurate, for the greater the accuracy, the more food will be brought into the colony in a set time. Once a plentiful source of food has been found the foragers also need to be able to locate it again and, in fact, do so as we have seen in the previous section. The importance of the pattern of polarized light from the sky as a guide for the bee returning to its hive has been mentioned already (p. 104).

Once bees have become accustomed to returning to a hive in a particular position they will continue to return there even after the hive has been moved. If the hive is merely turned so that the entrance faces in a different direction the bees still return to the position which the entrance occupied originally. Since, in the first instance, removal of the hive also removed all sources of stimulation apart from those arising from the surroundings, it is clear that the bees must have been depending upon visual clues, having learned the position of the hive and its entrance relative to objects in the neighbourhood.

A careful investigation of the effect of moving a hive has shown how the distance and direction in which it moved is correlated with the disturbance produced. In these experiments the disturbance was indicated by a reduction in the number of bees returning to the hive per minute while the extent of the disturbance was measured

by the time taken for the normal average number of workers returning accurately to be restored. The hive was moved either sideways,
backwards, or upwards from the flight line. In all instances it was
necessary only to move the hive a distance equivalent to its width
for disturbance to be caused. However, the effect lasted longer
when the hive was moved in one direction than another. It lasted
for the shortest time when the hive was moved backwards, twice as
long when it was moved sideways to left or right and three times as
long when it was moved upwards. At the end of each of these periods
of disturbance the foragers were returning directly to the hive in
its new position.[581]

If the hive was moved with its population of bees to a new place,
subsequent displacement of it did not produce these effects until
some time had passed. As the time went by the disturbance caused
by moving it in any of the three directions increased, thus after 14
hours it was slight even when the hive was moved 40 cms. upwards
but after 48 hours there was definite disturbance, which was the
same whichever way the hive was moved, and after 77 hours the
disturbance varied according to the direction in which the hive
was moved, in the same order and to the same extent as in the original
experiments mentioned above.

To discover what would be the effect of moving a possible landmark a 5 meter plank was placed on the ground beneath the line of
flight of the returning foragers. When the plank was moved sideways, having been in place for some time, the bees were disturbed
and did not home accurately.[582] In order to eliminate visual landmarks, screens were arranged around the hive and on the ground;
the disturbances produced when these screens were in place supported the view that knowledge of the surroundings arose from
learning the appearance of the objects in the vicinity of the hive.
Where orientation objects were few, returning foragers found the
new site of their hive less quickly than if it was standing in a place
rich in objects which could be discerned by the bees. The differences
between the amount of disturbance produced when the hive was
moved in the various directions are not surprising when they are
considered more closely. Movement back along the flight path
involves the least re-orientation for the forager since it has only to
continue on its flight bearing. If the hive is to one side of its original
position this involves a change not only of the bee's position along
the track but also sideways movement. It is fairly certain that the
acuity of a bee's eye is greatest horizontally and therefore when the
hive was moved upwards it moved into an area where the bee would
be less able to distinguish it, apart from adding to its difficulties the

necessity for it to displace itself in yet a third direction—upwards.

Bees can show great adaptability to alterations in the position of the hive entrance. Three brood chambers were piled one upon another with bees in the middle chamber. The entrance opened to one side. Then the middle and upper chambers were exchanged and at the same time the entrance was moved through 90° to open on the front face of the pile. Two days later the occupied chamber was moved to the bottom of the pile and the bottom empty chamber transferred to the top. Again the entrance was moved through 90° to open on the other side face (Fig. 93). The bees adapted themselves

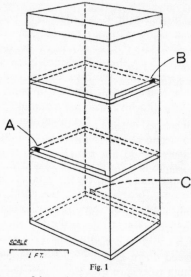

Fig. 1

FIG. 93. Arrangement of brood chambers for experiment on homing in bees, see text (Ribbands and Speirs[455]).

to these changes quickly. After the first interchange a few returned directly to the entrance in its new position and after the second change 50% were correct. The greater success of homing after the second change is probably due to the disturbance of the first change which made the bees less conservatively resistant to alteration of their flight positions.[455] The accuracy of the bees throughout the whole manoeuvre may have been due partially to their use of colony odour, and not vision, for locating the entrance. Here again we find orientation which begins visually in the whole process of finding the way back to the pile of chambers, after which perception of entrance is by scent.

How local knowledge is acquired can be studied by transferring a hive of bees into a part of the country where they are unlikely to have flown before. When individual bees from such a transported hive are taken and released a short distance away before they have flown in the new place, they are unable to find their way back to the hive. Their ability to return to the strange site after being carried away increases slowly in proportion to the number of hours they spend flying in the new area. They explore in an ever increasing circle around their hive, a circle which continues to expand unless they meet an obstacle like houses or thick woods when their area of exploration becomes distorted as they avoid these places.

Bees transported in a black box to some area in which they had not foraged would leave the box, forage, and return to it. Their attachment to their original point of release was a very firm one for pollen bearers continued to return to the site of their release from 9 a.m. until the afternoon even after the box itself had been removed.[581]

These experiments do not show conclusively that the surroundings were learned as objects. It is quite possible that they may be explained as increasing knowledge of the polarized light pattern from the sky (p. 104), for foragers would not return to the place to which they had been transported when the sky was overcast or when dusk was falling; at both times the polarized light pattern would be obscured or indefinite.

But more certain evidence of the use of landmarks was obtained by experiments which were carried out on a disused aerodrome, a sandy waste which could be considered as free of visual landmarks. The hive was placed down and the bees permitted to fly freely for a time, long enough to ensure that they knew the area.[582] Blue and yellow squares were placed along the track of the bees. When the hive was moved sideways the bees returned to the old position and searched for it there. If the marks were moved sideways the track of the bees was moved sideways as well and they searched at the end of the track for the hive. But when both hive and marks were moved sideways many returning foragers persisted in their correct track undeceived and searched the area of the old position of the hive. Therefore, though the landmarks had some influence, they were not of overriding importance and, when complete changes occurred in the marks and their relative position to the hive, the bees probably depended on polarized light to find their way back.

The evidence points to a preference on the part of honeybees for objects which have broken outlines and which throw shadows (p. 143). Since most natural objects fit both these requirements

there is no difficulty in suggesting that bees have in fact the ability
to orientate by natural landmarks.

Another group of insects can also navigate accurately. These are
the solitary wasps. They dig a burrow in which they lay an egg and
in which the larva develops. When the egg is laid it may be surrounded with food or, as the larva develops, it may have food brought
to it. In either case the female who does the stocking of the hole
needs to be able to find it again as she returns with her prey, the
food for the larva. It is not surprising that there is now considerable
evidence for the use of form vision among these wasps, as among
honeybees, to pick out landmarks by which to locate the nest.

It is quite plain that objects in the vicinity of the nest are observed
in detail by the bee-killer wasp, *Philanthus triangulum*. This wasp
makes a hole which is closed after each visit. It continues to visit
the hole until there are sufficient bees stored away for the grub
when it emerges from the egg, then it lays its egg, closes the hole
and abandons it. Although each time it leaves the hole the wasp
closes the actual entrance, the sand which it has kicked up in digging
out the hole in the first place is left. Often this sand fleck is plainly
visible contrasting with the surrounding darker top soil. Objects
can be placed around the nest entrance while the wasp flies to and
fro. These can then be moved to one side while the wasp is hunting
so that on its return it can either go to the objects, say, some pine
cones, where it will not find its nest or it can go to the sand fleck
and find the nest entrance. In such a case the wasp would go on its
return to the ring of fir cones so that it must have learned the shapes
of the objects in the immediate vicinity of the nest.[522]

Tests were also made with rings placed around the nest entrance.
These were either plain coloured or checkered. As might be expected
from the experiments on honeybees, the wasps showed a preference
for the more disrupted patterns and shapes. Black rings with half
circular cross-section were preferred to flat black rings. This preference for three-dimensional figures was tested further. Rings of eight
flat discs alternating with eight hemispheres of the same diameter
were placed around the nest entrance. Then, while the wasp was
foraging, the discs were placed in a circle to one side and the hemispheres in a circle to the other side of the nest. When the wasp flew
back it showed, by its attempts to find the nest entrance in the ring
of hemispheres, its preference for the solid objects since it apparently
identified the nest surroundings by the appearance of these rather
than the discs. The solid objects must be projecting from the ground
also, for black paper cones were not preferred if they were buried
in the ground with their bases open on the surface. If, however,

they were standing upon the ground projecting upwards the wasps preferred them to flat black discs of the same diameter; in one set of observations, for example, the wasps chose the cones 108 times and the discs only 21 times. Flat pieces of equal area to the cross-section of the black hemispheres were not preferred if they were arranged, during the training period, to radiate from the nest hole (Fig. 94). However, if they were arranged as the sides of an octagon centred on the nest hole they were preferred to the hemispheres. To an insect entering or leaving the hole the pieces arranged to radiate would only show their edges but arranged in an octagon each piece would appear like a hemisphere. Standing cylinders and cubes were

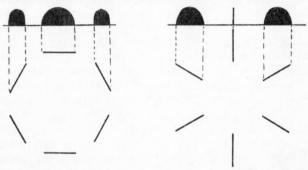

FIG. 94. The two arrangements of flat black shapes used in the experiments (see text) in plan and elevation (after Tinbergen and Kruyt[522]).

preferred to ones lying on the ground, and knobs were preferred above all else. Thus solidity, real or apparent, was an important attribute of a landmark.

The sand fleck itself was only important as a landmark when it was of light sand kicked up over the upper darker sand. When the flecks were visible in this way a wasp could find its own nest from the position of its neighbours' nests. It was apparently reacting to the whole pattern of nest flecks, the Gestalt. It was able to perceive the relationship of landmarks close to the nest to those further away. They could be trained to find their nest holes from the clue offered by a square so arranged that one corner pointed at the hole (Fig. 95). If a branch was thrust into the ground well over a metre away, on the opposite side of the nest hole from the corner of the square, the wasp continued to go to the hole as it had learned to do.[46] If the branch was then taken away and the square turned so that one side was against the hole instead of a corner, the wasp visited the two corners nearest the hole with equal frequency. If the branch was moved out sideways to stand opposite a corner, the wasp then chose that corner (Fig. 95). It was clear that the square and the branch were acting in concert to lead the wasp on its return. The insect was guiding itself by the pattern of 'corner of square and branch' and knew the position of its nest relative to this pattern. This reaction to the whole pattern or Gestalt also holds for its reactions to a constellation of landmarks around the nest. Sixteen fir cones arranged in a circle around the nest were recognized as a ring and continued to be recognized as such even when the number was reduced to ten. Recognition became uncertain as the number was reduced further and failed altogether when only four were left. So the number of elements in the pattern made no difference provided

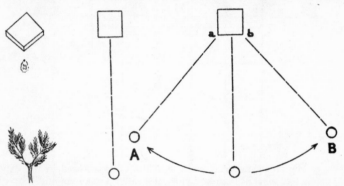

FIG. 95. Left, the arrangement of wooden square and branch (see text). Centre, the square is turned so that its side faces the nest; either of its nearer corners are now visited by the wasp. Right, when the branch is moved to one side the wasp visits the appropriate corner (after van Beusekom[46]).

that there were sufficient for the pattern to be distinguishable. The ring was also picked out of a more complex configuration. For example, when the cones were laid out in the form of the constellation of the Great Bear, the 'Dipper' was singled out from the pattern and the wasp searched its centre, ignoring the 'Handle'. Again the elements of the pattern were not recognized individually for the cones could be replaced by blocks and the cones heaped up beside them. It was the ring of blocks which was subsequently visited, not the heap of cones. These experiments showed that the visual field of the wasp is organized as a Gestalt with all the characteristics of the classic Gestalt; the pattern is distinguished from the background, it is transposable into terms of other elements, as in the change from cones to blocks, the elements are perceived as related in space to the nest hole and the configuration is recognized in a reduced form and in other patterns.

This wasp flies back to its nest with its prey at a height of 2–3 metres. It hovers above the nest and then descends slowly to the hole when it has identified it. On the other hand, the prey of the heath sand wasp, *Ammophila campestris*, is often so heavy that the wasp cannot rise into the air and has to drag the prey back to the hole. This wasp hunts caterpillars and stocks them in the nest in

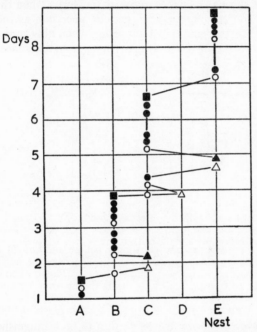

FIG. 96. Scheme of an example of visits paid by a sand wasp (*Ammophila campestris*) on successive days to various nest sites. Solid circles, visits with caterpillars; open circles, visits without caterpillars; solid triangles, egg laid in provisioned nest; open triangles, nest dug; solid square, nest closed finally (after Baerends[19]).

much the same way as the bee-killer does with its bees. This wasp, however, may be digging, stocking, egglaying or closing two or three nests at the same time so that its knowledge of locality involves remembering several different places at once[19] (Fig. 96).

Since the wasp flies out to search for its prey and may walk back, even walking backwards as it drags the caterpillar along, the problem of its navigation is more complex than in our previous example.

The various landmarks will be viewed from different aspects on the outward and return journeys. In the immediate vicinity of the nest small objects act as landmarks but further away larger objects are used. Trees standing clear of the heath land on which this wasp lives are good guides. A series of imitation trees were arranged along the normal flight line of the wasp. When these were moved sideways and the wasp released at a point near the end of the row, it flew along the row and searched for its nest at a place which in relation to the row was the same as its nest's true position (Fig. 97). Released in the

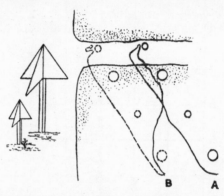

FIG. 97. Experiments with the effect of landmarks on *Ammophila*. Left, imitation trees. The solid circles on the right show the position of the 'trees' originally and the broken circles after they were moved. The tracks of the wasp from A and B when the 'trees' were in their original positions are shown by the continuous line and that from B, after the 'trees' were moved, by the broken line (after Baerends[19]).

same place, with the row back in their correct place, it flies to them following their line to the real nest.

As one of these wasps makes its way back dragging a caterpillar it makes frequent excursions to the top of the heather plants at which height it views the surroundings and apparently takes a bearing. Climbing down it walks on until it climbs another plant to take another bearing. When it flies out it does not go so high as the bee-killer but flies more slowly level with the tops of the heather so that, from its points of vantage on its return journey, it is observing the surroundings from an aspect similar to that from which it observed them on its outward journey. The landmarks which are effective seem to decrease in size as the wasp nears its hole.

Yet another wasp, *Bembex rostrata*, has its landmarks organized so that a return journey is taken step by step. It certainly appears that the landmarks close to the nest are perceived as being arranged in girdles round the hole so that if a disturbance is made to the marks in an inner girdle the wasp can still orientate by the marks in the girdle lying outside it. The whole return journey is probably organized in the same way, the wasp flying from one set of marks to another and so on to the nest.[278]

Objects put close to the nest will disturb one of these wasps when it returns. The disturbance not only affects the speed with which it locates its nest, for the wasp hesitates before entering, but also makes it perform a searching flight as it leaves the nest. The amount of disturbance which any object causes can therefore be measured by the increase in the time it hesitates and the time it takes over its

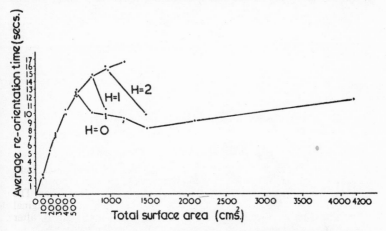

FIG. 98. Relation of average re-orientation time of *Bembex rostrata* to the total area of the disturbing objects. H is the height of the object, thus, H = 0 for thin sheets of cardboard (van Iersel[278]).

exploratory flight. Now a flat piece of cardboard placed beside the nest causes a disturbance which increases as the width of the piece is increased. A piece 18 cms. wide causes maximum disturbance so that if the width is increased to 25 cms. the extent of the disturbance is not increased (Fig. 98). This suggests that the girdle of landmarks close to the nest is, in fact, about 18 cms. wide. These experiments were done with pieces of the same length but varying width so that up to 18 cms. the whole area of the piece was probably perceived by the wasp. Apparently the edge of 25 cm. piece which lay furthest from the nest was not perceived so that although the whole piece was of much greater area only part of it was perceived—that part which lay within the bounds of the innermost girdle of landmarks.

The constellation of landmarks close to the nest seems to be a very complex one for this wasp, more so than the apparently simple pattern to which either *Philanthus* or *Ammophila* react.

ORIENTATION FLIGHTS

Bees on leaving their hives or their food, and solitary wasps on leaving their holes, fly round in circles before going to their feeding or hunting grounds. These orientation flights, as they are called, seem to enable the insects to memorize the appearance of their homes and the relationship of its position to the surrounding objects. A bee circles vertically opposite the hive entrance, a wasp will fly on horizontal circles around its nest hole (Fig. 99). There is little

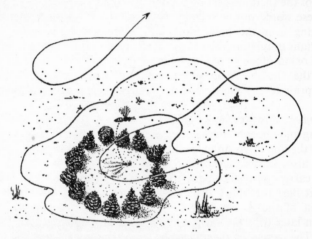

FIG. 99. Locality study by *Philanthus* (Tinbergen[521]).

information about the function of the orientation flight of a bee, but since the same sort of flight (p. 161) serves on leaving the food place to establish the relation between the place and the surroundings it is very probable that the flight outside the hive has the same purpose.

At least a bee-killer requires only one flight to learn the situation of a newly dug nest. After rain it may perform one again. But otherwise provided that no new landmarks have been put near the nest it usually flies straight off. The flight varies in length with different individuals and at different times, for example, two individuals made flights of 3–100 secs. and 7–40 secs., respectively. The learning is therefore possible in a variable but short time.[522]

Though this flight will give information on the more distant landmarks, the immediate vicinity of the nest is apparently memorized either as the insect emerges or as it enters the hole. This can be deduced from its preference for the flat half-circular plates as opposed to solid hemispheres only when they are placed broadside on to the nest hole, in which position, if they are observed from the nest entrance, they will have the same silhouette as the solids (see p. 167 and Fig. 94). Also cubes placed 12 cms. from the nest entrance are preferred to similar cubes placed 24 cms. away, but when the cubes placed further away are twice the height of the nearest ones, this preference disappears. With these dimensions both sets of cubes will subtend the same angle at the hole. The comparative unimportance of the shadows cast by solid figures is also supporting evidence, for these would not be seen by an insect which was just entering or emerging from the hole. Since the orientation flight seems to be important in relating the objects in the nest vicinity to those further away, or, in other words, to building up the Gestalt, it seems most likely that the objects around the nest hole are remembered immediately prior to the flight, that is, when the wasp emerges from the hole.

Bembex, however, apparently learns the nest vicinity while it is digging and appears to learn the shape and position of objects which are in the line of vision of the insect as it is digging the hole. *Ammophila*, also, learns the position of its hole while it is digging. This wasp carries away the spoil from its hole in its jaws and scatters it as it flies for short distances in a number of directions. The earliest of the flights have the same outward and inward tracks but on later trips the wasp may fly back by a different route[19] (Fig. 100). The increasing divergence between the outward and the return path seems to indicate an increasing knowledge of the ground which is covered so that, even though a wasp diverges from its outward track, it can still find its way. The plan of these consecutive tracks gives as it were a picture of the increasing education of the wasp.

A wasp's knowledge of a piece of country is limited to those parts it has flown over, albeit that those parts may be well known. Individual bee-killers transported beyond their accustomed hunting grounds did not return to their nest holes after they had been released. Transport and release experiments show the extent of the area which individual *Ammophila* know. They are able to return quickly to their nests when taken any distance up to 35 metres but thereafter they become confused and fail to return from the longer distances (Fig. 101). These experiments show also how the ground is learned in patches, each patch being an area over which the wasp has flown. In

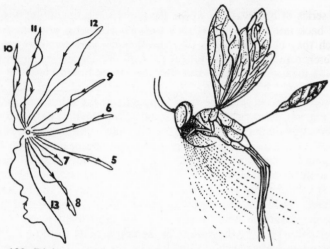

FIG. 100. Right, a sand wasp (*Ammophila campestris*) distributing sand which it has removed when making a hole. Left, the tracks of successive outward and return flights while digging (after Baerends[19]).

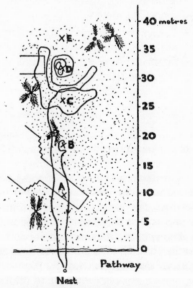

FIG. 101. Tests on homing abilities of 10 *Ammophila campestris* transported various distances from the path on which lay their nests. None returned directly from E, 3 flew from D; while 7 from C and 1 from B flew in spirals before flying off, the others returned directly. All returned immediately from A (Baerends[19]).

one series of observations wasps released from points along a path flew back immediately until they were released at a position from which they chose a long detour through the surrounding trees in preference to the direct route (Fig. 102). The patches which have

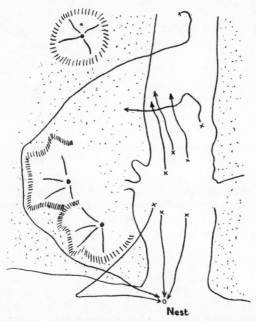

Nest

FIG. 102. Return tracks of a sand wasp (*Ammophila campestris*) after being released at various points, *x*, along a path leading to its nest. It returned by the most direct route from near places but took wide detours from more distant ones (after Baerends[19]).

been learned are not welded into a whole. On the other hand despite this limitation the landmarks which are known can be employed flexibly, the wasp does not necessarily follow the landmarks seen on the outward journey strictly in reverse order. Individuals of another species, *Ammophila pubescens*, will make detours around screens placed across their homeward tracks returning to the route when they have passed the obstruction.[514]

CHAPTER VI

REACTIONS TO HEAT

BEYOND the red end of the visible spectrum lie the infra-red rays of longer wavelength than any visible to the human eye. These rays carry heat and this form of radiant energy has great biological importance because of its effects on living systems. The length of the heat waves are from 0·1 mm. down to 770 mμ, which approaches the wavelengths of visible light. This light is not without a heating effect which is, however, minor in comparison with that of the infra-red.

Heat is not always equatable with temperature, which is a measure of its intensity, and heat capacity may differ widely from the intensity. An obvious example is the transformation of ice into water which requires a large amount of heat energy while the temperature remains constant during the change. But where the behaviour of animals is concerned heat and temperature are generally equivalent. We can consider the temperature as a measure of heat capacity for this purpose.

There are four ways in which heat energy can be transferred. Radiation of heat takes place in a manner similar to that of light, that is, heat can be considered to travel in straight rays consisting of waves. The heating effect of such rays depends upon the wavelength. Where this falls in the infra-red spectrum the effect is greatest. The heating effect of sunlight is due mainly to the infra-red component invisible to the human eye. The straightness of the rays gives this form of heat transfer a directional quality, though the possibility that animals may be able to guide themselves by using this quality is usually ignored, despite numerous examples of animals following light rays (but see later).

Masses of warmed air or water move in currents due to convection. Usually these will move away from the source of heat carrying heat energy with them. The direction of flow will therefore give an indication of the position of the heat source, but only if the direction of movement can be detected. In fact few animals locate heat sources in this way. Another characteristic of convection is that it produces a gradient of temperature decreasing regularly from the source as the moving water or air cools. Such a gradient can be scaled so that an animal following the increasing temperature will

176

arrive at the origin of the heat. Such behaviour is the commonest form of orientated reaction to heat.

Conduction occurs when heat is transferred from one object to another by contact. This heat flow can represent the difference in temperature between two bodies, for it will move from the hotter one to the cooler. Sensory equipment is not always sufficiently developed to register temperature accurately by measuring the amount of heat flow. One has only to think of one's own subjective impressions when touching a very hot or a very cold object, either of these may appear hot for the subjective sensation depends among other things upon the temperature of one's hands just previous to touching the objects. It is not clear whether the sense organs are stimulated directly or via disturbance of the gradient between the temperature of the circulating blood and the superficial layer of the skin, on contact with hot or cold objects. Animals are probably no more accurately sensitive to temperature than we are though the lack of such an absolute temperature sense does not prevent animals from detecting a gradient of heat.

The fourth means of heat transfer is by evaporation. Though this is of great importance in the control of an animal's body temperature it seems to have no part in determining its behaviour.

HEAT TOLERANCE

All invertebrates are poikilothermous, or cold-blooded; their body temperatures are approximately those of their surroundings. The temperatures at which they can continue to carry out all their life functions are limited to a range which is narrow compared with the range of temperatures actually occurring in nature. Within this range is a narrower band of temperatures at which they are living under optimal conditions. The actual ranges depend on the species for a few animals, like the marine bivalve, *Yoldia*,[4] can live only in water at about 0° C, while others live in hot springs at about 40° C. Only under special, and unnatural, conditions can animals resist temperatures far below 0° C, for example, rotifers or nematodes can be refrigerated to −253° C and will survive provided the temperature is reduced slowly enough.[446] A cave-dwelling beetle (*Astagobius angustatus*) inhabits ice crevices and grottoes whose temperature may be as low as −1·7° C and usually ranges between this figure and +1·0° C.[4]

Animals may die at temperatures above 0° C because they pass into an inactive state and cease to carry out actions that normally preserve their lives. Thus, after long exposure to 10° C, a cladoceran, *Moina macrocopa*, will die with blocked gill chambers because the water current which aerates the gills within the chamber and at the same time clears away detritus stops when the limbs become inactive at this temperature.[66] Moreover such temperatures may also cause death by their direct physiological effects. Other animals, particularly insects which survive through the winter in cold climates, are capable of surviving even when the temperature has dropped as low as −30° C. Sometimes their body fluids remain liquid but supercooled, though many can withstand the formation of ice in their tissues.[468] The low temperature may decrease the speed of metabolic processes that are necessary for normal life below a safe level. Thus a honeybee will die at 0° C largely because absorption of sugar from the gut is reduced below the point at which the bee can survive, yet the other metabolic processes in the cells are taking place actively.[287]

The extent of cold hardiness is dependent upon the water content of the body. When nymphs of *Chortophaga*, an orthopteran, hibernate their water content is only 65% compared with the normal 79%.[51] Their ability to resist cold winter temperatures seems to depend on maintaining the water content at this lower level.

The ability of animals to survive at temperatures at the upper end of their range of temperature tolerance also seems to depend upon the amount of water in their bodies. Large mealworm larvae, for example, can survive at temperatures of 43° C, while individuals of only one third their weight can survive only below 42° C. It appears that the larger individuals can lose more water and that the evaporation of the water cools them, so that their body temperature is below that of the surroundings.[369] Small insects cannot cool themselves in this way for, as the total body volume is reduced, the ratio of body surface to volume is increased, thus the evaporating surface is increased and cooling can only occur if a comparatively large amount of water is removed from the body. This amount seems to be more than the insect can lose and still survive.

The cause of death at high temperatures may lie in the increased speed of some metabolic process which produces an accumulation of harmful products faster than they can be conveyed away. Thus, blow-fly larvae kept at 39° C accumulate organic and inorganic phosphorus compounds in their haemolymph.[273]

It has been claimed that insect larvae have been found alive in water at 55° C or even as high as 65° C. Rhizopod protozoa have been reported in springs at 58° C. It seems probable, however, that the highest temperature at which animals can carry on active life is between 50° and 52° C. Animals in the encysted stage are resistant to higher temperatures as they are resistant to desiccation. In some

PLATE 2(a). Adult desert locusts (*Schistocerca gregaria*) orientating themselves perpendicular to the sun's rays, at the same time lying on their sides. The lines on the board indicate the horizontal projection of the rays (arrow) (Fraenkel [174]).

PLATE 2(b). Desert Locust hoppers sitting on the ground parallel to the sun's rays at noon. Photographed against the sun, the rays of which are indicated by the arrows.

(Fraenkel[172]).

hot springs in the Dutch East Indies the majority of the animals found there were living at 36° to 40° C, fifty-seven species being reported from this range, while twelve species endured 41° to 45° C, four 46° to 50° C and four were found in water at above 50° C. As the temperature rose the number and variety of animals decreased.[68]

THE TEMPERATURE RANGE AND THE OPTIMAL TEMPERATURE

The extent of cold hardiness and heat tolerance will fix the lower and upper limits of an animal's temperature range. But, before death occurs at either end of the scale, cold or heat stupor intervenes and the animals become immobile. They may recover when they are transferred to a higher temperature when they are cold or to a lower temperature when they are hot.

Between these limits lies the optimal range for all activities though the actual optimal temperature for each of the activities may lie at different points within this range. It is therefore necessary to state for what the temperature is an optimum. Thus *Daphnia magna* will live for only 26 days at 28° C but for 108 days at 8° C. But at the lower temperature the rate of heart beat and respiration are lower. In a lifetime at either temperature the total number of heart beats will be approximately the same. However, the optimum for long life differs from that for high reproductive rate, the former being at 8° C and the latter at 28° C.[346]

Though the temperature at which most animals aggregate in preference to higher or lower ones might be considered as the natural optimum for all processes, in fact this depends upon the temperature to which the animal has previously been accustomed, as will be shown later, and is therefore variable.

Provided that the animals have been kept under the same conditions of temperature as their normal environment or taken directly from natural conditions, the preferred temperature selected by the majority of a particular species does have some significance. It is frequently close to the temperature of their normal environments as would be expected. The larvae of flies breeding in dung, for example, choose temperature ranges close to those of their normal breeding places, that is, fermenting dung whose temperature will vary according to the extent to which it has fermented. Thus *Lyperosia* larvae chooses places at between 27°–33° C and *Haematobia* larvae ones at 15°–26° C.[510]

This preferred temperature bears a relationship to the thermal death point, that is, the temperature at which the animal dies from overheating. The flies of the genera *Musca*, *Stomoxys* and *Fannia*

G

pass into heat stupor at 45°–46·5° C, 43·5° C, and 39°–41° C respectively; the temperatures which they prefer are in the same order being 33·4° C, 27·9° C and 23·7° C respectively.[400, 401]

From all these considerations a graph of the temperature relations of an insect living under continental conditions in the middle latitudes can be derived which is also roughly applicable to most other invertebrates (Fig. 103).

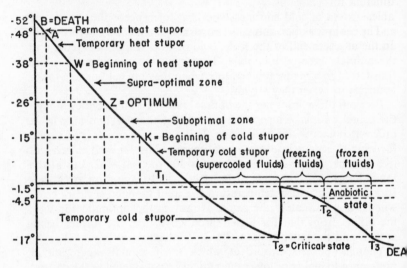

FIG. 103. Temperature relations of an insect (Allee, Emerson, Park, Park, and Schmidt,[4] after Uvarov and Bachmetjew).

SELECTION OF PREFERRED TEMPERATURES

As happens so often in descriptions of behaviour, it is easier to describe the reactions of an animal to heat in terms of human analogies. Animals collect in regions which are at the temperatures apparently most favourable to their continued life and it is convenient to describe this as being selected. In fact there is no selection involved in the human sense for there is no conscious comparison of two different temperatures, or their effects, which is the essence of human selection. Nor, indeed, is there any preference in the human sense. An alternative term has been suggested for 'preferred temperature' in 'eccritic temperature' but even that carries a flavour of anthropomorphism for those who retreat from such terminology. However, for descriptive purposes, selection and preference will be used.

A temperature gradient can be set up in a number of different ways all of which use a long trough parts of which are heated or cooled in various ways. The trough may be filled with water, or remain empty as required. It is difficult to avoid complications due to convection currents and differential cooling in the apparatuses which have been described but, by ingenuity of design, these unwanted sources of error can be reduced. However, results from different forms of this basic apparatus may not be directly comparable.

The behaviour of *Paramecium* in such a gradient is a good example. In these experiments a small water-filled trough was used with tubes

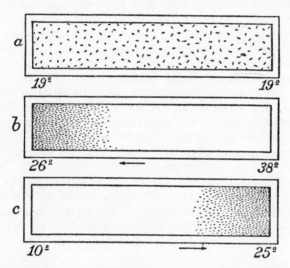

Fig. 104. Distribution of *Paramecium* in troughs of water under various conditions of temperature (Jennings[256] after Mendelssohn[370]).

running across it beneath the middle and the ends against the outside through which water at different temperatures could be passed. If the water in the trough was uniformly at 19° C the animals were evenly scattered throughout its length. If one end was warmed to 38° C while the other was maintained at 26° C, the animals congregated at the cooler end (Fig. 104). When the temperatures were reversed the animals moved as well. At lower ranges, for example, from 10° C at one end to 25° C at the other, they collected at the warmer end. The optimum appeared to be between 24° and 28° C. Preference for the end of the trough whose temperature was nearest the optimum was shown even when the temperature difference was only 3° C between the two ends, 10 cms. apart.[370, 371]

This aggregation seems to be due to avoiding reactions which occur when the ciliates enter zones at temperatures above or below the optimum. In both cases, as they leave the preferred area and as water at the changed temperature impinges on their oral surfaces, the animals stop and then begin to swing their anterior ends round in a circle, occasionally moving forward in what are apparently random directions. If these forward movements do not lead the animal into more favourable conditions, the direction of beat of their cilia is reversed and they move back again to turn once more and move forward again. This continues until they move into either cooler or warmer areas as the case may be. Then they move in approximately straight lines until they reach the further boundary of the optimal area when the turning movements begin again. The only difference between the avoidance of high and low temperatures is that the manoeuvres are performed faster at the higher temperatures. This is very probably simply due to the effect of the temperature on the metabolism of the animal, for at high and low temperatures the animals ultimately die from the effect of heat in very warm water or sink motionless to the bottom in ice water.

Temperature may affect behaviour either by its influence on metabolism or by an effect on the central nervous system. The first leads to increased or decreased speed of manoeuvre while the second may initiate behaviour movements which do not occur at optimal temperatures. The behavioural effect can be seen in *Paramecium* as the onset of the avoiding reaction, while the metabolic effect is shown by the greater speed of movement at the higher temperatures.

The optimum is rarely a particular temperature but rather a range. It may be partially determined by the conditions under which the animal has been kept previously. Thus, the optimal range for paramecia kept for some hours at 36° to 38° C becomes 30° to 32° C.[371]

Avoidance of both low and high temperatures is shown also by the human body louse, among a number of other examples. Here again when placed in a gradient, of air temperature, in this case, the animals aggregate at between 26·4° and 29·7° C (Fig. 105). Here too the avoiding reactions are apparently klino-kinetic, (p. 38), that is the lice begin to turn more frequently in the unfavourable parts of the gradient which brings them back into the preferred zone.[272] This preferred range is lower than the normal body temperature of its human host. Lice are repelled by high temperatures which suggests a reason why lice migrate from the bodies of feverish patients (whence the belief that a person with lice is healthy).

Movement in a trough of the sort used in these gradient experiments is restricted, especially if the animal is large compared with the width of the trough. It is not easy to judge whether the animals are comparing the temperatures at two points on the gradient under these conditions. A circular apparatus heated at the centre has been used to study the reactions of ticks, *Ixodes reduvius*, this avoids the difficulty of canalizing the animal's movement. In such an apparatus the tick ultimately follows a roughly circular path around the

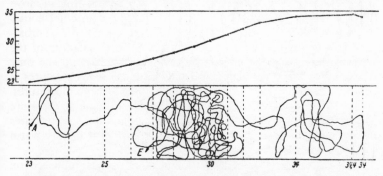

FIG. 105. Path followed by a louse in a temperature gradient, the slope of which is shown on the graph above (Homp[272]).

source of the heat at a distance from the centre which depends upon the temperature at the centre[528] (Fig. 106). They appear to avoid both higher and lower temperatures by klino-kinesis (p. 38), though similar behaviour by lice (*Pediculus vestimenti*) (Fig. 107) has been interpreted as a menotactic response to the source of heat (i.e. similar to a light compass reaction).[272] Ticks, tested in a trough heated at one end and cooled at the other, with precautions taken to prevent heat loss and to ensure that the gradient was as uniform as possible, did not aggregate in any particular zone. A great majority of unfed ticks which had been kept at 25° C collected at the cool end of the gradient, over 70% coming to rest between 8° and 11° C. This appears to result from their behaviour on entering high temperature zones, when they turn abruptly and move into cooler regions. But they move on in a roughly straight line, moving more slowly as the temperature drops, until finally they become completely immobilized in the low temperature zone. Ticks which had been taken from fields in the early spring, after having been exposed to temperatures between 5° and 13·5° C, were more evenly spread throughout the gradient being more active at the low temperatures than those kept at higher temperatures in the laboratory. They passed into chill-coma at about 1° C while those kept at 25° C became stupefied at 7° C.[329]

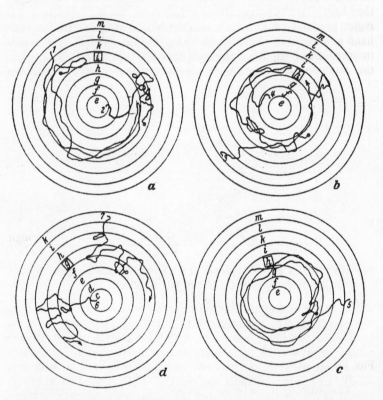

FIG. 106. Paths of ticks in apparatus with a circular gradient of temperature. a, imago, preferred temperature 10°–12° C; b and c, nymphs,
preferred temperature 16°–18° C; d, larva, preferred temperature
18°–20° C. The ring which the tick chooses is shown by a square
around the letter designating it. ● represents that the tick comes to
rest; → that it was moving when the record ended (Totze[528]).

The ticks avoid high temperatures but do not avoid lower temperatures. Flies also do not appear to perform avoiding reactions
to cold. When a number of active individuals of *Lucilia cuprina*
were studied as the temperature of their surroundings was raised
the proportion which were moving about rose from nothing at 5° C

to a first peak of about 33 % at 20° C followed by a period at which the proportion remained about the same, declining slightly between 30° and 35° C.[397] After this point activity increased sharply to a second maximum of some 60 % active at 42° C. Any further increase in temperature was followed by a sharp decline as heat stupor and then heat death supervened. It is clear that once a fly moves into a region of low temperature it is likely to be trapped there. On the other hand at higher temperatures than the optimum, movement increases in speed and it is likely to be carried into the favourable zone. If this reaction is purely an ortho-kinetic one in which the animal

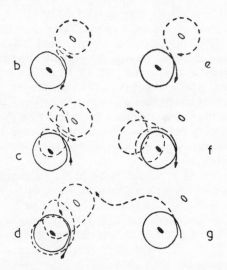

FIG. 107. A louse will follow a warm tube when it is moved and continue to circle round it suggesting that it is reacting to the radiant heat in a manner similar to a light compass reaction to a light source (Homp[272])

moves faster but without any increase in turning movements, it may be a consequence of the metabolic effect of heat and not a response of the central nervous system. Some insects show a purely ortho-kinetic response to heat. A cockroach stops moving when it moves into its preferred range remaining motionless for some time.[212] When it moves out into warmer parts its speed of running increases and it is ultimately brought back into the preferred zone. This behaviour only happens in daylight for at night time the animals are continuously active and do not come to rest for any length of time even in their preferred zone.

It is to be expected that the preferred temperatures observed in experiments should be closely related to the temperatures of the animal's environment. In the case of the flies, *Fannia canicularis* and *Musca domestica*, study of the relation between activity and temperature shows that the maximum activity occurs at very different temperatures, in *Fannia* at 21° C and *Musca* at 40° C.[397] The breadth of the range is also different in the two species for there is some activity in *Fannia* over the whole range between 9° C and 35° C while the range for *Musca* is 14° to 43° C. This is correlated no doubt with the emergence of *Fannia* earlier in the year than *Musca*.

Temperature preferences may alter at different stages in the life history. The larvae of *Musca domestica* show a preference for the range of 30°–37° C within which development takes place most quickly.[511] However, when they are fully grown and ready to pupate the larvae prefer a temperature of 15° C. These preferences are reflected in their habits of pupation. Though the larvae live in dung the temperature of which near the surface is between 30° and 34° C, they pupate in the soil surrounding the heap where the temperature is lower. Migration out of the dung must be caused by changes in the central nervous system which alter the temperature preferences as the larva grows.[510]

The preference may remain constant in an environment with wide variations in temperature such as occur daily in the tropics, and therefore some special response must occur to maintain the animal at its preferendum. Locusts, for example, orientate themselves to the sun in a manner which changes according to the time of day (Plate I).[172, 174] In the early morning they become active when the temperature rises above 17° C below which they are in a cold stupor. Adults and nymphs (hoppers) both bask with their long axes at right angles to the sun's rays until the air temperature reaches 28° C (Fig. 108). At this temperature both adults and nymphs move off on their migration. The warming up period seems to be essential. Their orientation to the sun is maintained with great accuracy as the sun rises. If the migration temperature has not been reached the adults tilt their bodies so that by holding them perpendicular to the sun's rays the maximum heating effect is obtained. To enhance this effect further, adults lower their abdomens and raise their wings so that more of the body is exposed. Midday temperatures may rise above 40° C and if they do the locusts react by turning to face the sun thus reducing the body area which they expose to about one sixth of that which they turn to the sun when temperatures are lower. In this position their body temperatures are 6°–7° higher than that of the surrounding air. But while they are broadside on to the sun their internal temperature may be 16°–17° C higher than the air.

This reaction to the radiant heat from the sun involves the heat-sensitive patches on the head, thorax and abdomen, which have already been mentioned (p. 13). But orientation when these alone are functional is not so efficient or so immediate as when their eyes can also be used. When adults are blinded they may not orientate

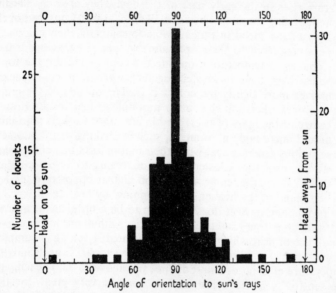

FIG. 108. Histogram of the distribution of the angles between the body axes of 112 adult locusts and the projection of the sun's rays on the horizontal (Fraenkel and Gunn[177]).

at all or, if they do, they do not turn directly into the correct position but get into it by a series of trials, so that at this stage the accurate movements of the intact animal are due to stimuli from the infra-red and from the visible parts of the spectrum. However, when young nymphs of the third stage or earlier were blinded they were still able to orientate fairly precisely, the role of the eyes apparently being less important than in adults.[172] The function of visible light stimulation is shown by the reaction of adult locusts to an artificial source of light and heat. As this is moved higher so the locust's head turns. This produces a twist in its neck and every so often this is corrected by turning of the body to nullify it. This is strongly

G*

reminiscent of the relationship between the head movements of dragonflies in response to gravity and the compensatory twists of the body (p. 213).

On the other hand, the change of temperature with time of day may control activity. Thus, slugs are stimulated into activity by falling temperature (between 20° and 4° C), and so begin to move about in the evening. But rising temperature suppresses movement with the result that they cease to move and feed as the air temperature rises in the early part of the day. They are very sensitive to change being stimulated by as small a fall as 0·1° C in one hour.[117]

Many of the social insects are able to maintain their colonies at temperatures close to their optimum by special behaviour evoked by a change in temperature outside the colony. During the winter broodless bees tend to cluster together when it is cold, packing themselves more tightly the colder it is. The outside of the cluster consists of workers which remain motionless, their heads towards the centre of the mass of bees. Within are other workers who move about and make body movements, such as shaking their abdomens. These actions generate heat while their motionless outer companions act as an insulator. Cluster formation seems to begin at about 14°–16° C. When the temperature is too high as opposed to too low, workers stand at the hive entrance 'fanning' by beating their wings. The production of heat does not seem to be a problem in a brood nest in summertime, rather, the activities within produce an over-abundance of heat which has to be dissipated. Fanning is comparatively efficient for when a hive was warmed to 40° C artificially the temperature of the brood nest did not rise above 36° C. The temperature sensitivity of honeybee workers may be very great, for they seem to be able to detect a temperature difference of 0·25° C. This figure was obtained when the bees were in a gradient grouped at their preferred temperature point, the whole gradient was allowed to cool and the bees were observed to move to a new preferred position when the temperature of their immediate surroundings had dropped by this amount.[244] The local warming of the air around a cluster is one of the stimuli causing other individual workers to join the group.[180]

When the heat becomes excessive bees bring into the hive water which they place on the top of the combs. The surrounding air is cooled by evaporation of this water and flows downwards over the comb. The effect of these actions is enhanced by the bees leaving the combs and clustering outside the hive, for otherwise the activities of the bees would produce heat within the hive.

The social wasps of the genus, *Polistes*, also fan and may bring water into the nest. The temperature at which fanning begins seems to be from 31·5° and 35° C and only a small further rise to 34°–37·5° C is necessary to stimulate this wasp to carry in water.[504] Ants will carry their larvae about the nest placing them in whatever chamber may be at the most favourable temperature for development. In summer, the older larvae will be found near the surface on warm days. In winter, however, the members of the colony bunch together a foot or so below ground to avoid the frosts at the surface. The wood ants, *Formica rufa*, control the air flow through the entrances of their nests in summertime. When the sun's heat is greatest the entrances are closed with nest material to prevent the entrance of warm air and as the temperature drops they are re-opened.[447] This is similar to the closing by bees of the hive entrance in hot weather, except that the bees stand in the entrance blocking it with their own bodies.

REACTIONS OF PARASITES TO HEAT

To many parasites of warm-blooded animals the warmth of their host's body acts as a guiding and controlling stimulus in their search for the host. This is particularly true of ectoparasites which attach themselves to their host only temporarily while they take a blood meal, dropping off when they are satiated. They require some accurate mechanism of host finding when they become hungry once again. In fact many of the responses which lead such animals to their hosts are actuated by hunger, the satiated animal showing no response, or a diametrically opposite one, to the same stimuli. Temperature is a token stimulus for their host's presence. Such a token stimulus is in a different category from a stimulus arising directly from the goal to which the response is aimed. For the parasite is not seeking warmth but food, and the stimulating warmth does not arise directly from the blood, the sucking of which is the goal of the activity.

The medicinal leech, *Hirudo medicinalis*, will move directly towards a tube warmed, by water circulating through it, to 33° to 35° C. Such a tube also elicits a contact reaction and finally the leech sucks onto it. This temperature is close to its host's which is usually about 34·4° C. If the temperature of the tube is raised to 39° C the leech shows alarm, and detaches itself when the temperature reaches 41·5° C. The fish leech, *Hemiclepsis*, reacts to a warmed tube in a similar manner but at a lower temperature, at 31° C, in fact. This is correlated with the lower body temperature of its host. And for similar reasons, *Glossiphonia complanata*, a parasite on invertebrates, adheres to a tube at 26° C.[250] Here temperature elicits attachment but the leech does not guide itself to its host only by the temperature gradient from it. In the case of the fish leech at least, temperature is not the main factor in orientation for the disturbance in the water caused by its host seems to be more important,[248] however, *Hirudo*, does appear actually to orientate towards the source of heat.

The South American blood-sucking bug, *Rhodnius prolixus*, is also able to make its way directly towards its host which can be imitated by a warmed tube at 37° C.[574] A bug placed 4 or 5 cms. away first moves its antennae about, extends them towards the tube and then moves straight to it, mounting and probing it with its labium (Fig. 109). That this is a reaction to the gradient of warmed

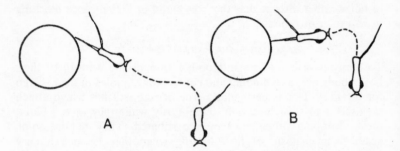

FIG. 109. Reaction of a blood-sucking bug, *Rhodnius prolixus*, to a warm tube at 37° C covered with fresh mouse skin. In both cases one antenna has been removed completely. The proboscis is put out to touch the tube at the last moment; note that in A at this time the bug swings sharply in the direction of the intact side (Wigglesworth and Gillett,[574]).

air around the tube is shown by the similarity of response to uncovered tubes and to tubes covered with aluminium foil at the same temperature. The latter radiate less than one-tenth of the total radiant heat from the uncovered ones though the heat convected from both is approximately the same. Since there is no difference in reaction it must be the gradient of heat which is supplying the guide. Even if one antenna is removed the bug can still orientate. It seems most likely that the receptors along the antennae are sufficiently sensitive to perceive the gradient up an antenna when it is held along the gradient. If the antenna is moved about, as it is in fact, then the direction, towards which the temperature drop along it is greatest, can be detected. Then, providing that the tip is warmer than the base, moving in that direction should lead the animal up the gradient to the source. Such a movement guided by alternate comparison laterally, in this case by the waving antenna, is a klinotaxis (p. 49).

Though receptors on the antennae are probably the main heat receptors in lice (*Pediculus vestimenti*), lice without antennae can still orientate. An intact louse will crawl straight to a warm tube and follow it as the tube is moved about. Should a louse be confronted

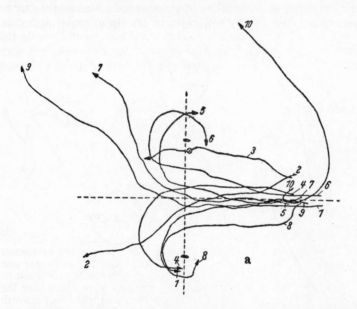

FIG. 110. Tracks of human body lice towards two warm artificial fingers, whose position is shown by the black ovals on the dotted line. Environmental temperature, 18·9° C, finger temperature, 66·5° to 71·3° C. The lice were started on the right. No. 10 did not react at all, but all the others first went between the sources; Nos. 2, 3, 7, and 9 went on past them, but the others curved round to one source or the other (Homp[272]).

by two warm tubes of equal temperature it may crawl either directly between them, or in a parabola to one or other, or directly to one of them, but the majority steer roughly halfway between the two (Fig. 110). In all probability the receptors, being spatially separated along the antennae and over the body, enable orientation to the gradient of heat, as they do in *Rhodnius*, for lice do not react to radiant heat.[272]

Similar types of experiments have been performed on the sheep tick, *Ixodes reduvius*.[329] Here a warm tube at 37° C may be repellent to female ticks (Fig. 111) though it is usually attractive at first, especially if that temperature is higher than the temperature of the floor on which they are being tested. Engorged ticks, replete with blood, are repelled, without exception. Covering the tube to reduce the radiant heat makes no difference to the reaction, so that they are clearly reacting to the gradient of air temperature around the tube. These ticks when hungry will move to the tip of grass blades, or

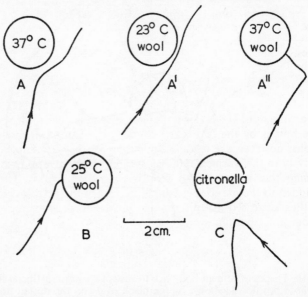

FIG. 111. The response of ticks to smell and temperature. A, A′, A″, tracks of the same hungry female approaching a warm odourless tube, a tube at room temperature with sheep wool wrapped round the base, and a warm tube in the presence of sheep wool; B, an example of attraction to wool in the absence of a temperature gradient (room and tube temperature 25° C); C, unfed female avoiding the odour of citronella (Lees[329]).

glass rods, and rest there until they receive some stimulus which could arise from their host. Then they begin to 'quest' by moving their forelegs upon which are the main sensory receptors (see Chapter II). Resting ticks will 'quest' when the warmed tube, covered or uncovered, is brought to within a $\frac{1}{4}$–$\frac{1}{2}$ cm. of them, some becoming so excited that they lose their footing.

Though with many of the hungry ticks a tube at 37° was repellent, the same tube wrapped in freshly cut sheep's wool was very attractive so that 40 out of 50 were attracted by it (see Table IV).

TABLE IV. The reactions of hungry ticks of all ages to a warm tube in the presence or absence of sheep wool and to the same wool at a lower temperature (from Lees[329])

Stage	No. of ticks	37° C, odourless		37° C, wool		20° C, wool	
		No. attracted	No. repelled	No. attracted	No. repelled	No. attracted	No. repelled
Females	50	11	39	40	10	6	44
Nymphs	50	48	2	49	1	17	33
Larvae	50	48	2	48	2	6	44

The same wool at 20° C is no longer attractive. Thus this response to the host is by the two token stimuli of warmth and smell. The nymphs, however, are less discriminating for they react quickly and positively to the warmed tube, clustering round it. The nymphs of *Rhodnius* find a warm tube exceedingly attractive also. The adult has added to the number of stimuli necessary to elicit the response and thus increased its discrimination which produces a greater economy of reaction.

CHAPTER VII

THE POSITION SENSES

A BODY has imposed upon it a force acting downwards through its centre of gravity towards the ground. When an animal is in water and has the same density as water, this force is opposed by an equal and opposite force thrusting the animal's body upwards. But if the weight of the animal is greater than that of the displaced water, the animal sinks under the influence of gravity. An important difference between this force and other sources of stimulation is that for all practical purposes the force acting upon an animal's body will be the same wherever it is and will always act in the same direction. There can be no occasion on which comparison between two unequal forces is made by the animal's sensory equipment, as a fly chooses between lights of different intensities. At all times work must be done to counteract the force. And if one part of the animal's body is more dense than the rest it will be subject to a greater force than the less dense parts and a strain will be set up, usually a bending strain, between the two parts. If the animal possesses the sensory equipment necessary to perceive this strain it may be interpreted in the central nervous system as being due to the action of gravity.

PERCEPTION OF GRAVITY

It is most important for many animals to maintain a definite attitude in space. Usually they are upright with the dorsal sides uppermost, though some animals such as *Artemia salina*, the brine shrimp, and *Notonecta* spp., the back swimmers, generally move with their ventral sides uppermost. In any case the animals have a normal position, be it right or wrong way up according to human convention. This means that their reactions are carried out with the effector organs on a known base, for example, if a leg is extended in the direction which is correct when the animal is right way up, it may be incorrect in any other position. Clearly if the animal were as likely to be upside down as to be right way up, its normal activities would be difficult to adapt to the two positions. Without this definite basis the interpretation of the stimuli received by the sense organs is also difficult and accurate motor responses become almost impossible. Since the animal exists by virtue of its responses these must be accurate, its movement being placed correctly in space.

The perception of position may arise from sensations in the

194

muscles, signalling their position and the strains set up in them, and in the skeleton, if there is one. Thus an insect standing across a slope will tend to have a compression force on the legs of the lower side as its weight bears down on them, and a stretching strain on the upper legs, forces which will be detected both by strains set up in the muscles and in the exoskeleton. But perception may be by special organs, the statocysts (p. 18). Within these the statolith is a body of high specific gravity, higher than that of the fluid filling the statocyst. Under the influence of gravity, this presses down upon the sensitive cells or bends fine hairs on which it is borne. There will be one patch of hairs of cells that is normally stimulated when the animal is upright. Stimulation on the sensory surface elsewhere is interpreted as a disturbance in the normal orientation and righting movements are initiated. Statocysts are often present in pairs, one on either side of the body, acting in concert, though they may be able to function individually in correcting posture.

For a variety of reasons, some animals require to move up or down vertically, along plant stems or to and from the water surface of a pond, for example. Their ability to sense the direction of such a movement often resides in some sort of gravity receptor. If the animal's limbs or body are in contact with some object, then the direction 'up' and 'down' can be recognized by the appropriate set of stimuli arising from the body or its musculature. If the animal is free swimming, however, the direction can only be given by a statocyst organ. A semi-fluid medium such as mud will have the same effect. Then the statolith will press harder upon the sensory patch at the bottom of the statocyst when the animal accelerates upwards, and less heavily when it accelerates downward. The statolith will only be induced to move if the movement is an acceleration or a deceleration, at steady speeds the statolith maintains its position relative to the rest of the body and is not displaced. Very little investigation of this sort of stimulation has been carried out among the invertebrates where the function of the statocyst in maintaining posture has been investigated more than its ability to be stimulated by acceleration or deceleration. Where regular guided movements up and down take place, statocysts are usually invoked, but they cannot always be demonstrated morphologically. For example, such sense organs are almost entirely absent in insects but nevertheless these animals will move orientated with respect to gravity. Dorsal, or ventral, light reactions are often important in maintaining correct orientation in space (p. 78).

ORIENTATION BY MEANS OF SPECIAL ORGANS

Even among the protozoa, statocyst-like structures have been described. In the gymnosomatous ciliate, *Loxodes*, they are in a row along the length of the animal, parallel to the line of the meganu-cleus[427] (Fig. 11D). The cavity of each vesicle is filled with fluid containing particles in suspension, while a large concretion is suspended in the middle of the cavity which vibrates when the slide upon which the animal is being observed is tapped. No function seems to have been ascribed to these structures, and no attempt has been made to correlate their presence, unique among the protozoa, with the animals' way of life.

On the other hand, *Paramecium*, which has a fairly clearly defined tendency to swim upwards, has apparently no special organ for perceiving gravity. It may be that the food vacuoles with their contents act as statocysts.[126, 127] Indeed when the animals are fed on finely divided iron particles, their geotactic response can be altered experimentally. When a strong magnet is held over them, they swim downwards, reversing the normal direction. Since this magnet will be attracting the iron particles, their weight will no longer be pressing on the lower part of the vacuole but on the upper, and as the animal usually swims away from the direction of the force it now swims downwards.[225] The effect of centrifuging paramecia also indicates that true gravity reception can occur. For if animals have forces of between 3·5 and 9·0 g. imposed on them, they move towards the axis of the centrifuge, that is away from the direction in which the force is tending to draw them. At higher speeds, imposing greater forces, they are thrown outwards, though observation of the beat of their cilia shows that they are struggling towards the axis but are unable to make any progress.[126, 127]

Radially symmetrical animals of the simple umbrella shape of the jellyfishes might be expected to have gravity receptors arranged around their periphery. Neither a single organ nor a pair diametrically opposed would be completely successful in maintaining balance as the axis of tilting might be along the diameter on which the organs lay so that they would not alter their positions relative to each other and the discharge from both would be alike. If another pair were to be introduced lying on the extremities of another diameter, particularly at right angles to the first, the arrangement will be more generally sensitive. Increasing the number of organs increases the sensitivity to inclination in all directions. In fact, the Cubomedusae bear this ideal smallest number, one statolith being placed above each of the four inter-radial corners. The medusoid

stages of such hydroids as *Obelia*, bear eight statolith organs, while
in the Scyphomedusae they may number hundreds. The statolith
of the hydroid medusa is contained within a vesicle which may be
closed or open to the exterior. But the statolith of the Scyphozoa
does not lie in a cyst, being surrounded and protected by a lappet
on either side and a hood formed from the upper surface of the
bell above.

In the majority of cases jellyfish swim vertically upwards, descend-
ing slowly between each beat of the umbrella. Some, however, swim
horizontally (e.g. *Rhizostoma pulmo*), others at an angle to the vertical
(e.g. *Aurelia aurita* and *Cyanea capillata*),[80] while *Gonionemus
murbachi*[587] swims vertically upwards but sinks downwards upside
down, the tentacles outstretched for catching food.

There is evidence that the statocysts of *Cotylorhiza tuberculata*
control the activity of the muscles in their vicinity.[167] When the
jellyfish is held with its main dorso-ventral axis lying horizontally,
the lower rim beats in complete strokes while the upper shortens its
stroke. The amplitude of the beat is greater on the lower side for
the umbrella relaxes completely there, increasing the length of the
stroke. There is no change in the synchrony of the radial muscles,
but the circular muscles do not relax as much as the upper side.
The result of these movements which disappear if the statoliths
('randkorper') are removed is to right the jellyfish. Swimming is
apparently dependent upon a rhythmic discharge from the statocysts.[60] (cf. Crustacea, p. 204).

Complete removal of the statocysts in *Aurelia aurita* stops the
pulsations of the bell, but if only one is left normal pulsations can
come from the stimulation of that one organ.[460] If the whole of the
centre of *Cassiopea* is taken away leaving only a ring of contractile
tissue bearing the statocysts, and then all the statocysts are removed
except one, a wave of contraction originating from the remaining
one may continue round the ring for as long as 11 days (travelling
at the speed of 46·5 cm./min.).[365] It is clear that the statocysts are
acting as excitatory organs stimulating the muscles into activity.
They will be brought into activity if the statocyst is stimulated when
the animal is tilted, but also each time the bell pulsates the statolith
will be moved and will stimulate the nervous parts of the organ.

It has been suggested that the normal posture of a jellyfish is not
due to the activity of its statocysts but simply to mechanical considerations of the different specific gravities of parts of its body, for
removal of the statocysts does not always destroy the ability to
maintain the normal position, though the rate of the beat will be
markedly affected and the diameter of the bell also changes. Such

observations on *Gonionemus*,[393] *Chrysaora hysoscella* and *Cyanea capillata*[330] show that the importance of the role of these organs varies among the different species.

Ctenophores, such as *Beröe ovata*, also generally swim vertically upwards, moving by means of their eight comb rows of cilia, mouth uppermost. If a negatively geotactic animal is gently tipped over, the cilia which are now uppermost cease to beat while the lower continue vigorously. This turns the animal so that it is once again swimming upwards. Under certain conditions the response can be reversed to a positive one. When such a positively geotactic animal is tipped, it is the lower cilia that cease while the upper continue to move and the animal turns downwards. In both cases the result will be to turn the animal back to its accustomed and preferred position.[31] Destruction of the nervous system prevents this differential inhibition of the comb rows.[210]

The organ responsible for this is a single statocyst borne at the opposite end of the animal to the mouth. The concretion within is carried on four pillars of fused cilia. Since the nervous control of the comb rows is an inhibitory one, the swimming cilia beat more vigorously after removal of the statocyst but at the same time without co-ordination so that balance cannot be maintained. Each pillar seems to be related to two comb rows for when a pillar is stretched by the displacement of the statolith, the row opposite the new position of the statolith is inhibited, the row on the under side, the side to which the statolith is leaning, being unaffected. The animal then turns upwards again. This will be the result in a negatively geotactic animal. If, however, it has been moving with positive geotaxis before tilting, the row next to the displaced statolith will be inhibited, the cilia of the upper one continuing to beat, and the animal swims downwards.

But this means of control of position does not seem to act in all circumstances. At times this mechanical reaction to displacement of the statolith seems to be suppressed. This occurs, for example, in *Pleurobrachia pileus* (= *P. pileata*) when the long tentacles are extended to catch food. The animal, swimming mouth upwards, turns in a wide circle tilting over sideways through 180° until ultimately it has turned through 360° and is upright again, with its tentacles fully extended. Clearly when it begins to tip over, the upper cilia are not inhibited for they continue to beat, driving it further over. So control by the statocyst is not obligatory.[80]

Concentration of the sense organs at one end of the body is the basis of cephalization. Statocysts do not escape this tendency, and many of the burrowing polychaetes, such as *Arenicola*, have a pair of statocysts on the head. If *Arenicola* is burrowing in mud between two sheets of glass so that its path can be observed, it can be seen to burrow downwards.[71] When the aquarium is tilted through 90°, the worm turns through 90°, still maintaining a downward direction, a positively geotactic movement. This compensation continues after further tilting, but it does not happen if both statocysts have been removed, or the nerves of them have been severed. One statocyst alone will permit the full reaction.

The position of the statocysts is the same in *Branchiomma vesiculosum*, and elimination of one or both produces the same effects as in *Arenicola*.[72] However, unlike the other two worms, *Branchiomma* burrows tail first. When it is placed in any position but the vertical, the tail turns downwards but the head retains its position. Any bends in the body move headwards as the tail burrows down. The head is only brought into the preferred vertical position at the last. Since the reaction does not immediately restore the sense organs to the normal position, the mechanism of control is probably more complex than in the other reactions where the end bearing the receptors is the first to react and then the remainder of the body follows. An ability to make its way into the substratum which serves as a protection and sometimes as a food source is clearly of great importance to a burrowing animal. The worm's reactions are not mathematically accurate to the vertical for it is not usual for them to go straight downwards, *Arenicola*, for example, often burrows at 30°–40° to the vertical.

Convoluta roscoffensis, a marine flatworm, appears in large numbers on the surface of the sand at low tide, but they disappear below the surface when the tide rises to cover them. This downward movement, which affects the whole population, is stimulated apparently by the mechanical effect of the water moving and breaking over them. But the direction is determined by a statocyst buried in the brain, and therefore inaccessible to experimental operation.[173] If the worms are permitted to crawl on a wet vertical glass sheet, they move downwards altering their direction to compensate for any rotation of the sheet in a vertical plane. Certain individuals in one collection of these worms did not, however, react in this way, being apparently unable to perceive the direction of gravity. Investigation showed that they were unusual in that they did not possess statocysts, unlike all the other worms examined.

Even though *Arenicola* has two statocysts, its reactions are apparently normal when one is removed, that is, the one statocyst can be stimulated by movement in any direction, and similarly a single organ is adequate for the reactions of *Convoluta* for it possesses only one. Theoretically this suggests that all the inner lining of such a statocyst is sensitive to movements of the statolith. In other animals, as we shall see, removal of one of a pair of statocysts leads to destruction of normal posture and movement. It appears that these statocysts are only sensitive to stimulation by the statolith in one part of the inner lining. The sum of the sensitive areas is similar to the sensitive area of the single organ in other animals. The first type, possessed by *Arenicola* has been said to have a two-way action responding to tilting in a clockwise or an anti-clockwise direction, or to be sensitive in two ways ('zweisinnige') while the second has a one-way action, or is sensitive to tilting in one direction only ('einsinnige').

Another test of the way in which statocysts function is to observe an animal's behaviour when it has to move on an inclined plane, going up or down according to the sign of its geotactic response. Animals with functional statocysts which are positively geotactic will tend to travel up the steepest gradient of a slope whatever may be its inclination. Thus the flatworm, *Otoplana*, goes straight up a slope whether it is at 30°, 45° or 90° to the horizontal.[283]

Despite the fact that stimulation, possibly proprioceptive, arising from the forces on the shell of pulmonates crawling up a slope in air may affect their orientation,[116] there is little doubt that stato-cysts also have their part in the reaction. For under water, where the natural bouyancy of the body and shell would seem to obviate any proprioceptive stresses, fresh-water pulmonates, and even land ones like *Helix*, will make their way vertically down an inclined slope.[283] This reaction is reversed in some of the fresh-water forms when their lungs are empty of air. They then move upwards towards the water surface to refill the mantle cavity. If *Physa fontanalis*, one of these snails, is living in well oxygenated water, it becomes indifferent to gravity, the necessity for a behavioural reaction which will bring it to its oxygen supply at the surface having been removed.[466]

Those molluscs which swim also have well developed stato-receptors. The scallop, *Pecten*, usually swims with its dorso-ventral axis at an angle of about 45° to the vertical. This posture may be the result of inequality in the size of the statocysts, for that on the left, and normally upper, side is large, while that on the right is smaller.[71] Removal of this smaller one makes little or no difference to the normal position of swimming, which is, however, upset by removal of the left-hand one. Since *Pecten* swims mainly by ejecting water past the hinge or between the valves of the shell, a horizontal or near horizontal swimming position is more advantageous than the upright position common in burrowing lamellibranchs.

The heteropod, *Pterotrachea*, possesses a pair of statocysts close to the cerebral ganglia. Removal of one of these causes a temporary disturbance by reducing the tonus of the muscles on the same side, so the animal bends in the direction of the operated side.[183] But after five minutes its normal posture is restored, the tonus being balanced once again. This compensation arises apparently from the activity of the remaining organ which has thus a two-way effect. Removal of an eye can also bring about the same changes. So removal of the statocyst on one side and an eye on the other produce results which balance each other. In this case normal balanced movement does not appear to be disturbed even for a short time. Removal of both eye and statocyst on the same side give a long lasting disturbance in balance.

Paired statocysts are also found in cephalopods. Here, however, each organ has a one-way effect so that removal of one leads to

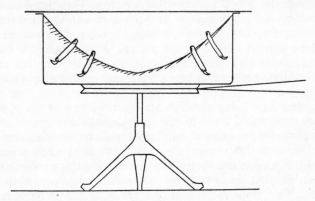

FIG. 112. Razor shells, *Ensis ensis*, placed in a trough, containing sand and filled with sea water to the top so that no air bubbles remain below the cover, are rotated for one hour. Afterwards they are occupying the positions shown (after Fraenkel[169]).

rolling towards the injured side; this is a permanent injury. Some vestige of balance is retained, however, to be lost completely if the remaining statocyst is removed.[80]

In much the same way that burrowing marine worms have strongly geotactic behaviour, so also have burrowing lamellibranchs. *Ensis* (= *Solen*) *ensis* and *E. siliqua*, the razor shells, will burrow downwards when placed on the surface of wet sand. In a rotating box filled with sand they dig in a direction which is the resultant between the centrifugal force and gravity (Fig. 112). The downward direction is the result apparently of the stimulation of statocysts, which are in the foot, as in most lamellibranchs. The foot is the burrowing organ of these bivalves, thus the receptors are within the part of the body which leads the movement, just as in *Arenicola* which burrows head first the statocysts are in the head.[169] Other burrowing bivalves, such as *Cardium* and *Venus*, behave in a similar manner.[80]

THE POSITION SENSES OF ECHINODERMS

The righting reaction of starfishes, which has been so extensively studied, does not seem to depend upon perception of position by statocysts, though the influence of the contents of the digestive tract have been invoked to explain the apparent absence of statocyst structures. This is more likely a kinaesthetically perceived activity and as such will be dealt with later. In sea-urchins, where the righting reaction also appears, and among which there are numerous cases which indicate the use of statocysts, it is probably the sphaeridia which perform this function. Their removal slows down the reaction to gravity in *Echinus esculentus, Paracentrotus* (= *Strongylocentrotus*) *lividus*,[125] *Psammechinus miliaris* and *Echinarachnius parma*[421] but does not prevent them righting themselves. *Echinarachnius* also shows a definite orientation when burrowing, since it travels horizontally beneath the sand instead of going deeper and deeper.

Holothurians, many of which also burrow, possess five apparent statocysts arranged close to the oesophageal nerve ring. Like the other burrowing animals already mentioned, holothurians are positively geotactic going vertically down into sand when placed on top of it.[71] Unlike the worms they cease to do this as soon as they are buried. The behaviour of *Synaptula hydriformis* when it is crawling on a slope shows that its reaction to gravity remains after removal of the 'statocysts'.[403] Despite this evidence, it is not necessary to deny these organs the functions of statocysts for, under these particular conditions, kinaesthetic perception of the direction of gravity may take precedence over the statocysts. In the majority of cases only those echinoderms which possess statocysts show definate gravitational responses when tilted.

THE POSITION SENSES OF ARTHROPODS

Statocysts are known in very few insects, but occur commonly among the Crustacea. With few exceptions, their place is taken in insects by kinaesthetic mechanisms in the form of sense organs capable of detecting stresses and strains in the cuticle. The chitinous integument of Crustacea, being impregnated with calcium, is more rigid than the pliable cuticle of insects and deformation under strain will not be as great. This may be a partial explanation for the differences in the character of the position receptors in the two main groups of the arthropods.

Limnophila fuscipennis, a dipteran, is an example of a larval insect possessing statocysts (p. 20). There seems little doubt that the organs do serve to detect gravitational forces, for the normally positively geotactic behaviour is abolished if they are removed.[507]

But it is among the Crustacea that statocysts are best developed and exercise a good deal of control over the activities of the animals. They are present in many malacostracans but they are apparently absent in most animals outside that group. The statoliths within the organ are frequently sand grains placed inside the sacs after each moult when the old statoliths are lost. A crucial experiment to demonstrate the function of these organs was, therefore, to induce a prawn to refill its statocyst with iron filings.[312] Then when it entered a magnetic field it took up a position which was the resultant between the direction of the force of gravity and that of the field, showing that the direction of pull of the iron filings on the sensory hairs influenced its orientation.

The function of the statocysts of the crayfish, *Astacus fluviatilis*, have been studied closely.[317] The sensory hairs with a statolith resting on them lie in a half circle in a sac within the basal joint of each antennule. A normal animal hanging freely in its upright position makes few movements but when it is tilted sideways beyond 5°–10° out of the vertical the legs on the lower side make swimming movements which tend to turn the body back into the vertical position once again. At the same time the legs on the upper side are drawn up to the body. The eye on the upper side is depressed, the antennae on the same side pointing dorsalwards. The reaction is strongest when the crayfish is lying on its side. The animal becomes still again when it is upside down, within 20° on either side of the vertical (Fig. 113). If one statocyst, say the right one, is removed entirely or if the statolith is simply plucked from the hairs of this organ, the legs on the operated side are drawn up, while those on the unoperated side make swimming movements, and the stalked eye is depressed even when the animal is upright. The position of no response, normally the vertical, is now at an angle of 20°–30° to the right of the vertical. At this inclination the eyes and legs take up their normal relaxed position. Similarly the upside down equilibrium position is changed to 40°–50° to the left of the vertical (Fig. 113). Similar observations can be made on the lobster, *Homarus gammarus* (= *H. vulgaris*), a prawn, *Palaemonetes varians*, and a shrimp, *Crangon crangon*.[486]

It was once believed that this was proof that the organs had only a one-way action (p. 200), but more recently it has been shown that deflection of the hairs of the sensory surface after removal of the statolith produces different reactions according to the direction in which they are pushed.[484] Thus if they are forced outwards by a stream of water impinging on them, the legs of the same side will make swimming movements while the opposite legs are raised and the opposite eye depressed. But if the jet is arranged to bend the hairs inwards the actions are reversed. The sensory cells can be stimulated without the presence of the statolith to cause the animal to roll away from the side on which the hairs are deflected. The

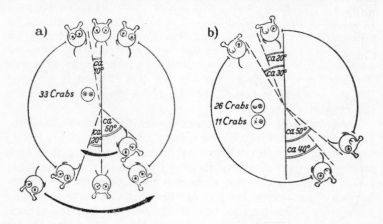

FIG. 113. Leg and eyestalk movements of the crayfish, *Astacus*, when tilted, (a) the intact animal, (b) with either one whole statocyst or one statolith removed (Schöne[486]).

tendency to roll in the absence of the statolith will be balanced if the bodies are missing from both sides, but if one whole statocyst is taken away, the animal will tilt towards the operated side. If the statolith is present, however, it will stimulate tilting away from its own side so long as it is bearing down upon the outer part of the sensory epithelium, but towards its own side when it bears down on the inner side. Thus it will reinforce the tendency produced by the sensory epithelium alone only in the first position described above. The organs therefore have potentially a two-way action but are only called upon in the intact animal for one-way action. The sensory epithelium is responsible for a continuous nervous discharge, whose modifications are enhanced when a statolith is present.[101]

It has been known for some time that the statocysts of certain crustacea such as the brachyurans, *Uca* (= *Gelasimus*) *pugilator* and *Platyonichus ocellatus*, contain no statoliths and yet appear to take part in the crabs' responses to gravity. They are extremely small in the shore crab, *Carcinus maenas*. Tipping experiments have also been performed on this crab and its reactions are very similar to those of the crayfish, for it shows non-response points both right way and wrong way up and the same kicking and righting reaction when it is tipped from these positions[486] (Fig. 114). The experiments on the function of the sensory hairs in the organs of crayfish show that the hairs are alone capable of being sensitive to gravity; this no doubt explains why, where statoliths are absent or small, responses to gravity still may be apparent.

Experiments in which the force of gravity was increased by putting *Crangon vulgaris* and *Palaemonetes varians* into a centrifuge show

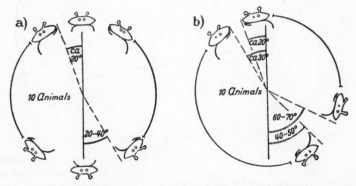

FIG. 114. Leg and eyestalk movements of the crab, *Carcinus*, when tilted, (a) the intact animal, (b) with one statocyst removed (Schöne[486]).

that the angle, determined by the statocysts, at which they swim downwards when released at the surface, is altered under different forces (Fig. 115). This suggests that action of the statocysts can be explained on the reafferentation principle,[270] for the motor activities of the animal are matched to the sensory input from the statocysts, which will be altered when greater forces are applied in the direction of gravity.[488] Under these admittedly unnatural conditions a rigid concept of positive, negative or transverse geotaxis breaks down and is replaced by a more plastic system of explanation.

The presence of the statocysts of the prawn, *Palaemon xiphias*, is not essential for equilibrium for it is clear that the position sense of this animal depends upon the interplay of impulses from the statocysts, of a dorsal light response and of the sense of touch in the tarsi.[5,6] This prawn reacts to tilting in much the same way as the crayfish. Hanging freely and lit from above, it kicks with the legs which are lowest when it is tilted through 45°, its upper antenna turns dorsalwards, the lower one downwards, its upper eye turns down and the lower one upwards. When it returns to the right way up, the symmetry of the position of the antennae, eyes and legs is restored. It has a second position of equilibrium in which it remains still, for when upside down it makes no attempt to right itself though as soon as it begins to tilt away from this position, it makes compensatory movements, just as a crayfish does. In turning it may go either clockwise or anti-clockwise (Fig. 116). When its statocysts are taken away it still reacts in the same way.

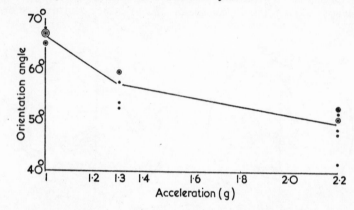

Fig. 115. The influence of centrifuging (and thus increasing the gravitational force) on the path towards the bottom taken by a prawn or shrimp released at the surface (from Schöne[488]).

If at the same time that a prawn is tilted over, a piece of board is held against its legs, it remains standing on the board in a symmetrical position, though its eyes may bend towards the light.

After removal of both statocysts the dorsal light response takes control (p. 81). Even with one eye only the prawn will still regulate its position when it is tipped sideways, such an operated animal has a new position of equilibrium with its dorso-ventral axis at 45° to the vertical, the intact eye uppermost (Fig. 116).

There are other observations from which the importance of statocyst function in crustacea can be inferred. Lobster larvae, which are free swimming members of the plankton, do not possess

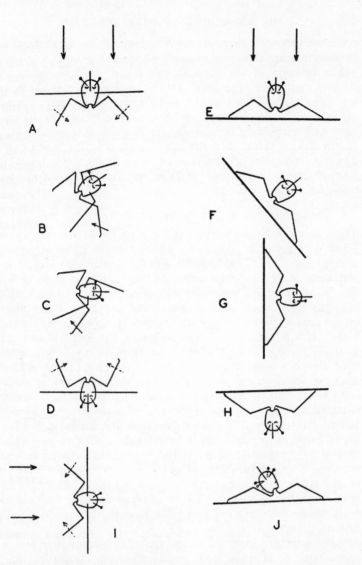

FIG. 116. Orientation reactions of the prawn, *Palaemon xiphias*. A–D, reactions of intact animal to tilting; light from above. E–H, the prawn is tilted on a board, note that though body movements are suppressed the eye-stalks move. I, animal without statocysts lit from the side, a new equilibrium position is taken up with reference to the light rather than gravity. J, same animal on a board, note that the light from the side causes the prawn to tip towards the light, the dorsal light reflex is not suppressed when there is tactile stimulation on the feet (Alverdes[6]).

statoreceptors when they first begin to move about. Until statocysts develop they are extremely unstable swimmers.

The function of the statocyst-like organs of gammarids was doubtful until the behaviour of *Gammarus pulex* and *G. locusta* was compared. *G. locusta* has well developed statocysts ('frontal organs') while in *pulex* they are very much reduced. On the other hand a dorsal light reflex is hardly developed by *locusta* but is manifest in *pulex*.[327] Here then the two species maintain their position by each making use of a different attribute of the vertical, one, the force of gravity, the other, the light from the sky which will normally fall from above.

RESPONSES IN WHICH STATOCYSTS TAKE NO PART

There seems to be much evidence for a position sense, often combined with geotactic movement, which depends upon perceptions arising from parts of the body, though the animals may also possess statocysts. A well-known example of this type of perception is in the burrowing sea anemone, *Cerianthus membranaceus*, which normally lives buried in sand in a mucus-lined tube. When placed on the sand it will burrow vertically down, its foot entering the sand first.[338] If it is placed on a wiremesh mat, the foot will also turn vertically through a cavity of the support. If the mat is then turned over, the foot turns through it once more. This can be repeated until the anemone has woven itself into the mesh. Under natural conditions, though its position sense may be satisfied, contact stimulation is also required if the animal is not to move away.[389] Indeed, if it is allowed to enter a glass tube, it will remain in a horizontal position, provided the tube is small enough to stimulate it greatly by contact. Attempts at righting will only be made when the tube is raised to about 35°–45° to the horizontal. Since this animal apparently possesses no statocysts, its perception of position must be due to mechanical effects of its position on parts of the body which are perceived and passed on to the central nervous system.

When kept in aquarium tanks, starfishes, sea urchins and sea cucumbers can often be seen moving about on the vertical walls. Sea cucumbers and starfishes are as likely to go up as to go down, *Asterina gibbosa*, for example, may creep up or down, according to the phase of behaviour it is in. If a cork float is attached to it, applying a strong upward pull, then the direction of its movement may be altered.[115, 288] Instead of moving upwards in the negatively geotactic phase it will go down, and vice versa, Thus, apparently, the pull of the body plays some part in the determination of the direction of gravity for this animal. Since it is supported on its tube feet, it may be that an uneven stress is applied to the musculature of the feet which results in the perception of the direction. But this is not a highly sensitive response, for a slope of 5·6° fails to produce a response from the sea cucumber, *Thyone briareus*.[426]

Statocysts, or sphaeridia, can be removed and gravity perception still occurs. It has been suggested that movement up vertical faces may be simply continued movement in one direction, an animal crawling horizontally continuing to move when it reaches the wall of an aquarium but now moving upwards. This would account for the changes between going up and down, and remove these movements from consideration as true responses to gravity. But this is an unsatisfactory explanation, for it does not account for the behaviour of *Asterina*,[115, 288] for example, when it creeps towards the centre of a horizontal rotating turntable. Such behaviour is more consistent with a true gravitational sense, kinaesthetically perceived in the absence of statocysts.

An animal with statocyst gravity reception would be expected to go straight up an inclined plane. If it does not do so, and if the angle of its inclination to the horizontal across the plane alters smoothly as the angle of tilt of the plane increases, some perceptive mechanism other than statocysts suggests itself. A number of invertebrates have been tested on slopes in this way and it would appear that the stresses and strains set up in the musculature have much to do with the orientation.

A particularly clear case is that of *Liguus*, a tree snail.[116] When this creeps up a vertical face, it appears to orientate itself so that its shell is hanging downwards, over the hind end of the foot, so that the base of the visceral hump is not twisted. If the shell is held horizontally sideways, the animal turns to crawl across the slope, compensating for the twist of the body caused by the displacement of the shell. Similarly though it is normally negatively geotactic, if the shell is pulled round to the vertical by a thread attached to it and supported, the snail turns and creeps downwards (Fig. 117). A possibility remains, however, that, rather than from proprioceptors in the shell muscle, the sense of change of position arises from the lack of stimulation of areas of the body surface normally touched by the shell.

For the animals tested, the relationship between the angle of the slope, α, and the inclination of the animal's path to the horizontal across the plane, θ, is:

$$\theta = K.\log(\sin \alpha)$$

This original equation is probably not perfectly valid for K does not

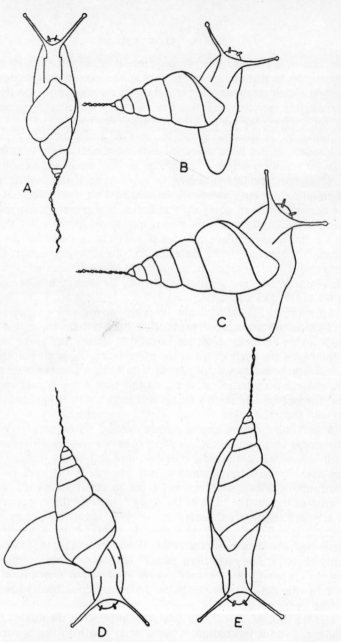

Fig. 117. Geotactic orientation of the tree-snail, *Liguus*. A, the snail is crawling up a vertically placed board, a string attached to the shell hanging loose. B and C, when the shell is drawn to one side the animal turns. D and E, if the shell is drawn upwards, the snail turns and crawls down the slope (after Crozier and Navez[116]).

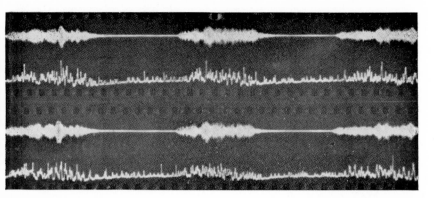

PLATE 3(*a*). Response in the tympanal nerve of a female *Chorthippus parallelus* to repeated stimulation by the recorded song of a male *Chorthippus brunneus*. Upper trace: male song; lower trace; action potentials in the nerve. The action potentials vary despite the identity of the two phases of the song shown above (Haskell[231]).

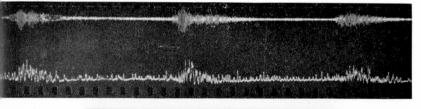

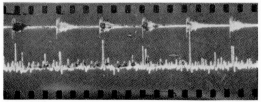

PLATE 3(*b*). Responses (lower traces) in the tympanal nerve of a male *Omoscestus viridulus*. Above, to stimulation by the natural song of another male (upper trace). Below, to stimulation by an electric imitation of the natural song (Haskell[231]).

[*face p. 210*

seem to be a constant in all cases. It is difficult to evaluate this in terms of the animal's reaction. The only satisfactory conclusion seems to be that walking across the slope imposes unequal stresses on the two sides of the body which are levelled by orientation across the slope. An insect crawling up such a slope will undergo compression strains on its lower legs and stretching of the upper legs, as well as the usual tendencies to slip down the slope. By taking up its particular path at an angle to the horizontal, it minimizes these strains.

But the possibility of a passive mechanical effect as well cannot be excluded. The tick, *Rhipicephalus sanguineus*, will wander in any direction over a slope if it is unfed.[367] But after a blood meal with its abdomen engorged it will crawl upwards. It seems that the enlarged abdomen simply drags the body round by its weight so that the head points up the slope. An unfed tick with its abdomen weighted with plasticine moves in the same way. This is an imposed orientation similar to that of siphonophores buoyed up by their gas bladders, for it is inflicted on the animal without reference to its behaviour responses.

The existence of proprioceptors among arthropods is no longer in doubt for muscle receptor organs and other proprioceptive devices have been described in various decapod crustacea (e.g.[1, 2]) and in insects (e.g.[406, 498]). Apart from these, nerve endings are connected with the cuticle of insects in such a way that they are stimulated by stresses in this outer covering, acting as proprioceptors. Nerve endings may simply lie in the general body surface or in the softer, more pliable, intersegmental membranes. Flexion of the joints of the legs of *Periplaneta* can be detected by tactile sensory hairs on the inner side of the joints.[438] Chordotonal organs stretched across the internal spaces of the exoskeleton can detect alterations in position. These are found in the base of the wings and in the halteres.[252, 430] There are tension receptors in the leg of *Periplaneta*, campaniform sensilla, of a type which are also found in the halteres.[435] Sometimes they have an elongate shape reacting only to compression and stretching strains along their length, in other positions they are round reacting to a greater variety of strains.

These organs are well developed in insects but apparently are absent in Crustacea where, however, muscle receptors seem to be fairly widespread. Their absence may be correlated with the structure of the cuticle in the two groups, that of the insects being generally pliable and therefore deformable, while the cuticle of crustacea is heavily impregnated with calcium, becoming hard and inflexible. It might be expected that no form of muscle receptor or position

H

receptor of the insectan type would be of use in the orientation of a crustacean swimming freely. It is therefore not surprising that statocysts are particularly well developed in this group.

A special type of proprioceptive organ, the versatile Johnston's organ in the antennae of insects, may be pressed into service as a position sense organ. The waterbugs, *Notonecta* spp. and *Plea* spp. swim with their ventral side uppermost, while *Corixa* spp. and *Naucoris* spp. swim with the dorsal side up. Their position is indicated by the movements of the antennae caused by an air bubble trapped between it and the underside of the head.[445] Each antenna is held in the air-water interface of the bubble, the buoyancy of

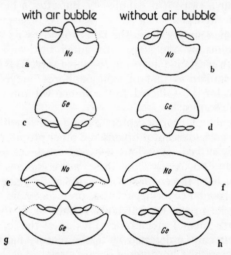

FIG. 118. Function of antennae as position indicators in aquatic bugs. a–d, *Notonecta* and *Plea*, e–h, *Naucoris* and *Corixa*. Those diagrams on left are of animals with the air-bubble between antennae and head, those on right, after removal of air-bubble. *No* = normal position; *Ge* = inverted position (after Rabe[445]).

which causes the position of the antenna to be altered when the animal's orientation is changed. Strains are set up between the first and second joints and are detected by Johnston's organ in the articulation between these joints. In the normal swimming position, the antennae of *Notonecta* are strained away from the head, but are drawn towards the head if the insect turns upside down (Fig. 118). These conditions are reversed in *Corixa*. If the air bubble is removed and the insects placed in the dark, notonectids will swim in the reversed position, for the antennae now tend to strain away from the head under their own weight (Fig. 118). In the light the ventral light reflex corrects the deficiencies of the position sense organ. Similar considerations apply to *Corixa* but in an inverse sense.

EQUILIBRIUM IN FLYING INSECTS

Since an animal in flight has no contact with the ground no stimulation on their feet can aid them to keep upright. Therefore flying animals have other methods of perceiving their position. Flying vertebrates, such as the birds and bats, depend upon the statolith systems in their inner ears, but such organs are absent in insects, the only flying invertebrates. Other receptors of a special form are developed in their place.

Dragonflies are powerful and accurate fliers. Level flight in *Anax imperator* is ensured by two pairs of pads in the neck which are covered with sensory hairs. If the head is twisted on the thorax, parts of the exoskeleton press on pairs of these pads so that the hairs are stimulated.[385] If small pieces of iron are attached to the head, it can be twisted by using a magnet. In either case the wings make compensatory flight movements so that the thorax is twisted sideways to take up once again its normal alignment to the head, the neck being untwisted. In normal free flight the reverse happens, for it is the thorax and wings which are tilted sideways by up currents of air. Since the head is large it has sufficient inertia not to follow the thoracic movement, this produces a twist in the neck membranes, and the sensory pads are stimulated. The wings then make their compensatory movements and the thorax swings back into the horizontal position. Level flight is important apart from aerodynamic reasons, because dragonflies catch their prey when they are on the wing in a sieve arrangement formed by the hairs of their legs. Therefore if the insect is aiming at some prey visually it is clearly necessary for the catching device and the eyes to be in a definite relationship to each other.

The two-winged true flies have a hind pair of reduced wings modified into halteres which seem to be necessary for normal flight in most flies, though the flight of tabanids is unaffected by their removal.[79] They are short rods with heavy knobs on the end which vibrate vertically when the wings are beating. A turn to the right or left during flight, that is about the vertical axis, will produce lateral forces attacking the beating haltere. This produces shearing forces in the cuticle at the base of the rod.[136] At this point there are groups of campaniform sensilla, just as there are in the cuticle of the joints of the cockroach's legs. These are sensitive to shearing forces of this sort. They are stimulated therefore when the fly makes a turn.

Physiological investigation of their function in *Calliphora, Eristalis* and *Lucilia* suggests that the halteres are responsible for the reception of turning about the vertical axis, that is yawing, for the impulses arising in the nerve leading from them are different in a yawing movement from those in a rolling or pitching motion, both of which give similar responses.[436] Thus it seems unlikely that the halteres control displacement about a transverse or a longitudinal axis both of which movements are probably indistinguishable to the fly. Also it seems that such a fly as *Muscina stabulans*[268] maintains itself in an inherently stable position for pitch, though it may be somewhat unstable for roll; there is no evidence for any inherent stability in yawing, however. Observations of haltereless *Calliphora* indicate that compensatory movements after rolling are less efficient than in unoperated flies. So the haltere may aid in maintaining horizontal flight about the longitudinal axis in some species. It must be admitted that this does not agree with other observations that haltereless *Calliphora* are completely unbalanced until they are restored to normal flight by attaching a small piece of cotton onto the tip of the abdomen.[178]

PRESSURE

Since air is light, decrease of pressure as the height above sea level increases is likely to be small except over great differences of altitude. This renders alteration in pressure almost useless as a means of perceiving movement up or down in air, for over short distances the changes will be too small to stimulate any known sense organ. Though there is ecological banding at various height levels on mountain sides the distribution must depend upon other factors than a direct barometric response to the right height.

In water, however, the position is different. The medium is denser and the pressure changes with vertical position much more rapidly than in air. Therefore, decrease or increase of pressure can be used with accuracy as a sign to distinguish between up and down movement. Not only this but pressure receptors placed at opposite ends of the animal may react to pressure differences, which can be interpreted in the central nervous system as one end being higher than the other, in other words pressure reception can be used as a postural sense as well.[517]

The diurnal movements of plankton have long been known (see also p. 319). Various organisms swim towards the surface until at mid-day, when the sun is at its zenith, the planktonic plants and animals are nearest the surface. Then as the sun sinks and the light wanes the plankton also sinks down to its night level. This is very clearly connected with light values, but it is very possible that perception of pressure plays a part. Zooea and megalopa larvae of *Carcinus* and *Portunus* swim upwards when subjected to an increase in pressure.[220] Such increased activity with change in pressure (barokinesis) is typical of various copepods, adult pelagic and larval polychaetes, ctenophora and hydromedusae. Most of these concerned have a higher specific gravity than sea-water, and therefore sink when they cease swimming. Probably increase in pressure as they sink initiates a new period of activity so that they swim upwards once more (some are stimulated into activity by pressure changes equivalent to 50 cms. of sea water). Other animals e.g. *Calanus, Tomopteris* and *Sagitta* do not sink as rapidly and do not appear to react to pressure changes.[303] Benthic animals may cease their activity when pressure decreases; this would prevent them swimming far upwards from the bottom. Response to moderate increases in pressure have also been observed in protozoa, for example, *Polytoma uvella* and *Colpoda cucullus* became more active and *Colpidium campylum* and *Paramecium aurelia* come to rest.[300a] No sense organs responsible for the detection of pressure changes have been identified in any of these animals.

Many aquatic insects possess efficient pressure receptors, all of which are based upon exposing an air bubble or air layer to the water pressure, sensory cells reacting to changes in its volume. The same bubble may or may not be used as an air store for breathing. But the pressure sense air bubble is almost always connected with the tracheal system.

Nymphs of *Nepa* and *Ranatra* hold their air stores in grooves along the undersides of the abdomen. These grooves are roofed by long hairs. But at intervals this hair layer is interrupted, giving place to shorter sensory hairs which lie in the interface between air and water, for the air stores are exposed to the water at these points. Any change in shape of these air bubbles will be indicated by movement of the sensory hairs which, being hydrofuge, remain in the interface. This will stimulate the nerves leading from them. Apparently these organs do not respond to absolute pressure, but rather to pressure difference along the series under the abdomen. In other words, they do not indicate absolute depth, but differences in position of different parts of the body.[35]

The aquatic bug, *Aphelocheirus aestivalis*, however, has only a small amount of air trapped on its body, the film acting as a plastron.

The amount is insufficient to make the animal bouyant. Since the efficiency of the plastron as a physical gill depends upon the insect remaining in the better oxygenated upper layers of water it is essential that they should have some sense organ capable of responding to absolute differences of pressure and indicating when they have swum too deep. The bugs react to sudden increases of pressure by vigorous upward swimming movements. A dorsal light response aids in directing the bug towards the surface, thus, when the organs are destroyed, the bugs can still make their way about provided that there is light falling on them from above, but in the dark they are unable to orientate themselves.[517]

Similarly, *Nepa cinerea*, the water scorpion, is heavier than water. Unlike *Aphelocheirus*, this bug requires to return to the surface to replenish its air store. A row of three pressure receptors are arranged along each side of its abdomen. These function as differential manometers and indicate the longitudinal inclination of the body (p. 16). They do not react to changes in absolute pressure. Placed on a see-saw beneath the surface, one of these insects will walk upwards until the see-saw tips under its weight when it will reverse its direction though continuing to move upwards. After removal of the complete set of the organs the bug cannot make the correction in its direction on the see-saw.[35] It appears that at least two pairs of symmetrically placed organs must be intact for efficient orientation. As might be expected the presence of the anterior and posterior pairs is most effective; extirpation of the middle pair seems to have little influence on the efficiency of the insect's reactions.[517]

Just as the pressure organs on one side of *Nepa* act in concert, so do the pair in *Aphelocheirus*. They are interconnected by the tracheal system and serve as differential manometers for balance in the transverse plane.

The two insects show characteristic differences which are connected with the environments in which they live. *Nepa* is heavier and lives in still water. Its oxygen supply is obtained from the atmosphere and carried as a film of air below the wing cases. Provided that it maintains its orientation in the vertical axis, changes in absolute pressure are relatively unimportant, for it can still rise to the surface. But *Aphelocheirus* inhabits swift-flowing streams and is a better swimmer than *Nepa*. It depends for its oxygen on the air film into which the gas diffuses from the surrounding water, it does not rise to the surface to replenish the film. Therefore absolute pressure is most important in this case, since alterations in pressure will alter the rate at which oxygen can diffuse from and carbon dioxide into the surrounding water.

CHAPTER VIII

THE PERCEPTION OF VIBRATION

A HUMAN being is very liable to construe the sensory abilities and apparatus of animals on a basis of his own subjective sensations and often credits an animal with sense organs similar to those which he possesses. If an animal is capable of smelling, then he seeks a nose built on the human plan; the possibility of other means of receiving chemical stimuli may be overlooked. So also with the ability to hear sounds. Hearing in human beings depends upon the reception of mechanical disturbances of the air though the term is colloquially used to describe the central process of interpretation of the impulses received from the ear. The sounds which are heard are restricted to a certain band of frequencies. Though this constitutes hearing in humans, and indeed in all land-living vertebrates, there is little doubt that other animals can sense the presence of moving objects by the mechanical disturbances which they cause in other media than the air. For sound can be transmitted through solids and liquids, as well as gases, so an animal can detect movements in the water surrounding it or of the ground on which it stands. Then if these movements are vibrations due to sound produced by another animal, the animals can be said to have heard the sounds though the vibrations are not airborne.

In general this form of hearing has no counterpart in human experience, though low-frequency vibrations may be felt, for example, deaf people become peculiarly sensitive to vibrations. So an invertebrate may be said to hear 'when it behaves as if it has located a moving object (a sound source) not in contact with it'.[440] Further this implies a definition of sound beyond the colloquial, thus 'sound is any mechanical disturbance whatever which is potentially referable to an external and localized source'.[440]

Thus touch stimulation is restricted to the location of objects, moving or otherwise, in contact with the animal. The differences are akin to those distinguishing smell from taste, in that one is a distant sense while the other, touch, is a contact sense. But a sound wave is a movement of the particles in the transmitting medium set in motion by the transmitting organ, while the chemicals received in smell are parts—albeit minute ones—of the transmitter.

A difference between sound and touch would also seem to lie in the phasic nature of sound and the unfluctuating, or, at best, irregularly fluctuating nature of touch stimulation, both often depending upon alterations in pressure. If a sensory hair is deflected, moves back to its original position and is deflected again, regular phasic movement of this sort is due to sound stimulation. If the hair is bent into one position for the whole of the stimulation time returning to its original position only when the stimulation ceases, it is being touched. Sound receptors that utilize the movement of a membrane as the main receiver will not react to this second type of stimulation.

THE NATURE OF SOUND

It is of the very nature of sound that it is phasic for the waves are produced by vibration causing alternate compression and expansion of the medium adjacent to the vibrating object. The sound waves emitted may be represented as regular fluctuations in the form of a sine curve about a normal position. The curve traces the fluctuations of pressure which correspond to the chain of alternate compression and rarefaction which forms the sound wave. At the same time the particles of the medium are displaced sideways making small oscillations about a mean position in the direction in which the wave is moving, energy being carried forward in the same direction. The louder the sound the greater is the amplitude of the pressure fluctuations, and, therefore, the depths of the wave troughs, and the longer are the oscillations of the particles. From this point of view loudness is equivalent to intensity.

Sound can travel through gases, liquids and solids. An animal may detect a sound wave by its pressure or displacement characteristics; thus the receiver may react to changes in volume caused by the fluctuation of pressure, or to the displacement caused by the movement of particles in the passage of a wave. In both cases organs utilizing a stretched membrane may be involved.[439] If the membrane covers the opening of a solid walled cavity, then movement outwards will follow when the pressure outside the cavity is reduced in the passage of a sound wave, and movement inward when it is increased. The human ear functions in this manner.

Among the invertebrates, only the insects give clear experimental evidence of being able to hear, and many insects have hearing organs of various sorts (see Chapter II). These organs usually consist of a cavity one wall of which also bounds a trachea, or some other space. A small area of the wall is membranous forming a tympanum. A system of enlarged tracheae, or air-spaces, may connect this tympanum with another tympanum often on the other side of the body and facing in the opposite direction (p. 20). A hearing organ of this kind can react only to displacement of the membrane caused by the translational effect of the sound wave which impinges upon it, for two opposite walls are movable. It is the displacement characteristic which is also responsible for the reception of sound by sensory hairs, for they are moved back and forth in such way that the nerve cell supplying them is stimulated.[439] Further the movements of the substratum which are detected and interpreted as sound are caused by this same factor. These movements are perceived when they in turn move the legs or any parts of the animal which are resting on the substrate.

Since sound can be said to have a wave form, any particular sound will have a definite wavelength, the distance between one peak of pressure and the next, and a frequency, the number of complete waves passing a fixed point in unit time. In fact high notes have high frequencies and therefore short wavelengths, while low notes have low frequencies and long wavelengths. Now if two pure sounds of very widely different frequencies are sounded together, the result theoretically will be an impure sound which has rhythmical changes of amplitude, or beats. This is because at definite intervals, a wave of each sound will rise to its maximum amplitude at the same moment, these two amplitudes being summed to give an intensity higher than that of either sound alone. And at points midway between these maxima, the beats, will be troughs of low amplitude. The intervals between the beats will depend upon the frequencies of the two notes. If the intervals are long, that is, if the frequencies of the two sounds differ widely, the beats may not be heard by a human being. Probably among insects, the high shrill note forming much of the song acts as a fixed frequency 'carrier' upon which a variable lower note enforces modulations. Experiments seem to indicate that it is these beat modulations to which the insect reacts.

One last property of sound is important in our context. Unlike light, sound waves are not restricted to straight paths. Hence though 'sound shadows' may play a part in the localization of sound, these are not so well defined as shadows made by light, the penumbra being greater in a sound shadow. At high frequencies, however, the shadow is sharper.

THE PERCEPTION OF SOUND BY MEANS OF TYMPANIC ORGANS

The crab, *Coenobita clypeatus*, is found both on dry land and on the shore. Individuals taken from the two habitats show a difference in structure of the statocysts for those of the dry land forms have a cavity closed by a thin membrane which has been called a tympanum,

H*

and a function as a hearing organ has been ascribed to this statocyst. Indeed the crabs of this genus and of the genera *Uca*, *Ocypoda* and *Birgus* have statocysts with a similar structure and have stridulation organs of which that in *Coenobita nigrosa* will serve as an example. It consists of ridges on the large left claw and a ridge on the last joint of the second leg on the same side. These crabs are sensitive to sounds. Unfortunately no detailed investigation into the function of the organs has been made.[223, 224]

So, apart from these possibilities, it can be said that tympanic organs have not been described among the invertebrates outside the insects. They occur in the Orthoptera, Hemiptera and Lepidoptera (p. 22). The organs are paired, the two members of the pair being often interconnected by a series of chambers, as has been mentioned above. Their positions on the body varies among the groups. Thus, in the super-families of the Lepidoptera in which they are found, the organs are on the first segment of the abdomen in the Geometridea and the Pyraloidea, but on the third thoracic segment of the Noctuidea. Among the Hemiptera, as well, they occur on the abdomen in those families, the Cicadidae and Corixidae, in which their function has been confirmed. Among the three Orthopteran groups, the Acrididae have abdominal organs, while the Tettigonidae and Gryllidae carry them on the proximal end of the tibiae of the forelegs. In all these they are fully developed only in adults. Frequently the membrane is sunken beneath the level of the exoskeleton in a pit which acts as a collector for sound.

The sounds made by grasshoppers, crickets and cicadas are plainly heard by humans. Since song, if such it should be called, appears to play such a part in the life of these insects, it was a reasonable conclusion that in all probability they would be able to hear the sounds that they made. But detailed analysis of their hearing abilities could not be made until methods had been devised to produce pure tones of variable intensity. Linked with this development has come the manufacture of sensitive microphones and methods of recording and analysing sound both within and outside the human range of sensibility.

The first experiments using electrical techniques for sound production were carried out on a cricket, *Gryllus campestris*, and a long-horned grasshopper, *Pholidoptera aptera* (= *Thamnotrizon apterus*).[448–452] Both male and female crickets have tympanal organs which make their first appearance in the last nymphal stage. They appear as two slits on the upper (proximal) end of both left and right fore tibiae. When the chirps of a male were transmitted through a telephone to a room in which females were kept, the females were attracted to the instrument, despite the distortion of the sound which was clearly noticeable to the human ear. This was good evidence that the song plays a part in the courtship of these insects, serving to bring the opposite sexes together. Later work has fully supported this. Mated females, that is, those already fertilized, were not attracted, only the unmated virgin females moved towards the instrument. Thus the physiological state of the animal affected its reaction to the noise.

The song of the male long-horned grasshopper is complicated, for there is a prelude ('Vorspiel') followed by an alternating duet, if two males are within hearing of each other, and finally a coda ('Nachspiel'). So that it is possible to judge whether a male interprets a particular sound as another male by testing whether he will perform a duet with it. Clearly the fact that such duets are heard indicates that these grasshoppers can hear their partners in song. When artificial sounds were made to older adult males, the only result was that singing stopped. It was only with males which had just become adult, that is soon after the final moult, that success was obtained. These insects would sing alternate duets with artificial sounds of between 400 cycles per second and 2,800 cycles per second. Removal of both tympanic organs prevented duet singing, and removal of the organ from one side only prevented organized concerts though the insect retained some sensitivity to sound generally. This is an example of the inability of a young animal to discriminate between similar stimuli, a common feature of many behaviour patterns. For reaction to a narrowly specified stimulus, in this case, the real song of the male, does not occur until the grasshopper has heard its companions singing. Thus the innate reaction is one to sound in general, but the particular sound to which reactions must occur has to be learned. The particular sound is the one which will have most biological importance, in this case, the sound which keeps the males together in a chirruping band, which probably, though this is not proved, attracts the females to it. This prevents wide distribution of the insects, which, if they are not large, very active, or in great numbers, makes the meetings of the opposite sexes less likely.

A number of different songs may be produced by individuals in different circumstances (e.g. 12 distinguishable songs in the genus *Chorthippus*[160, 161]) but that of the domestic cricket *Acheta* (= *Gryllulus*) *domesticus*, is less complex but serves much the same purposes as those outlined above. The males have a 'normal song' of an irregular series of chirrups. They do not perform duets but this song stimulates the females to move towards the noise. This has a fundamental frequency of 3,500 cycles per second. 'Courtship song' with a fundamental frequency of about 2,000 cycles per second causes the female to stop moving and also to permit the male to attach his genitalia. The males do not apparently react to the sound of other males. Only about 60% of females do react to either of these songs. This figure is diminished to 27–37% when the tympanal organs are destroyed. If the anal cerci are then coated with vaseline, the number of positive reactions is further reduced to 10–15%.[230] This makes it clear that though the tympanal organs do partake in hearing, the anal cerci are also stimulated. That these are certainly sensitive to sounds particularly of low frequency will be shown later.

That the tympanic organ of the long-horned grasshopper can react to a wide range of sounds is proved by the way in which young adults chirrup in unison with sounds over a wide range of frequencies. Since an older adult restricts its reactions to a narrower band of frequencies its behaviour is no longer a reliable indicator of the ability of its tympanic organ to receive sound; there is in fact central suppression of reaction. A direct method, however, is to study the impulses arising in the nerves leading from the organ while it is being stimulated. By this method the range for a cricket has been found to be 250–10,000 cycles per second and for a long-horned grasshopper, 800–45,000 cycles per second.[566]

Now of great interest is the fact that the electrical response in the nerves from the hearing organs of all these insects, though it is of course intermittent, does not necessarily have the same frequency as the pure sound used to stimulate the organ. Responses in the auditory nerve of a number of Acridids were asynchronous with pure tones of frequencies up to 20 kcs.[231] Thus the frequency of discharge in the nerve does not reflect the note of the stimulating sound. Discrimination between sounds according to their frequencies is not therefore possible by insects, though it is the method used by humans. There must be some other quality of the natural songs which gives them distinction. And to judge from the reaction of grasshoppers to sounds transmitted through telephones (above) this quality must survive the distortion caused by the instrument. Since the greatest sensitivity to sound appears to be at about 5,000 cycles per sec., though sounds were still being perceived at 20 kcs. (outside the range of natural songs) this distinctive quality must be one which sounds of these frequencies can have.

Orthopteran noises are usually produced by a scraper moving across a vibrating structure, for example, the inner side of the femur being drawn across the fore-wing. From this there will be two sources of noise, a high frequency sound arising from the resonance of the vibrating structure, the wing case, and secondly, a lower frequency sound arising from the teeth of the scraper and dependent upon the speed with which the scraper is moved. Interaction of these two frequencies produces amplitude modulation, as explained earlier. It has been shown that if the tympanic organ of a locust is stimulated by a pure tone of 8,000 cycles upon which other lower frequency sounds are imposed, the impulses in the nerve are synchronous with the modulations produced up to 300 cycles.[231, 441] Such modulation in the form of pulses is characteristic of natural songs (e.g. in Acrididae).[231] Indeed different pulse repetition frequencies particularize different songs and are constant for individuals of any one species. On the other hand, frequencies and waveform within the pulse (modulation envelope) are very variable (as indeed are the spikes in the nerve, though the bursts of spikes are synchronized with the pulse frequency) (Plate II). This demonstrates that the mechanism to receive the pulses exists. Although pure sounds which are characterized by sudden increases or decreases in amplitude (transients) may stimulate insects,[89] it seems unlikely that the transients are the characteristic components of natural songs. The telephone experiments support the view that the pulse frequency is the main factor for though notes and amplitudes may be altered by transmission through a telephone, the pulses would remain, hence the identity of reaction of a female cricket to the transmitted sounds of a male and to the male itself.

Further it is possible to remove the fundamental frequency of a sound electrically by filtering it with the appropriate valves, this leaves the beat frequency unaffected. Such filtered sounds have been used to prove the effectiveness of modulations in both the courtship and normal songs of male house crickets. When the unfiltered sounds were used 54% and 58% of the females reacted positively to 'normal' and 'courtship' songs respectively. When the fundamental frequencies were removed, the proportions reacting were reduced very little, to 40% and 52% in fact.[230]

But not only has the sound to be distinguished, but it must also be localized so that the insect can be guided towards its source, in the case of a courting female, a chirping male. Unmated females will make their way towards the males over distances of 10 metres or more along a substantially straight path. And unmated females of the locustid, *Ephippiger ephippiger*, will choose noisy males rather than ones that have been prevented from stridulating, making their way even to a box in which the males can be heard but not seen.[154] For this it is not essential that the organs on the two sides should be constantly comparing the stimulation arriving from the two sides, for removal of one organ affects the female very little showing that the power of guidance resides in one organ alone, though the path followed is not so direct as with both organs.[448-452]

Now when we consider the structure of the tympanic organ lying in the upper end of the tibiae of these crickets, we see that it opens by two slits facing slightly outwards. Within the cavity behind each slit lies a tympanum. The level of activity in the tympanal nerve varies when the organ is stimulated from various directions with pure tones of equal frequency and intensity (Fig. 119). Activity is

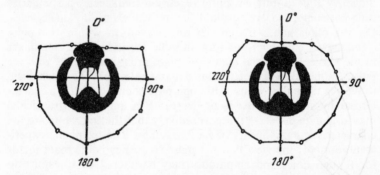

FIG. 119. Diagram of the directional sensitivity of the tympanal organ of *Tettigonia viridissima*. The distances of each circle from the centre shows the size of the action potential set up by sound (of equal intensity and frequency in each case) from that direction (from von Buddenbrock[80] after Autrum[12]).

least, that is, the sensitivity of the organ is lowest, when the sound strikes the organ parallel to its plane of symmetry.[12] However, at about 35° to both left and right of this plane, the sensitivity begins to increase sharply, so that a small angular movement of the sound source produces a great increase in activity in the nerve. Now in normal walking the legs are moved forwards through an angle of about 50° and the hearing organ likewise swings forward scanning the surroundings (Fig. 120). Sounds reaching an organ within about 35° of its plane of symmetry will require to be of high intensity before they are perceived, but on each side of this wedge is a narrow angle within which change of position of the organ with respect to the sound source will be most easily detected (Fig. 121). The impulses from the organ on the side towards the sound source will show a marked diminution in frequency when the source passes through and out of the zone of greatest sensitivity. As a result of this the leg bearing the organ may not swing forwards through its full pace. The leg on the other side, however, makes its full pace, for the sound, if it reaches the organ, will impinge on a part of the organ which does not give rise to sharp changes in nervous activity with angular movement. Thus the animal will turn towards the source.[12, 15] This hypothesis is supported by the ability of an insect with only one fore-leg to steer towards a sound source, though less accurately than an intact insect.

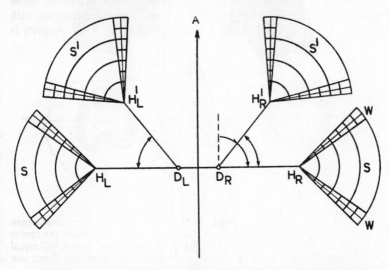

FIG. 120. Diagram to show the position of sectors of reduced sensitivity during the movement of the legs of *Tettigonia*. A, longitudinal axis of insect; D_L, D_R, centres of rotation of the left and right legs; H_L, H_R, positions of the left and right tympanic organs when the legs were at the most posterior part of the pace; H'_L, H'_R, position when the legs were advanced as far as their anterior limit of the pace; W, sectors of maximum sensitivity (Autrum[15]).

The abdominal tympanal organs of locusts (*Locusta*) also show differences in intensity according to the angle at which the sound strikes them (Fig. 122).[439] Sounds reaching them from either straight ahead or from behind are least likely to be detected, but on either side of the longitudinal axis, both forwards and backwards, are areas over which sensitivity changes with angular displacement are rapid. It might be that these areas function in much the same way as in the tibial organs of *Tettigonia*, though in this case turning must bring the direction of sound to lie within the angle at which it evokes least activity of the sense organ. So navigation may be by altering

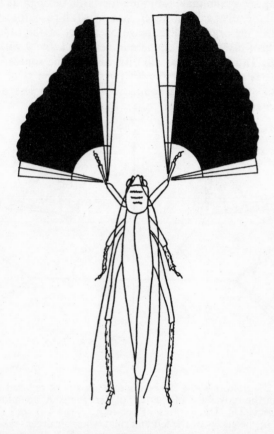

FIG. 121. *Tettigonia cantans* showing the sectors of reduced sensibility to sound in black. Sounds which enter the plain sectors of high sensibility from the black areas produce a sudden increase in discharge in the tympanal nerve (Autrum[15]).

direction until no nervous activity occurs in the nerves, swinging to left or right of the correct course causing impulses to travel in the tympanal nerves.

Possibly differences in phase may also aid in sound location. Thus if one tympanum is towards the source, a wave will strike that one earlier than the other by a time interval proportional to the extra distance that the second tympanum lies from the sound's source. The two tympana will tend to vibrate out of phase, being brought back into phase again only when the whole organ is turned so that the tympana are now equidistant from the source. At lower frequencies intensity differences might play their part, for the organs are very sensitive to such differences over the lower ranges.

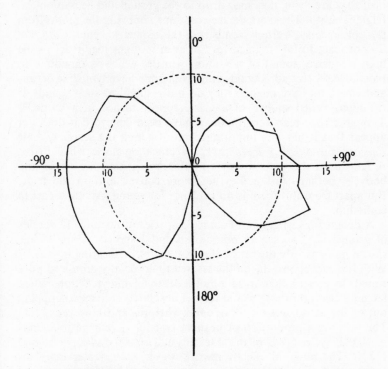

FIG. 122. Directional sensitivy of an isolated abdominal tympanal organ of *Locusta*, plotted on polar co-ordinates as a function of the direction of incidence of the test stimulus. Sensitivity (log. reciprocal of threshold amplitude) is plotted radially and the minimum sensitivity is arbitrarily taken to be zero. The line 0°–180° lies in the sagittal plane of the animal, and for angles of positive or negative sign the test stimulus is incident on the external or internal aspect of the tympanic organ respectively (Pumphrey[439]).

HEARING AMONG THE LEPIDOPTERA

Abdominal tympanic organs are found in both sexes in some moth families, such as the Geometridae and Hydriomenidae, while the Caradrinidae, Lymantriidae and other families possess organs on the metathoracic segment. Tympanic organs do not occur in

Hepialidae and Sphingidae. But the noises produced by these moths, if they do all make noises, are with a few exceptions inaudible to humans. Nevertheless they do react to various sounds. When they are on the ground, the moths may fly up on hearing the sound, or if they are flying they may drop to the ground and lie motionless, feigning death. These are escape reactions removing the moths from possible enemies. Certain members of the geometrid genus, *Catocala*, do not react to low frequencies but even in flight they react to the high frequency sound of a Galton whistle, which is inaudible to most men.[531] Not all noctuids and geometrids have tympanic organs and where they are missing they do not respond to such sounds as the high-pitched squeak of a glass stopper turned in a bottle.[156] Though escape reactions to sound have been described it does not appear that it has any importance in attracting the sexes. A male *Endrosa aurita var. ramosa* makes a crackling noise when flying. A female on the ground reacts to this by shaking her wings and body;[428] perhaps this makes her more conspicuous to the male. But apart from this there is no evidence for sound playing a part in courtship.

A detailed investigation of some 23 species of noctuid, 12 species of geometrid, 2 species of notodontid and 1 species of arctiid has shown more exactly the range of sensitivity of the hearing organs.[473] With few exceptions, the moths reacted to artificially produced pure sounds by either a flight reaction or a death feigning reaction. When feigning death the moth would remain absolutely still, even dropping out of the air to rest on the ground wherever and however it fell. The maximum proportion of positive reactions occurred to sounds of 60,000 cycles (72% of those tested) and 80,000 cycles per second (76%). The range of effectiveness, however, was greater than this for a sound of 15,000 cycles produced positive reactions in 45% of those tested, and one of 175,000 cycles in 47% of those tested. The intensity threshold was not measured, but sounds were effective even if the oscillator was 4–5 metres away. As would be expected removal of the tympanic organs abolished this behaviour; but less expected was their cessation in decapitated moths, though in other respects these mutilated insects were behaving normally. This suggests that the behaviour evoked by the sound is not due to a peripheral reflex, but that reference must be made to the brain before the behaviour appears. The responses of the two sexes are similar and such sounds do not evoke courtship behaviour in either male or female.

But the range of sensibility is very like the frequency range of sounds produced by bats[232] whose high-pitched squeak of 30,000–80,000 cycles serves as the sound wave whose reflection from objects warns the flying bat of obstacles. When it is remembered that bats are probably one of the main predators of flying geometrids, it seems very probable that the hearing ability of these moths has a protective function, for both of their escape reactions, the one, active, the other, passive, will take them away from the danger threatened by their predator.

Further, electrophysiological studies of the tympanal organs of *Phalera bucephala* and *Arctia caja* show that they respond, asynchronously, to frequencies of 3-20 kcs., but synchronously to modulation frequencies up to 45 kcs. This suggested that they are most effective in detecting short bursts of high-frequency sound, such as those produced by bats.[232] The tympanic organ of *Prodenia eridania* functions in an essentially similar manner, for its greatest sensitivity is over the range 15-60 kcs., though some preparations would discharge in response to a stimulation frequency as high as 240 kcs. Ultrasonic impulses from bats flying in the same room evoked near maximum discharge in the nerve at a frequency of 650 impulses a second. The after-discharge effect, so prominent in these preparations, would suit the organ to the reception of these short bursts of sound as the previous experiments had suggested.[458] Moths without hearing organs do not react to bat noises, as would be expected.[529]

While flying on wires moths (*Prodenia*) produced high-frequency sound at 15 kcs. and above, which induced impulses in the tympanic nerve of a preparation of the hearing organ of another moth placed 8 inches away. Possibly there may be a system of monitoring their own flight sounds which permits moths to avoid obstacles, in a similar way to that employed by bats, and indeed there is evidence that in moths, as in bats, there is a device by which the auditory organ is put out of action while the sound is being produced.[458]

HEARING AMONG THE HEMIPTERA

Among the noisier insects are the cicadas with their strident song. Though the structure and position of auditory organs are known their functions had not been tested with any degree of exactness until recently. South American cicadas will sing alternating solos. Cicadas have been heard to sing in response to the drums of soldiers. On the other hand an attempt to interfere with the song of cicadas by the firing of a cannon was quite unsuccessful. Such a sound might perhaps be of too low a frequency to evoke any reaction.

Other members of the group, *Auchenorrhyncha*, which also contains the small plant bugs the Cercopidae, Membracidae and Jassidae, produce sounds in a somewhat similar manner to the cicadas. But since these are usually very small insects the noise is not loud. The sounds are very varied and are apparently mainly connected with courtship for there are invitation calls, pairing calls, and rivalry calls as well as calls concerned with other things such as distress. But the means by which this code of sound is appreciated remains unknown, no auditory organ having been detected.[407]

More is known of the functions of the tympanic organs of the lesser water boatman, *Corixa*; this is also the only example among the insects about which anything is known of sensitivity to water-borne sound. The organ exists in both sexes but only the males stridulate. They are stimulated by the sound of other males to chorus, and also can be artificially stimulated by sounds from a whistle of 2,000–10,000 cycles, and by electrically produced sounds of 20,000, 30,000 and 40,000 cycles.[474] These two sources induce different sorts of stridulation, the first, intermittent 'chirps', and the second a continuous 'chirrup'. Normally the females react to the 'chirps' of males by swimming jerkily in circles. This appears to make them more visible to the males, who are stimulated to copulate with them. After copulation the males may continue to sing for no apparent reason for after copulation females no longer react to male sounds. The typical jerky and circling swimming movement is not always evoked by artificial stimulation of the females particularly if the sound is a continuous note; the best frequency is 20 kcs., but more certain results are obtained with intermittent notes. It may be that it is not the frequency of the note but the frequency of the bursts of sound which release this action. Both the ability of males to chirp in concert and the ability of the females to react to male chirping is abolished when the hearing organs are destroyed.

Song seems to serve to bring the sexes together in cicadas as well. Groups of individuals of various cicadas of Ceylon are each of one species only, even when two species found in the same area, such as *Platypleura octoguttata* and *P. westwoodi*, have similar song patterns. Sound in these insects is produced by pulling in a tympanum which clicks back into position. An organ occurs on each side of the body and they are synchronized, giving a song consisting of a succession of short pulses (at a repetition frequency of 390 per sec. in *Platypleura capitata*, for example). As in orthopteran hearing organs it is the modulation envelope which characterizes the songs of the different species. The specialization of the song for special functions has not been analysed in detail but in *P. octoguttata*, at least, the male produces a distinct courtship song before attempting copulation.[437]

SOUND RECEPTION BY SENSORY HAIRS

Clearly if sound can cause the displacement of a tympanum it can also cause the displacement of a lightly hinged hair. It was found that crickets, e.g. *Gryllus campestris* and *Pholidoptera aptera*[448, 450] retained some power of hearing after the removal of their tympanic organs. Therefore there must have been some other part of the body sensitive to air-borne waves. Both sexes of most orthoptera have paired cerci at the end of the abdomen. The nerves supplying them are readily seen on dissection and the electrical responses passing along them can be studied. The cerci themselves are covered with hair sensilla, that is, sensitive hairs whose movement will stimulate a nerve cell at their base. At one time it was believed that these were olfactory hairs, but if a pure tone is directed upon the cerci, the electrical responses in the nerve are synchronous with the frequency of the sound between 50 and 400 cycles per second. That is, each sound wave deflects the hairs, and each deflection of the hair results in a response which can be detected with suitable apparatus as an electrical wave travelling along the nerve. Above this frequency the discharge is asynchronous except on occasions when the synchrony may remain up to 800 cycles per second. The upper limit of sensitivity is about 3,000 cycles per second. That the hairs are the receptors can be shown by covering them with vaseline, when the electrical response is much reduced. The vaseline will prevent the movement of the delicately hinged hairs. So responsive are they that they can be seen, under a microscope, to move in air currents too slight to be felt by a human. The deflection of the tip will move the lower end in the opposite direction about the pivot of the hair. Since the length of a hair is usually greater above the pivot than below, the distance through which the lower end moves will be very small. An estimate of this distance can be obtained if the movement of the tip under the influence of a sound of a controlled intensity is measured. Thus in an example, a tip deflection of 560 A° produced an estimated movement of the lower end of about 0·5 A° (an amplitude of the same order as the smallest movement capable of stimulating the subgenual organ of *Locusta*[13]). Since even this was sufficient to start a response in the nerve, the sensory cell at the base of the hair must have been very sensitive.[440] Clearly a stubby hair whose tip was deflected by the same amount as a longer one will produce greater movement of the lower end, if the distance between pivot and the lower end was the same in both. On the other hand a long hair may be more mobile than a shorter one, and it will certainly apply a greater magnification factor to the force deflecting it than will a short one.

Hair sensilla occur on the ventral side of the abdomen of *Chorthippus parallelus* and probably function as short-range receptors of song.[231] It is probable that in crickets the cercal hairs serve to detect vibrations travelling through the ground, while in cockroaches, where cerci are held erect over the end of the abdomen, they probably serve to detect air currents. In both cases they will be detectors of danger and as such it is not surprising to find them developed in all nymphal stages that have been investigated, unlike the tympanal organs, which being a prerequisite for courtship, an adult prerogative, do not appear in the nymphs.[439] The few sensilla which occur on the cerci of some acridids respond to a limited range of frequencies and it is likely that being stimulated mechanically in copulation,[231] they serve to raise the level of central excitation (as seems to be necessary in *Gryllus campestris*[275]).

The whole body of many caterpillars is thickly or sparsely covered with hairs which function as sound receptors. When some caterpillars are stimulated by noise they rear up the anterior third of the body, or sometimes the tail end. This comes about by contraction of the longitudinal muscles of the back. Thus the sign that the sound has been perceived is the contraction of these muscles.[380, 383] It will occur, not only in the whole animal, but also in a decapitated caterpillar, or even in pieces of the body. Again the response is abolished if the hairs are clogged with flour or with water droplets, reappearing again when the flour is removed or the water dries off. Like the hairs on the cerci of orthoptera, these hairs are responsive to low frequencies, indeed the lower limit of sensitivity does not seem to have been reached at 32 cycles per second. The upper limit appears to be about 1,000 cycles, but if the intensity is increased this limit can be raised. It seems that, like the threshold for response in cercal hairs, the threshold is greater for the higher frequencies. Thus both systems have a decreasing sensitivity with increase in frequency.

Since the hairs on a caterpillar vary in size and length, it is possible that different frequencies of sound are received by different sized hairs, thus long fine hairs might be expected to vibrate slowly and therefore be resonant with the lower frequencies, and short stumpy hairs to vibrate faster and be resonant with the higher frequencies. Since most sense organs may be fatigued, the use of one tone continuously might eliminate the hairs resonant with it by fatiguing them. If the caterpillar still reacted to sounds of other frequencies, then discrimination of tones by a variety of different sized hairs would be proved. But when this is done the results are very different from those expected on this assumption, for continuous stimulation with low-frequency noise inhibits reactions to

high frequencies,[380] but the reverse is not true. It is unlikely therefore that there is frequency discrimination by different hairs. The
result probably arises from the great sensitivity to low-frequency
sound which would imply that for the same intensity of stimulation
low-frequency sound will have a more fatiguing effect on all hairs
equally.

Prey is located by some water bugs (*Notonecta* spp.) by the vibrations set up by its movement. These stimulate sensitive hairs on the
swimming legs of the insect. By comparison of the intensity of
stimulation on the two sides (tropotaxis) the insect can direct itself
towards the source of the vibrations.[445]

It might be thought likely that the trichobothria (hairs supplied
by nerves) on the forelegs of spiders enable them to receive the
vibrations of the prey caught in their webs.[408] Spiders are attracted
onto the net by the note of a tuning fork showing that they also
receive airborne stimulation. But removal of the hairs decreases the
sensitivity very little, so that it is very possible that the hairs are not
the only organs involved.

THE SENSITIVITY OF OTHER ORGANS TO SOUND

Logically one would expect that other parts of the insect's body, if
they are lightly hinged and easily deflected, might also be moved by
incident sound waves. The only obvious parts which fulfil this condition are the antennae. Like a sensitive hair, they are hinged at the
base. They are often light and may even have some knob developed
at the end which will endow the whole antenna with a natural frequency of vibration. In many species, the second antennal joint is
very much enlarged and packed with chordotonal organs. This is
Johnston's organ, first observed in a male culcine mosquito. The
chordotonal organs are connected between the base of the third
segment and the wall of the enlarged second segment so that movement of the funiculus, that is the rest of the antenna on the second
joint, or pedicellus, will stretch these organs. They are of the same
type as those which are stimulated by movement of the tympanum in
tympanic organs. Unlike the sensory hairs of caterpillars and orthoptera which appear to be receptors for stimuli indicating danger, the
antennae of male mosquitoes are hearing organs attuned to receive
the sounds made by the female mosquito. The reactions of a male
Aedes aegypti to such a sound are to take to flight if it is at rest, then
to fly towards the sound, to seize the female, and finally to clasp
the female's genitalia.[461] All these responses can be elicited by a
tuning fork vibrating at frequencies between 275 and 700 cycles per
second. This frequency range depends on whether the males have

previously copulated or not and on their ages, thus unmated males 48–50 hours old have an average range of 395–709 cycles per second, while those 203–309 hours old have an average range of 276–702 cycles per second. The upper limits are less variable than the lower. All the responses remain even when all of the antennae beyond the third segment is removed, but when all the antennal hairs are taken off, few of the mosquitoes seize females flying in the cage, though they will still react to a tuning fork, seizing the cloth of the cage wall opposite the fork and in a few cases they turn their abdomens into the copulatory position. The response is abolished if the John-ston's organ is waxed to prevent movement of the third joint upon the second, and if drops of wax are put on the end of the antennae. When the wax is removed the reactions are restored.

The young adult mosquito does not have a full brush of hairs on its antennae for many of them adhere to the shaft for some time. These hairs may act as amplifiers for noise. This might explain the absence of reaction to females by males with shaven antennae while they still respond to a tuning fork, for the sound of females is less intense than that of the tuning fork. The increase in numbers of erected hairs with age probably also explains the shift in the limits of the range received with age (Fig. 123). And while it is possible to adapt a young male, 25 hours old, to 400 cycles per second so that he shows no mating responses to sounds in this frequency, he will also not respond to 500 and 600 cycles per second immediately afterwards. This may be because the full complement of hairs is not extended and therefore the same adapted nerve cells are being stimu-lated at all these frequencies. Later when other hairs extend, differ-ent nerve cells may be stimulated by different frequencies.

Females do not respond to the sound of males, though they may perform any of a number of movements which can be classified as shock reactions in answer to mechanically produced sound. Bio-logically the sound the females produce has an important function in courtship. For, by it the male can perceive the presence of a flying female and can locate her direction. His ability to discriminate the female's sound from others alone allows the male to react appro-priately suppressing the shock reactions which he would show to other sounds. But in addition he can then fly to and seize the female. Location of a tuning fork is quite accurate even if the male lacks one antenna, but his ability to seize a female is greatly reduced.

Johnston's organ picks up vibrations of a different sort in *Gyrinus maximus*, the whirligig beetle.[157] This beetle moves around on the surface of water in swarms but individuals do not collide. They feed on insects trapped in the water surface film. The antennae of each beetle rests in the surface film. Vibrations transmitted through the surface, that is, waves set up by other beetles, or prey, move the funiculus of the antenna on the pediculus. So Johnston's organ is stimulated and the presence of prey or of a neighbour is detected.

Chordotonal organs similar to those in Johnston's organ are found elsewhere in the insect body and were so named because they were thought to play a part in sound perception. They were later considered to be organs of a kinaesthetic sense, but some at least

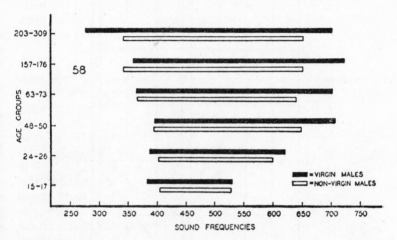

FIG. 123. Shift of limits of sensitivity to sound of various frequencies in virgin and non-virgin males of *Aedes* with advancing age (Roth[461]).

appear to be sensitive to vibration of the substrate upon which the insect is standing. They probably detect surges in the blood contained within the limbs when the limbs are accelerated up and down by the vibration.[16] They are developed as bundles in the subgenual organs of the tibia of Orthoptera, Lepidoptera and Hymenoptera.[122-124] The typical orthopteran organ consists of 20–30 scolopidia (p. 22) attached at two opposite points on the wall of the leg, while in other groups one end of the bundle is attached to the main trachea running down the tibia. Insects having these organs are extremely sensitive at their optimal frequencies, for the amplitude of displacement required to stimulate the organ is very small (Fig. 124 and Table V, Group I). Other insects which possess tibio-tarsal chordotonals, or hair sensilla at the tarsal joints, in place of subgenual organs are less sensitive (Group II), and those without any such organs the

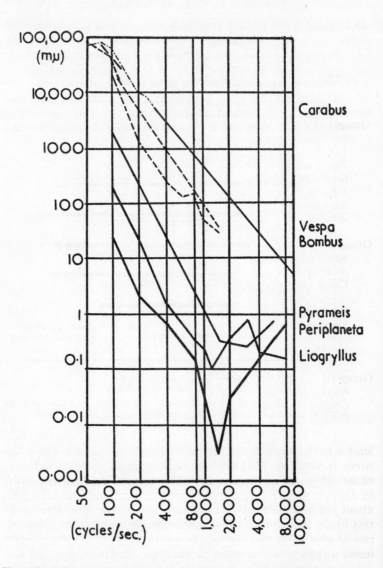

FIG. 124. Threshold amplitudes of movement of substratum causing reactions in a number of insects at various frequencies. The level at which the acceleration of the vibrating substratum is equal to g is indicated by the straight line (from Autrum and Schneider[16]).

TABLE V. Sensitivity of various insects to vibration of the
substratum (from Autrum[13]).

Species	Optimum Frequency (cs)	Threshold Amplitude (mμ) at Optimal Frequency	at 400 cs.
Group 1			
Periplaneta americana	1400	0·004	0·72
Locusta cantans	2000	0·068	0·64
Tachycines asynamorus	1000	0·1	2·2
Gryllus campestris	1500	0·1	1·6
Vanessa atalanta	3000	0·29	26·0
Satyrid	2000	0·4	2·0
Acridid	3000	0·9	12·0
Group II			
Apis mellifera	2500	13·0	400·0
Andrena nitida	1000	18·0	1490 0
Camponotus sp.	2000	19·0	177·0 (@ 300 cs.)
Bombus soroeensis	1500	32·0	270·0
Vespa crabro	1500	36·0	1950·0 (@ 300 cs.)
Agrotis sp.	1500	57·0	630·0
Group III			
Rhodnius prolixus	400	1300·0	
Carabus hortensis	300	5500·0	
Eristalis sp.	200	6590·0	

least sensitive (Group III). In this last group it is likely that the
nerve endings are stimulated directly by the vibrations. Removal
of the sub-genual organs lowers the sensitivity of the insect markedly,
in *Locusta* and *Decticus*,[13] increasing the amplitude threshold by
about 100 times at frequencies below 1,500 cs., though at and above
this figure the sensitivity is less affected. Since this vibration sense
can be used to localize a source of vibration not in contact with the
insect we can term this sound perception.

HEARING AMONG OTHER INVERTEBRATES

With the construction of better detecting and recording apparatus
it is being found that more and more of the 'silent' invertebrates do
in fact make noises, though their function, if they have any, is
undetermined. Many of these new discoveries refer to marine

animals, particularly Crustacea. No sound-receiving organs are known in this group, unless statocysts are indeed responsive to sound waves as was once believed (but see p. 219). Their original name of octocysts implies that they are ears. In mysids they do seem to receive sound stimulation[243] though an abdomen isolated from the rest of the body will also react to sound and vibration.[80] Theoretically there is no reason why they should not. The sensory hairs are often attached to the statolith, which is itself denser than water. Therefore when a sound wave travels through the soft parts of the body, which have a density not very different from water, the wave will have little or no displacement effect until it reaches the calcareous statolith. Its difference in density will render this liable to a greater displacement and thus the distortion of the sensory hairs will be greatly enhanced. But this is speculation.

CHAPTER IX

THE TACTILE SENSES

WE have chosen to consider the perception of low-frequency vibrations as hearing, but it has been stressed that as these frequencies become lower, one approaches the final conditions where the stimulus consists of only one wave phase, becoming a simple on-off type of stimulation without rhythmic fluctuations. This was defined as a tactile stimulus, that is, a stimulus in the form of a localized, and usually sudden, increase in pressure which is maintained, sometimes with variations in strength, until the end of stimulation when the pressure returns to its original level. The receptors for this sense will be mechano-receptors.

The stimulus may be received directly, as when a food particle touches an amoeba, or when a fly's foot touches the ground. But pressure received may arise from objects at a distance from the animal, thus the duck leech reacts to currents, which are pressure waves in the water set up by its host when it is some way from the parasite.[249] Also the pressure received may be a sign of conditions to be found elsewhere, a token stimulus, in other words. Thus, when a gravid planarian worm turns upstream against the current,[38, 39] the current itself is of no importance to the worm, but the fact that upstream, in the new direction it is going, lie the optimum conditions for egg-laying is of great importance.

Touch plays a part in many different activities of the animal's life. It is impossible to generalize about its different roles, for the receptors involved differ and the relations of the sense organs to the stimulating source differ. The only common factor of all is that the behaviour is a response to pressure on the body, which is often localized.

THE DISTRIBUTION OF RECEPTORS

It is often very difficult to discover the actual receptors involved in responses to touch, for they are most frequently extremely simple. Often they are free nerve endings lying in the surface layers of the body. Sometimes sensory hairs are tactile in function. They are stimulated when they are bent over in the same way as hairs that react to vibrations (Fig. 125).

Whether the receptors can be distinguished anatomically or not their distribution can be mapped by stimulating various parts of the body locally and noting whether or not there is a reaction. For various reasons this yields only an approximation to the true distribution but it is usually a close approximation. The organs are often grouped upon that part of the body which comes into contact with the surroundings most frequently but obviously those parts are used to touch the surroundings because they are sensitive. Thus the tentacles or antennae of heads of polychaete worms, snails, insects and crustacea are usually well provided with touch receptors. Similarly legs, and particularly feet, are often very sensitive to touch, and are usually in contact with the ground. But in general, sensitivity is also

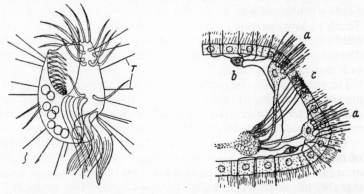

FIG. 125. Touch receptors in protozoa and turbellaria. Left, the ciliate *Diophrys hystrix*, showing the touch bristles, T. Right, a schematic cross-section through the flatworm, *Mesostoma lingua*; a and b, two different types of touch or current receptor cells; c, chemosensory cells (from von Buddenbrock[80]).

widespread over the body, especially if an animal is not clothed in a protective covering. Those parts of the bodies of molluscs, and in particular gastropods, which remain within the shell are insensitive to touch. The exoskeleton of arthropods being leathery or even hard also prevents touch stimulation reaching the underlying tissues. This is no doubt why tactile hairs are almost exclusively the touch receptors of arthropods.

Clearly if the receptors are localized, responses to their stimulation will probably have this locality as their focus. But even an animal with general sensitivity may be able to localize the spot at which it is being stimulated and react accordingly. This will be dependent on the ability of the central nervous system to distinguish nerve impulses coming from one part of the body from those from elsewhere. Though widespread among the vertebrates the ability is apparently less well developed among invertebrates, or, more accurately perhaps, has been less well investigated in this sub-kingdom. However, insects can clean the part of the body which has been made dirty, the manubrium of a jellyfish will bend towards the source of stimulation on the edge of the bell[460] and foreign bodies on the mantle of *Pecten* may be localized so that the foot may eject them from the shell.[534]

THE PLACE OF TACTILE SENSITIVITY IN FEEDING

Feeding consists of location of food and then taking it into the body. Touch plays its part in the detection of food which is usually some solid object, another animal, for example, or some plant debris. The search for the general area in which food lies may be at random, or it may be directed by stimuli arising from the food itself, or from the surroundings in which it is usually found. Such directive stimuli are usually chemical and will be dealt with later. But the final grasping and eating the food is often the result of tactile stimulation, though its selection may depend upon its chemical characteristics.

The surface of some ciliates, such as *Diophrys*, bears stiff bristles of protoplasm which appear to be touch receptors; they are often arranged at the ends of the body (Fig. 125). It does not seem likely that they are used to locate food for the food of a ciliate is usually minute and taken in at random from the surrounding water. However, these animals have a clear tactile response to surfaces, coming to rest against them. The reaction of an animal by which it comes to rest after random movement as soon as it touches a solid object can be called low-thigmo-kinesis, for when tactile stimulation is low or non-existent, the animal moves about (p. 247). *Paramecium*, for example, will come to rest against a surface, such as a large piece of detritus. Those cilia which are in contact with the object cease to beat but the feeding current is maintained.[286] Since at such places bacteria will probably abound feeding on the detritus, such behaviour is advantageous for it brings the animal into regions where its own food is plentiful. It is a common observation to see ciliates 'nuzzling' detritus particles; this is particularly striking in such forms as *Spirostomum*. The touch of a single bacterium suffices to stop, or, at least, to slow down the cilia of *Tetrahymenea geleii* but high carbon dioxide concentration prevents this response. This has the result that the ciliate escapes out of dense bacterial crowds when the carbon dioxide tension is high but feeds on the fringes where the touch response slows it down.[67]

The heterotrichous ciliate, *Stentor*, remains attached while feeding. So long as it is stimulated by contact at its lower end, its reactions to various stimuli, such as light, differ from those it shows when unattached and swimming free. While feeding it will bend over so that it maintains contact with objects touching the oral disc and stimulating the animal slightly. This occurs only if contact is light, if it is strong, avoiding actions are taken[286] (p. 249).

Amoeboid protozoa, such as *Amoeba* itself, engulf food by putting out parts of their body to form a food cup around it. If a stationary food object touches the body surface, the sides of the cup are put out in close contact with it. Probably this is due to gelation of the protoplasm at the point of contact and the production of pseudopodia around the gelated area. But if the food is mobile, the bases of the pseudopodia are wider apart. The food is not so closely wrapped by the enveloping cup and thus lies in a larger vacuole than would have been made around an immobile particle. Perhaps a mobile organism produces greater contact stimulation, and therefore a wider area of gelation separates the bases of the pseudopodia. The moving object need not, however, be in contact with the amoeba, for carmine grains 20 μ across evoke pseudopodia formation when 100 μ away from the animal. Also objects hitherto rejected as food when stationary may be accepted if they move; probably some sensitivity to vibration is involved.[471]

The ability of *Amoeba* to localize its response to that area in which stimulation has occurred is obviously necessary, for pseudopodia put out from other parts of the body would be useless for trapping the food. A similar localized response is seen in the jellyfish, *Tiaropsis indicans*. The manubrium hangs within the bell, the mouth at its tip being approximately level with the tentacles fringing the bell edge. A touch on the bell edge causes the manubrium to contract at first and then to elongate once again bending towards the stimulated area until with great accuracy it touches it with its tip.[460] If other points are stimulated the manubrium will move to them and will continue to touch them after stimulation has been discontinued. It can be observed, however, to retouch more frequently those that have been stimulated most intensely. The feeding method of this jellyfish can be conjectured from these movements. In fact, food organisms are caught on the marginal tentacles and are picked off the margin by the mouth.

This localization is dependent on the integrity of the nervous system. If an incision is made in the bell, which will sever part of the connections of the nerve net, the manubrium can no longer accurately localize stimulation occurring on the margin below the

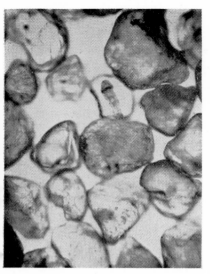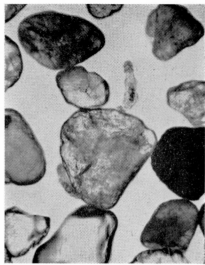

PLATE 4(*a*). Settlement of *Ophelia bicornis* larvae (approx. 35 ×). *Left*, an unmetamorphosed larva is attached to a sand grain by its anal papillae. The region of the prototroch is dark and distinct. *Right*, a larva in early metamorphosis crawling on the bottom of a glass dish. The larva is elongated, hence the dark prototrochal tissues are less distinct (Wilson[577]).

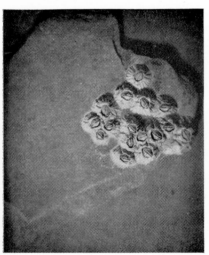

PLATE 4(*b*). The position of a patch of adult *Balanus balanoides* on a piece of slate has been outlined by a scratch (*left*). The barnacles are removed and cyprids of *B. balanoides*, allowed access to the whole slate, settle almost exclusively on the area previously occupied by the adults (Knight-Jones[302]).

[*face p. 242*

incision. But as the point of stimulation comes to lie nearer to one or the other end of the cut, localization becomes more accurate, first, the manubrium bends to the correct side of the margin, and then when the stimulation lies outside the strip which has been cut, the correct position is found. Similar disturbances occur in the hydroid, *Corymorpha*, when cuts are made at various levels in its column. Here the mouth and tentacles may be bent over to touch any stimulated part of the column. The column will bend even after the mouth and tentacles have been cut off.[527] Stimulation may arise from food, clearly, but the reaction may be protective as well for nudibranchs, which live on hydroids, may nibble at the base and application of the nematocyst-covered tentacles to them make the predators move away.[419]

Localized food capture responses are well developed in all coelenterates which catch their food by means of tentacles around their mouths. In *Hydra* and sea-anemones, for example, unstimulated tentacles will bend towards the one on which the prey is entangled. The number of tentacles which are involved will depend upon the strength of the stimulation caused by the food, so that if living food struggles violently more tentacles are recruited by the more extensive spread of the excitation round the disc.

The tentacles and tube feet of various echinoderms are also highly sensitive to touch. It is these parts that are responsible for grasping and holding food, as well as the location and lifting of material for the covering reaction (p. 32). The roughness of objects can be distinguished by the suckers of the arms of *Octopus vulgaris*. These animals can be trained to discriminate between perspex cylinders bearing different numbers of grooves, but though the percentage of the surface which is grooved is the characteristic which determines the choice the octopus can apparently not distinguish between patterns of grooves which involve similar amounts of roughness[563] (Fig. 126). Thus there does not appear to be any central spatial projection of the stimuli received by the suckers but rather the distinction seems to depend upon the frequency of discharge in the nerves reaching the brain.

It is important that contact stimuli arising from food should be differentiated from stimuli arising from objects which have no food value. Thus if the tentacles of the jellyfish, *Gonionemus*, are stimulated by a stationary object they contract, but if the stimulating object moves, they carry out the movements usually associated with food-catching.[587] Food is recognized as such merely because it moves. In other words movement of an object gives it valency as a food object. This can be compared with the behaviour of *Amoeba* and many other animals to moving and non-moving prey.

Food capture is often only mediated by touch stimulation reinforced by the necessary chemical stimulation. Thus the cnidae of the anemone, *Anemonia sulcata*, cannot be released in any quantity by simple mechanical stimulation, but a chemical factor is required, probably a surface active substance, before numbers of nematocysts will discharge.[410]

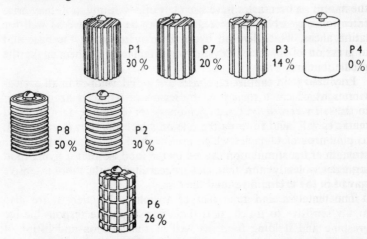

FIG. 126. The objects used in tests of the touch sensitivity of *Octopus*. The series is arranged so that there is a decreasing proportion of grooved to flat surface from left to right. This proportion is indicated as a percentage for each object. The top row contains objects that differ only in the number of vertical grooves cut in them. P_2 differs from P_1 only in the orientation of the grooves cut into it. P_6 has very nearly the same proportion of grooves as P_1, but the grooves are arranged to form a pattern of squares. Octopuses apparently find P_1, P_2 and P_6 difficult or impossible to distinguish, but can be taught to discriminate between the members of the top row (and between P_8 and P_4) relatively easily (Wells and Wells[563]).

On occasion searching for food may be stimulated by chemical factors diffusing outwards from the food, but actual grasping of the food will not take place without contact. Planarians in the vicinity of food move in an unorientated manner whenever they pass out of the sphere of influence of the chemicals arising from food. Since they also turn more frequently, they will be brought back into the immediate area around the food, where their paths are straighter (Klinokinesis, p. 38). This will bring them close to the food ultimately, but they do not grasp it unless their everted proboscides make contact with the food.[309]

Tactile hairs occur in large numbers on the mouthparts and body appendages of arthropods. They are no doubt used in the search for, and the manipulation of, food. Once again, however, chemical stimulation is often required as a reinforcement before the animal reacts. Thus flies, butterflies and honeybees, surfeited with water, will not attempt to suck or lap pure water, but will do so if food substances such as sugar are dissolved in the water though proboscis extension may be evoked in *Phormia regina* by mechanical stimulation, alone, of tarsal hairs.[137] The amphipod *Amphithöe* will attempt to grasp at food which touches its antennules but is indifferent to a needle touching these organs.[269]

Prey caught in the net of a web-making spider is located by the vibrations which it sets up in the strands as it struggles.[27] Return to the lair when the prey has been secured is made by visual landmarks (p. 83) but the tensions in the strands of the web seem also to play a part. After a spider (*Agalena labyrinthica*) had found its prey, the frame upon which it had spun its nest was distorted, changing the tensions in the threads. The spider was not able to find its way back to the lair, though when the original tensions were restored it immediately returned.[23]

PROTECTIVE REACTIONS TO TACTILE STIMULI

In much the same way that animals will react to strong vibration of their surroundings by taking protective action, so they will frequently do the same in answer to tactile stimulation. It is in the consideration of these two forms of stimulation, both of which produce similar results, that the distinction between sound and touch becomes vaguer. For the sake of consistency shock reactions to vibrations set up by striking the substratum and so forth, where a fluctuating stimulus may be in action, have been considered at the end of Chapter VIII.

Ciliates avoid obstructions by means of trial and error behaviour, described for the first time early in this century. When *Paramecium*, for example, touches a solid object in its forward path, the direction of beat of its cilia is reversed and it moves backwards for a short distance.[286] Halting once again, it turns through a small angle and advances once more. If it still meets the obstacle, backing, turning and advancing is repeated, until there is nothing to prevent it from continuing on. This behaviour is evoked by the tactile stimulus of striking the object and has protective value in that the animal is not prevented indefinitely from moving on for it is bound ultimately to move in a direction which leads it pass the obstruction. One supposes that where the obstacle is a possible food source other stimuli, probably chemical ones, evoke the adhering reaction in place of avoidance.

It appears that touch stimulation can be crudely localized on the body by *Paramecium aurelia* and *P. calkinsi*, at least. For a touch on the anterior end of a feeding animal causes an immediate avoidance reaction, the *Paramecium* retreating and then pivoting to the left to continue feeding if the stimulus is light but to swim away if the stimulus is a strong one. On the other hand, a touch on the posterior end causes the animal to swim quickly forward. Thus, the behaviour differs according to where the stimulus is located.[85]

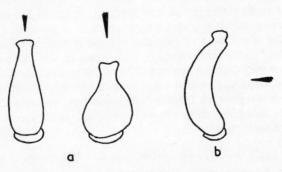

FIG. 127. Reactions of a leech, *Hemiclepsis marginata*, to touch. Note that the leech flattens itself, as well as withdrawing the head end when touched on the anterior end, but may bend away from an approaching paintbrush before contact is made (after Herter[249]).

Such avoidances are common though not always so complex. *Amoeba* reacts to touch stimulation as it flows forward by withdrawing its pseudopodia and coming to a halt. New pseudopodia are put out from some other point of the body and the animal moves off in a different direction. Again if the stimulation is from possible food, the reaction is different for pseudopodia are put out to grasp it. There is some discrimination of possibly harmful from possibly beneficial stimuli.[286]

The leeches are very sensitive to tactile stimulation. Even at some small distance the point of a needle can be detected as it approaches the body through the water, no doubt by the disturbance set up in the water. The nearest part of the body bends away as the needle approaches (Fig. 127). If the leech is attached and undulating near the surface in a dish of shallow water, it is only necessary to touch the surface film above its back to stop the undulation and cause the animal to press closely to the substrate.[571]

A whole group of protective behaviour patterns arises from low thigmokinetic behaviour. An animal moves about, sometimes at random, sometimes under the influence of other stimuli such as light until it comes to rest in a position in which the maximum area of its body makes contact with something solid so that maximum contact causes movement to stop. Such behaviour is probably typical of crevice-dwelling animals, though the reaction has not been studied in by any means all of them. Often when maximum contact has been achieved, behaviour towards other stimuli will be altered. Thus earwigs are photonegative, moving away from the light when moving about freely, but given glass tubes of an appropriate bore they will enter them and remain there whatever the lighting conditions. Even the right-angled edge of a petri dish will suffice to give the necessary stimulation.[568] Again *Nereis* will crawl into a glass tube and remain there, even in sunlight so strong that they are killed. In all these cases the diameter of the tubes must be such that maximum contact between the animal's body and the glass is achieved.[364]

Under natural conditions such reactions will lead the animal into sheltered places where it is protected not only from predators but also from a variety of other factors. Strong light is harmful to many animals and sheltered in crevices they are shaded from the sunlight. Likewise within a crevice the humidity is often high so that loss of water from the body surface is considerably decreased.

Vigorous contact or jarring may produce death feigning in insects, such as earwigs and stick insects. The cataleptic state of complete immobility is difficult to break, for locomotor reflexes are inhibited and sensitivity is reduced. Normal reflexes for righting the animal fail to function with the result that to all intents and purposes the insect appears dead. Probably this has a double advantage for not only will cessation of movement make the insect less conspicuous to its enemies, but also should those enemies see the insect its very immobility may render it unattractive.

This type of death feigning is very striking in many beetles, caterpillars and plant bugs, where it occurs as soon as they are knocked or jarred off whatever they may be walking upon. It appears to be caused by loss of contact between the feet and the substratum, be it plant or ground. Such stimulation of that part of the body which normally touches the ground is important in many animals for altering their methods of moving. The medicinal leech swims automatically whenever its suckers are unstimulated by contact, but a glass coverslip placed against one of the suckers will stop the swimming undulations the the leech will sink immobile through the water. The swimming activity of dragonfly larvae (*Aeschna* sp.) also ceases when a ball of paper is placed against their feet and grasped by them.[525] In a similar way, the prawn, *Palaemonetes varians*, will continue to swim until its legs make contact with the ground. But more particularly this change of activity occurs in flying insects when their feet make contact with the ground. A captive fly suspended by the top of its thorax will fly normally but will stop flying and crawl as soon as a piece of paper is held against its feet. The tarsi seem to bear the receptors for contact, since once these are cut off a fly will not stop flying when its legs are touched. Contact with all the legs at a time is not necessary and indeed stimulation of only one tarsal claw causes flying to cease.[176] Contact with

FIG. 128. *Meconema varians*. A, suspended with tarsi off the ground; B, the same but in an air stream (von Buddenbrock and Friedrich[81]).

one leg of a flying cockroach, stops the wing movement, even after the tarsi have been cut off. Flight is initiated in a falling cockroach by movement in the joint between prothorax and mesothorax deflecting trichoid sensilla situated at the articulation.[146]

Loss of contact may also produce an unusual posture. Thus the oak bush grasshopper, *Meconema varians*, throws its legs upwards over its back when it falls through the air[82] (Fig. 128). This has the effect of altering the position of its centre of gravity so that it lands the correct way up. Similar reactions probably occur in other insects and in spiders, for, like the proverbial cats, these invertebrates also land on their feet.

Maintenance of contact by the feet is important in many animals since their normal orientation demands it. Beetles and caterpillars thrown onto their backs struggle to right themselves but cease their struggles if their feet are touched with paper. The righting behaviour of inverted starfishes has been much studied as a piece of nervously co-ordinated activity. At the beginning of the movement the tip of each arm turns downwards, that is towards the starfish's back when it is inverted. The arm which first makes contact 'leads' the rest of the movement by turning further under while the arms on the opposite side of the disc turn upwards and towards the leading arm. A starfish (*Astropecten irregularis* or *Asterina gibbosa*) will attempt to turn over if freely suspended in any position in water. But no attempt is made to right itself if its tube feet are touched. Removal of much of the epidermis of the back has no effect, for it does not prevent attempts to turn when the starfish is put down on its back.[171] Thus contact on the back is not the stimulus, nor, indeed, does the stomach with its contents act as a statocyst-like gravity receptor,[580] for its removal does not prevent the starfish righting itself. Removal of the tube feet does, however, prevent righting.[171] But to remove the tube feet, the ambulacral spines must also be removed and it remains to be proven whether they, in fact, are not responsible for tactile position reception rather than the tube feet.

Fixed animals such as sea anemones, when inverted also perform righting movements so that their bases by which they are attached are once again in contact with whatever substrate they are inhabiting. The reaction is held in abeyance in *Hydra* while it moves by looping, which entails attachment alternately by foot and tentacles. The large area of the foot of gastropod molluscs is also kept in contact with the ground. In these cases stimulation of statocysts may also indicate the position of the animal, but this source of stimulation is minor compared with the foot's lack of stimulation in the upside down position. For, provided that the foot is fully in contact, moving in an upside down position is tolerated despite impulses which must be arising from statocysts.[36]

Sluggish, fixed or temporarily fixed animals require to be protected from being covered with unwanted debris. Thus if a stream of carmine particles are poured on to an attached individual *Stentor*, a series of avoiding reactions take place, developing in intensity if the stimulus remains. First, its body is bent away from the particles; if this fails to free the animal from stimulation, the ciliary beat reverses momentarily, and finally, if all these actions bring no relief, the animal contracts sharply, becomes detached and swims away.[286]

The pedicellariae of echinoderms are independent effectors responsible for cleaning the surface of the sea-urchin or starfish, that is, their reactions occur without reference to the main nervous system of the animal. Tactile stimulation causes them to close, but since the sensitive part is a pad within the jaws, an object must be well within the jaws before it is gripped.

Usually the ciliary currents over the surface of the mantle lining the shell of lamellibranchs are sufficient to carry debris out and to keep the mantle cavity generally clean. But on occasion pieces of debris are removed by the foot. Thus in *Pecten*, the scallop, contact stimulation by such pieces can be localized so the foot is brought round, and irritating material is removed in its hollowed end and ejected over the mantle edge.[534]

Many animals will survive better when there are two or more present. Brittle stars in glass tanks tend to clump together, wrapping their arms about each other. Glass rods will be accepted as substitutes. Contact is apparently the important stimulus in such crowds, for companions are in nature replaced by eel-grass.[3]

Individual worms may roll themselves up into a tangled mass; this behaviour is very typical of Nemertines, such as *Lineus* spp., and seems to arise from a need for maximum contact.

ROLE OF TACTILE STIMULI IN THE CHOICE OF A SUBSTRATUM

Many marine animals produce their young in very large numbers which are scattered at random into the sea, most of them joining the plankton. Since they are not laid in a suitable situation chosen by the parents they must be capable of reacting to favourable conditions whenever they may encounter them so that they may themselves select a suitable place for development. Not only should these conditions be suitable for larval development but also for future adult life as the demands an animal makes at these two stages of its life may be very different. Under experimental conditions the larvae of the polychaete, *Ophelia bicornis*, tend to choose sand similar to that of their parents' habitat. They will metamorphose better on particles which are smoothly rounded and of the size of the quartz particles of the sand of their breeding grounds (Plate IIIb). Smaller sharp particles are not chosen and in fact are not satisfactory for adult burrowing life.[577, 578] The distribution of the adults is limited to loose, clean sand. Though it seemed at one time that simple size and smoothness determined the acceptability of the sand, it now seems that the larva also requires that the grains be covered with certain microorganisms before they react with certainty.[579]

Sand grains of a particular size (149–295 μ) are most attractive to the burrowing crustaceans, *Cumella vulgaris*.[572] Oven dried, but re-moistened, sand of this size is, however, less attractive than fresh moist sand; it appears that the layer of microorganisms on the surface of the grains, used for food by these animals, is an important part of the group of stimuli by which the cumaceans recognize a favourable area. Since they leave their holes in the sand to swim some distance—the males being particularly active—it is important that recognition of a favourable substrate should be easily and accurately established. The most favourable size of grain seems to be dictated by the size of particle most easily handled by the mouth-parts.

In a somewhat similar manner gregariousness of the barnacles, *Balanus balanoides*, *B. crenatus* and *Elminius modestus* is ensured by contact of the antennules of the cyprid larva with other settled barnacles of their own species, or with the cemented bases left by them (Plate IIIa). This reaction to the correct settling place seems to be mainly to its chemical features, though roughness is important for cyprids avoid glass upon which other barnacles are fixed, preferring to settle on stones in the vicinity.[302] Thus the cyprids are led to settle and metamorphose only in those areas in which the very presence of other barnacles guarantees that conditions for development are good.

The texture of a surface, distinguished by tactile receptors, may affect the reactions of a number of other animals. A honeybee's foot bears claws and a pad; if the surface upon which it is walking is smooth, the claws are folded back, the pad making good contact with the surface, but if the surface is rough, the claws are extended so that the pad no longer makes contact.

A preference for rough surfaces is shown by the hermit crab, *Eupagurus bernhardus*, in choosing a new shell. The size and volume of the new house is perceived by touch.[208] Clearly it would not be sufficient to choose any other shell, for it must also be larger than the one that has been vacated. Both texture and size are probably perceived by the antennae.

But tarsal receptors more probably are responsible for the clustering of lice (*Pediculus*) on the rougher surface when they are offered the alternative of silk and cotton stockinet on which to walk (Fig. 129). This is an example of undirected orientation, for restriction to the rougher stockinet occurs only because on crossing onto silk, their path becomes more convoluted, (higher klinokinesis (p. 38)) usually bringing them back quickly onto the rougher surfaces, where their path is straighter.[573]

REACTIONS TO CURRENTS IN WATER

Many invertebrates show clear reactions to currents in the water in which they are living. *Paramecium*, for example, in a current, performs avoiding reactions which lead it to head upstream, it then proceeds against the current. This appears to be due to the disturbance to the beat of the cilia which occurs whenever it is orientated so that it is heading down or across the stream.[286] This behaviour

1*

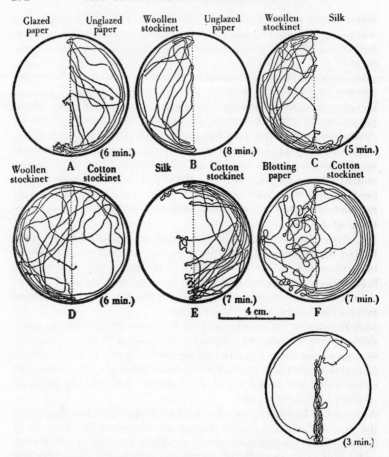

Fig. 129. Reactions of lice to rough and smooth materials (A–F). Also the path followed (during three minutes observation) by a louse in in a petri dish with a strip of flannel on a floor of blotting paper, its activities are almost entirely confined to the strip. (Wigglesworth[573])

can only be observed when the paramecia are swimming in a small bore tube where there is a difference between the speed of the current at the centre of the tube and at the wall.

Much attention has been paid to the activity of *Planaria alpina*, in currents, for this flatworm inhabits cold mountain streams. When it is sexually mature and provided that the water is below 12° C it responds positively turning into the current (positive rheotaxis). Therefore it moves towards the source of the stream where under natural conditions the water is even cooler. Here the worms congregate and lay their cocoons. It happens that the lower temperatures of the stream heads are most auspicious for development.[38] But the crowding produces food shortage. So that after releasing their cocoons the adults become starved. Release of the cocoons and starvation produce physiological changes which induce a change in their reactions to the stream, so that they now become negatively rheotactic and move downstream again.

When a stream of water is played on the head of a planarian it turns to face the pipette and follows if the pipette is moved. It responds in this way only when its head is stimulated, yet a decapitated animal will respond, turning into the current as before. It seems that the receptors, probably free nerve endings, are distributed all over the body but that there is a physiological gradient of sensitivity, those at the head end being more sensitive than those towards the tail. After the head has been cut off, those receptors immediately behind the cut gain ascendency. A very steep decline in sensitivity takes place behind the head.[309] This agrees with many other physiological gradients which have been demonstrated in flatworms.

In clear streams fish can be seen with their heads upstream swimming slowly into the current so that they keep to one position. Maintenance of their position does not depend upon tactile sensitivity to the current, but on visual stimulation arising from the movements of images across the eye if the fish swims forwards too fast or is swept back. However, a combination of tactile and visual stimulation is common in aquatic insects. The dragonfly larva, *Aeschna*, moves forward by ejecting water from its rectal chamber. As it moves forward its legs are folded against the body, decreasing the total resistance to the water, but this occurs only if the front of its head is stimulated by a current of water. If the larva is in still water, at each pulse as water is ejected from the rectum, the legs fold back.[525] But between each pulse when the animal almost comes to rest, its legs return to their normal position. Removal of the antennae or covering them with gelatine eliminates leg movements of this sort, indicating that tactile stimulation of the antennae by the current is of over-riding importance and that visual stimulation alone cannot compensate completely. But if a normal animal is observed in red light or with its eyes blackened its legs do not fold up. So that light falling upon the eyes seems to be necessary, the two stimuli reinforcing each other under natural circumstances. The water boatman, *Notonecta*, seems however to depend entirely on visual stimulation for maintaining its position in a stream[489] (p. 137).

Barnacles feed by straining off plankton from the water with their thoracic limbs. For the maximum efficiency the net formed by the hairs on these limbs should be orientated to fish against the current, for not only does the current make the catching easier but also brings with it abundant supplies of food. The barnacles settle particularly where there are currents passing over rocks or along the sides of ships and whales. Orientation is affected in the metamorphosed larva, that is, the early adult stage, for the cyprid larva shows no response to currents.[112]

Individual organs may react to water currents. The antennules of brachyurans and anomurans turn to point in the upstream direction of a water current striking the animal, so that when one of these crustacea is placed in water which is swirled round by rotating the vessel, its antennules bend in the direction in which the vessel is turning for the current will be travelling in the opposite direction.[64] When the vessel is halted, the antennules swing round to point to the other side of the animal as the after swirl, travelling in the reverse way to the current, strikes it. The antennules of crabs which are running sideways point in the direction in which they are heading. Even in still water the antennules show a typical flexion which appears to be a reaction to the water stream passing out from the gill cavity. In this way the antennules, which bear important chemoreceptors, are always turned in the direction from which chemical stimulation may come.

REACTIONS TO CURRENTS IN AIR

A flying insect will receive stimulation on its head from air currents unless it is flying in a completely homogeneous current, in much the same way as a swimming insect is stimulated by water currents. Most insects take off into the wind for aerodynamic reasons. The locust, *Schistocerca gregaria*, has hairs on the front of its head which are sensitive to bending by air currents. When these are stimulated the insect will fly, though the normal complete adduction of its legs to the body does not happen. A suspended locust can also be induced to fly by taking away paper which is touching its tarsi, though if the paper is taken away very slowly the locust may not fly. Stimulation of the hairs always results in flying. Painting the hairs with cellulose prevents these reactions. If the air stream strikes the head horizontally but asymmetrically the pitch of the wings is altered to turn the body into such a position that the current now is met head on. The locust nymphs, or hoppers, also possess patches of these sensitive hairs although they do not fly, and it is known that the bands of these hoppers moving across country are orientated to some extent with regard to the direction of the wind.[553, 554]

Movement of the whole antennae by the current is the stimulus in some Diptera. In a gentle air stream, *Limnobia* flies with its legs hanging slightly downwards but, in a stronger current, its forelegs are extended forward and its mid and hind pair backwards in the line of its body (Fig. 130). Similarly in *Muscina stabulans*, an air current striking the front of the fly's head causes the front two pairs of legs to be drawn up, while the hind pair are extended along the body. This is in contrast to a fly suspended in still air, for then its legs hang limply down.[268] Waxing the antennae down or waxing

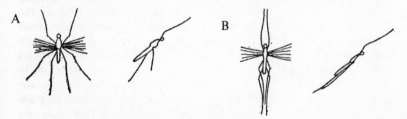

FIG. 130. Posture of *Limnobia* when flying, A, in a light current of air, and, B, in a strong current (von Buddenbrock[80]).

the various joints together did not prevent the air stream from being effective unless the third joint was prevented from moving on the second. Within this second joint is Johnston's organ which is stimulated by movement of the third joint. A suspended fly will continue flying in still air unless its head and antennae are enclosed in a transparent capsule. This would shield its head from the air currents caused by its own wings and its antennae would not be stimulated. The arista of the antenna of *Calliphora erythrocephala* flutters when a non-uniform air stream passes over it. When this occurs a train of impulses is set up in the antennary nerve, the frequency of which varies with the wind speed. It has been suggested that the antennae may also serve to detect the rate of beat of the fly's own wings.[87]

Normally as the wind strength increases the wing tip ceases to travel in a rough oval and begins to move through a figure of eight which produces aerodynamic compensation enabling the insect to maintain its equilibrium (Fig. 131). But flies with the antennae totally removed will fly in an air stream. However, in this case, the path travelled by the wing tip showed no compensatory alterations when the stream was increased in strength which implies that the strength is perceived by the intensity with which the antennae are stimulated.

Locust hoppers have been mentioned as orientating themselves to the wind. Similarly the blood-sucking flies, *Stomoxys calcitrans* and *Lyperosia exigua* will walk into an air stream.[313, 314] *Drosophila* does not react to a current of pure air but it will turn to head up-wind if a scent of mashed pears is wafted towards it.[163] In none of

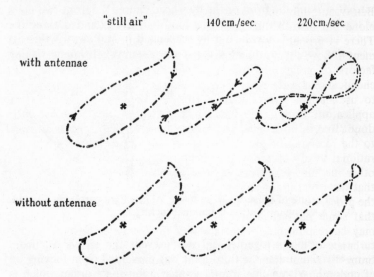

FIG. 131. Effect of the speed of the air current on the path traced out by one wing tip of *Muscina stabulans* (above); increase of the speed produces little change when the antennae have been removed (below). The crosses mark the position of the wing base. Insect flying to the left with body axis horizontal (Hollick[268]).

these cases is it certain that tactile stimulation is the cause of the orientation, it is just possible that the currents tend to upset the equilibrium of the animal. Contractions of various muscles are necessary to compensate for this and it may be that it is these contractions rather than the current itself which are perceived. If, for example, the air current strikes an insect from one side it will tend to bowl it over and the legs on the downward side will extend to counter this effect.

CHAPTER X

THE CHEMICAL SENSES

BEHAVIOUR does not consist of reacting to the physical environment alone but also to the chemical characteristics of the surroundings. There is probably no animal which does not perceive its environment in both chemical and physical terms for these stimuli represent factors of great importance to the survival of the animal. The chemical senses are effective in smelling and tasting the environment, to use human terms, unsatisfactory as they may be for general application throughout the animal kingdom. There seems little doubt that in both smell and taste molecules of the chemical travel to the receiving organ; there is little support nowadays for a vibrational theory of odour, in which vibrations of the 'ether' or some other medium pass from the odoriferous substance and it is clear that taste sensations are aroused by chemicals in solution. Though the process of stimulation remains obscure, it seems highly probable that some physical aspect of the molecules, such as their shape, may be responsible for their ability to stimulate (perhaps by disturbance of the ordered molecular arrangement of the cell membrane[392]) rather than any chemical reaction they may be capable of undergoing. We know little or nothing of this process for certain but we can gain indications, though no more, from the properties which are common to the substances which stimulate[138] (p. 261). Detection of impulses in the nerves leading from the sense organs to the central nervous system has been successful in several invertebrates, the king crab,[25] and a housefly (*Phormia regina*)[265] are examples. Though the ways in which these impulses are analysed centrally and perceived as arising from qualitatively different chemical stimuli is another unknown stage in the process between emission of chemical molecules from a substance and an animal's reaction, there appears to be some peripheral classification, probably only into 'acceptable' and 'non-acceptable' substances in the sensory hairs of the housefly labellum. Here sugars evoke a small spike, while substances, usually rejected by the fly, such as salts and acids, etc., produce a large spike, as a response in the nerve.[266]

Analysis of the chemical senses presents a number of difficulties which are not encountered in studying the effects of physical stimuli. First it is difficult, and even impossible, at times, to measure the strength of stimulation at the surface of a sense organ of this sort. In tests, chemicals may be presented in known concentrations at measured distances from the organs, a practice which gives at least an indication of the strength of stimulation when we are dealing with substances perceived in solution, but the amount of chemical which reaches an olfactory organ in air is impossible to measure. For similar reasons it is impossible to map with certainty the distribution of scent, though the passage of streams of scent-laden air can be traced by replacing it with smoke and attempts have been made to detect the pattern of scent diffusion by using talc sprinkled on the surface of mercury. A third difficulty is that the human vocabulary is not designed to be used for elaborate descriptions of chemical stimulation, no doubt because man is microsmatic. This produces a semantic problem, particularly in the subjective analysis of smell and taste. Further the chemical sensitivities of animals are so different from our own that it is difficult to appreciate their abilities in the same way that it is difficult for us to appreciate the perception of polarized light.

We have a distinction between taste and smell which is in common usage, but it depends upon the fact that the set of sense organs which respond to air-borne chemicals are in our noses, while those that respond to contact with chemical substances are in our mouths. In general such a distinction breaks down when we consider invertebrates and it becomes especially difficult when we have to decide whether an aquatic invertebrate can smell or taste a substance. And the choice is further confused when both substances which we perceive by their odour and those by their taste are perceived by one set of organs in the animal. Perhaps the distinction is unimportant and is merely a matter of difference in threshold, but in our present state of knowledge when we are not certain whether the processes of stimulation in an olfactory and a gustatory organ are the same, it would be unwise not to attempt some separation, at least for convenience.

Smell is distinguished by the comparatively very small amount of substance which is required to stimulate the sensitive cells. It has been estimated that between 10^5 and 10^6 molecules are sufficient to stimulate.[388] This means that the weight loss of an odoriferous substance is very small. For example, if muscone, the active principle of musk, loses weight at a rate of $\frac{1}{1000}$ mgm. in 100 years or about 1 % of its original weight in 10^6 years, it will be losing molecules at the rate of 8×10^5 molecules a second. The number lost in one minute would be perfectly detectable by humans, and probably the number per second also. The threshold for taste is much higher

(Table VI) than the olfactory threshold though it is difficult to compare these levels for all substances for many which have a taste are not perceived by the nose.

TABLE VI. Thresholds for smell substances in man (from Skramlik[492])

Alcohols	Molecular Weight	Weight $10^{-6}g/50$ cm^3	No. of mols. in 50 ccs.
Methyl	32	30	5.7×10^{17}
Ethyl	46·1	12·5	1.6×10^{17}
Propyl	60·1	0·25	2.5×10^{15}
Butyl	74·1	0 05	4.1×10^{14}
Acids			
Formic	46	1·25	1.6×10^{16}
Propionic	74·1	0·0025	2.1×10^{13}
Butyric	88·1	0·00005	3.5×10^{11}
Substituted Compounds			
Chloroform	119·4	1·5	7.6×10^{15}
Bromoform	252·9	0·01	2.4×10^{13}
Iodoform	393·8	0·0028	4.3×10^{12}
Other substances			
Skatol	131·1	0·00002	9.2×10^{10}
Vanillin	152·1	0·000025	1.0×10^{11}

Animals detect chemical substances from a distance in air by their smell. The bulk of the scent-producing substance does not have to come into contact with the sense cell, though molecules of it do so. A far larger quantity of the substance has to affect a taste cell and, practically, this means that the substance as a whole actually comes in contact with the sense cells. Therefore it can be called a contact chemical sense, thus avoiding the human subjective conotations of taste. Here we find one of the difficulties of applying these distinctions to aquatic animals; should one call the detection of substances in solution in water taste or smell? It is not always possible to determine the concentration of substance in the water bathing the sensitive surface, which might help in making the decision for a very low concentration would indicate smell and a higher one, taste. And when a substance like skatol, which we and other animals do smell, is detected in solution are we to call this smell by analogy?

The sensory cells responsible for the two different modalities of chemical sensitivity are not always morphologically distinct; in some invertebrates the structure is not even known. Though there may be little or no morphological distinction between the organs, taste and smell sensitivity may be restricted to different parts of the animal's body. This can be most easily shown in terrestrial animals but the behaviour of some aquatic animals indicate that such localization also occurs there (p. 289). Taste is usually restricted to the mouth, its appendages, and the buccal cavity, smell sensitivity is centred elsewhere.

The reactions which are produced may also help in distinguishing the two senses. In general smell leads to locomotion as it is used to distinguish substances at a distance and the animal moves towards the source of the chemical or away from it according to whether it is attracted or repelled by it. While taste, the contact sense, is particularly concerned with eating and therefore stimulation of these receptors often leads to feeding movements. There are a number of exceptions particularly among insects in which the contact sense is utilized for other purposes than feeding (e.g. egg-laying).

The distinction is not then always clear. But for our present purposes, we shall consider smell as sensitivity to very low concentrations of chemicals, detected at a distance from their source, and often localized on the body somewhere apart from the mouth region, while taste has a higher threshold and is essentially a contact sense often localized in the mouth region and concerned with feeding. Thus, we shall call smell the detection of chemicals in solution by an aquatic animal for it conforms with our definition in all respects except that threshold may vary enormously, from very low ones usually associated with smell to higher ones similar to those of taste. The position is confused by the undoubted existence especially in insects of a generalized chemical sensitivity widespread over the body (e.g.[497]).

The methods used to investigate whether an animal can perceive chemical substances are much the same whether we are concerned with taste, smell, or the generalized sense. We can note whether the animal reacts to a substance or whether the presence of the chemical inhibits reaction to another substance which is normally, for example, attractive to the animal. The lowest concentration of the substance required to give a reaction is the threshold concentration. Alternatively an animal can be permitted to exercise choice between a number of substances, or be trained to perform some action when it perceives particular substances which it has to differentiate from others. The site of the sense organs can be found by removing parts of the body or by masking parts with impermeable coverings. If the animals which have not been operated upon show reactions to chemicals which the operated animals do not, then it is a reasonable assumption that the operation has removed the sense organs responsible.

THE SENSE OF SMELL

On the whole substances which are perceived from a distance in air have high molecular weights (Table VI). They appear also to need to be lipoid soluble as well as water soluble, whereas the substances which stimulate on contact are mainly water soluble. For example, to humans an ether extract of an odorous substance is more easily perceived than a water extract of the same substance. Vapour pressure seems to be of secondary importance and indeed considering the comparatively small numbers of molecules required for stimulation, it is likely that a substance with even a low vapour pressure will produce enough molecules, though clearly an absolutely nonvolatile substance will not be perceived by smell.

THE OLFACTORY SENSE OF INSECTS

Receptors responsible for distant chemoreception in insects seem to be largely confined to the antennae. A great deal of work has been devoted to the study of the reactions of insects to a very large number of different substances for these results are important in devising repellants and attractants for pests. The list of substances is too long to repeat here. The insect's reaction has usually been tested by observing the insect's behaviour in a stream of air laden with the odour of the substance. The amount of material in the stream can be varied by passing the air over different concentrations of the substance. The insects react by moving either towards or away from the stream. An insect which is repelled by the substance even at a low concentration will continue to be repelled from it at all concentrations, but those which are not may be attracted to it when the concentration is low. The attraction is more intense as the concentration rises, even though the concentration may be above the threshold of the most sensitive cells. This suggests that more and more receptors, less sensitive than the original ones, are being called into action. But a point is often reached where the concentration becomes great enough for the insect to be repelled and it retreats downstream instead of moving up it. Such a substance is iso-valeraldehyde. Flies (*Phormia regina*) do not respond to concentrations of less than $2 \cdot 0 \times 10^{-6}$M, but above this concentration they are attracted, maximum attraction occurring at $1 \cdot 2 \times 10^{-5}$M. As the concentration is increased further, their reaction changes to repellance, thus between $2{\cdot}0 \times 10^{-5}$ and $2{\cdot}8 \times 10^{-5}$M, they are partly attracted and partly repelled, but there is complete aversion to an air stream containing more than $6{\cdot}0 \times 10^{-5}$M[143] (Fig. 132). *Nassarius reticulatus* shows a similar change from attraction to repellance when stimulated with solutions of acetic acid of increasing strength.[242] It may be that at these concentrations receptors of high threshold which mediate rejection are being called into action.[137]

But the animal's behaviour is determined in other ways. There are, for example, clear genetic differences shown by the different reactions of closely allied species. Thus three species of the fly,

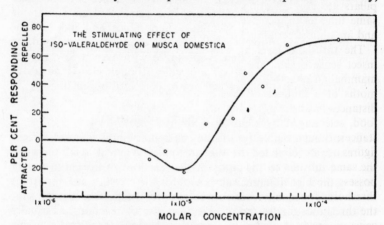

FIG. 132. The stimulating effect of the vapour of iso-valeraldehyde on the house fly (*Musca domestica*) illustrating the phenomenon of attraction at low concentrations and repellence at high (Dethier[134]).

Dacus, are attracted by different compounds of eugenol, though all are unattracted by benzoeugenol and eugenol itself[274] (Table VII)

TABLE VII. Attractiveness of eugenol and its compounds for three species of the fly, *Dacus* (from Howlett[274])

Species	Eugenol	Isoeugenol	Methyleugenol	Benzoeugenol
Dacus diversus	—	+++	—	—
D. ferrugineus	—	++	++	—
D. zonatus	—	—	+++	—

Also the sign of the reaction can be altered by conditioning, thus the odour of peppermint, normally repellent, can be made attractive to *Drosophila* after the larvae have been raised in a medium containing $0{\cdot}5\%$ of oil of peppermint. On emergence $67{\cdot}0\%$ of flies cultured in this way were attracted by an air stream containing peppermint while only 34·9% of flies reared on a normal medium were attracted to this stream.[513] Or, again, the reaction may vary according to the physiological state of the insect. The caterpillar of the pine shoot moth, *Rhyacionia buoliana*, is parasitized by *Ephialtes* (= *Pimpla*) *ruficollis*. On emergence from the body of its host, the adult parasite leaves the pines to feed elsewhere.[516] At this time in its life history it is repelled by pine oil, but after three or four weeks, its reaction to the oil changes and the scent becomes attractive, so that the insect returns once more to the pines, where the host caterpillars are now awaiting the parasite. These changes occur at the same time as an increase in the size of the ovaries of the parasite and are almost certainly correlated with this change.

The threshold level at which many chemicals are detected by insect sense organs are probably very much lower than those of mammalian olfactory organs. The almost legendary ability of male moths of a number of species to find females over considerable distances has been proved beyond doubt and many insects find their food, selecting it by scent most carefully from among many substances, though the odour of it is imperceptible to humans. Where figures are available for the sensitivity of both insects and humans to the same substances it is clear in some cases at least that the insects possess the higher sensitivity. Though earlier work had shown the thresholds for man and the honeybee to be similar, it appears that the thresholds for bees may be very much lower, for they can perceive one part of methyl heptonone in 40,000,000 parts of ethylene glycol whereas humans could not detect more than one part in 1,000,000,[454] and their ability to detect scents in mixtures is greater than that of humans. Experiments with other insects, however, suggest that sensitivity may not always be greater in the insect.

If the reactions of *Agriotes* larvae to various substances are taken as being reactions to smell, as it is on our definition for the wireworms live in moist soil and perceive certain substances at a distance in solution in the soil water, the thresholds will be seen to be very low. The number of molecules necessary for stimulation is small, about 10 times smaller than the average for humans, though admittedly measured against other substances (Tables VI and VIII).

Though the main site of olfactory organs is the antennae, there are also subsidiary sites on the maxillary palps. The thresholds of the organs on these two sites may be different. The caterpillar of *Pieris brassicae*, the cabbage white, will reject benzaldehyde at a concentration of 0·058 mg./l. of air. But the threshold rises to 0·077 mg./l. when the antennae are cut off, though it is unaffected by removal of the maxillae alone. Removal of both maxillae and antennae, however, causes the threshold to rise to 1·0 mg./l., indicating that both palps and antennae bear chemical sense organs.[129] The receptors on the antennae and palpi of the fly, *Phormia regina*, have different thresholds in a similar manner; indeed intact flies, with both antennae, have a lower threshold for rejection of pentanol vapour than those with only one. This behavioural summation may be a matter of the total number of receptors involved rather than any central nervous summation.[132]

The olfactory abilities of honeybees seem to be very close to those of humans though the thresholds are different. Bees were trained to take food from a box in which was placed a solution of an essential oil in liquid paraffin as well as a supply of food. Later a box with the same scent mixture but without food was placed among a number of odourless, foodless boxes. The bees continued to visit the scented box for preference. Later, after being trained to an essential oil from sweet Italian oranges, bees were offered a choice of this oil placed among twenty-three other varied scents. Once again they chose the scent to which they were trained, only showing confusion when three other oils derived from citrus fruits, and therefore containing common substances, such as limonene, were offered them.[454] Though it was clear that despite the confusion they still preferred the training scent to any of the citrus-derived oils. These oils smell alike to humans. Substances of different chemical composition but, to man, similar odours, such as benzaldehyde and nitrobenzene, were also indistinguishable to bees. And intra-molecular rearrangements like those converting para-cresol methyl ether to the meta- form alter the scent for man and bees alike. But this similarity though great is not complete, for example, isobutyl benzoate and amyl salicylate, indistinguishable by man, can be differentiated by bees.

The honeybees' ability to detect mixtures of smells is acute. After being trained to 1 % benzyl acetate they can detect the addition of only 0·93 % of linalol. They can also recognize the presence of a new addition to a set of scents to which they are trained and distinguish the training mixture from a mixture of the same scents in other proportions.[454] These abilities have obvious importance in the selection of flowers by their scent and recognition of nest mates by their body odour. In fact it has been suggested that mutations producing alteration in the scent of flowers pollinated by honeybees and bumblebees will be more effective in producing sympatric speciation than mutations producing colour changes.[353]

A study of the relative efficiency of various organic compounds in attracting or repelling insects can give some indications of what are the important characteristics of an odorous substance. The attractiveness of members of a homologous series of aliphatic alcohols from methyl to amyl and of a series of esters from acetates to valerates to flies was tested in the field.[104] In one set of experiments it was clear that the threshold concentration of the compounds in the two series decreased as their boiling points increased (Fig. 133). An increase in the chain length of the compounds also

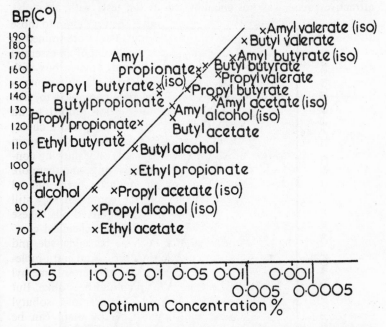

FIG. 133. Relation between boiling point and attractiveness (as measured by the number of flies taken from traps containing the substance) for members of an aliphatic series (from Cook[104]).

increases their effectiveness. Again the addition of —CH groups to the acid side of the esters increased their efficiency more than a similar addition to the alcohol moiety. These experiments indicated that at least the efficiency as measured by the threshold level was proportional to the boiling point, chain length, and molecular weight and inversely proportional to the water solubility.

Another series of laboratory tests on the rejection thresholds of a series of aliphatic alcohols (from $CH_3OH \rightarrow C_{12}H_{25}OH$) gave a somewhat similar result for the thresholds decreased logarithmically as the number of carbon atoms in the chain increased (Fig. 134). The thresholds were directly proportional to the vapour pressures of the substances.[145]

This work has been repeated with a series of aliphatic aldehydes with results similar to those obtained with the alcohols, though the thresholds were usually lower than those of aldehydes of the same chain length (Fig. 134)[134], (at lower concentrations aldehydes are attractive, becoming repellent as concentration increases, a similar attractive phase was not encountered in the tests with alcohols).

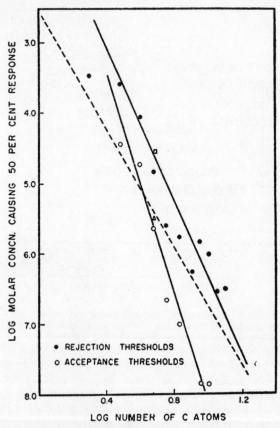

FIG. 134. Relation of olfactory thresholds (acceptance and rejection) for aldehydes to chain length. The broken line represents the relation for alcohols. The square and triangle represent rejection and acceptance thresholds respectively for iso-valeraldehyde. Acceptance thresholds are based on maximum response (Dethier[134]).

When the threshold concentrations are translated into thermo-dynamic activities (i.e. the amount of work required to transfer one molecule of a compound from one phase to another) they become nearly equal especially over the middle part of the range of chain length. This applies also to the alcohols tested (Fig. 135) (though calculations from the results of field experiments in which the measure of effectiveness was the number of flies trapped by different

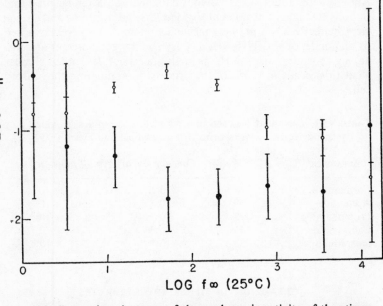

FIG. 135. Comparison in terms of thermodynamic activity of the stimu-lating effectiveness of the first eight normal alcohols acting in aqueous solution (open circles) on tarsal chemoreceptors and as gases (solid circles) on olfactory receptors. In each case the value represents a threshold of rejection. The vertical lines represent 2·575 standard errors for aqueous thresholds and 2 for vapours (Dethier and Yost[145]).

chemical baits indicate that this relationship did not hold in those particular conditions for thermodynamic activity at threshold diminished as chain length increased[104]). This suggests that olfaction is dependent ultimately upon an equilibrium.[145] Indeed in many other ways characteristics of olfaction support this conclusion,

maximal effect is reached rapidly after application of the stimulus
and remains at that level if stimulation is continued but is rapidly
reversed when the stimulus is removed. Further the effects produced
show characteristic relationships with special physical properties of
the homologous series.[135]

The importance of the position occupied by the side groups in
the molecule was well shown in the investigations of the activity of
various amides in attracting *Agriotes* larvae (Table VIII).[113] Here
again efficiency increased with increasing molecular weight but it
was clear that the —NH group was the active part of the molecule
for whereas acetamide was detected, acetic acid had no influence.
Amongst the amino-acids tested, guanidine and arginine produced
responses at a concentration of 10^{-9} gm./ccs. but ornithine and glycine
were ineffective. This implies that such a grouping as —NH possessed
by an amide, or —C(NH)NH$_2$ as possessed by guanidine or arginine
are active while —CO—NH$_2$, as in glycine, is not. It is not at all clear
what this means in terms of the process of stimulating the sensory
cell.

TABLE VIII. Threshold concentrations for various amides at which they
are detected by wireworms (from Crombie and Darrah[113])

Substance	Mol. Weight	Concn. gms/cm^3	No. of mols. in 1 cc.
Formamide	45	10^{-11}	$1·3 \times 10^{11}$
Acetamide	59	10^{-9}	$1·01 \times 10^{13}$
Propionamide	73	10^{-9}	$8·23 \times 10^{12}$
Caprylamide	143·2	10^{-9}	$4·19 \times 10^{12}$
Stearamide	283·5	10^{-8}	$2·11 \times 10^{13}$

OLFACTION IN OTHER INVERTEBRATES

Terrestrial arachnids with their impermeable cuticle approach the
insects most closely among the other land living invertebrates. The
tarsal organ of spiders has already been described (Fig.16d). Spiders,
e.g. *Araneus diadematus* (= *Aranea diadema*), retreat from clove oil
and oil of turpentine even when they are 1–5 mms. away from the
substance. These organs are also sensitive to contact with odorous
materials and it seems that they function mainly in this manner to
stimuli of natural strength.[50]

Odour plays a part in the courtship of salticid spiders though not
the major role.[109] To ourselves young females smell stronger than
old ones and also evoke courtship display by male spiders when old

females, which have barely any detectable odour, will not. Males take no notice of the dried dead body of an older female until the fresh abdomen of a young female is placed near the dead spider when they begin to display to the dead body. The courtship is directed towards the whole spider which is seen and not towards the fresh abdomen from which the chemical stimulation is emanating. Visual stimuli are essential but the fact that paper models of females would not evoke display by males, though paper models of males would evoke threatening postures from another male, shows that in courtship at least, chemical stimuli are an essential part of the stimulus situation. The chemoreceptors responsible seem to be generally distributed over the body but occur in greater numbers on the tips of the palpi and on the first legs.

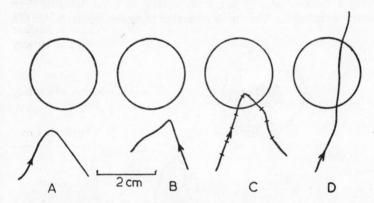

FIG. 136. Tracks of four unfed female ticks approaching a patch of citronella. A, normal tick. B, forelegs intact but tips of palps cut through. C, forelegs amputated but palpal organs intact. Positions where the tips of the palps touched the substratum are indicated by lines across path. D, forelegs and palpal organs amputated (Lees [329]).

Such receptors are also present on the forelegs of ticks which hold these legs in front of them as they walk, palpating and moving them in a manner very reminiscent of the way in which an insect uses its antennae. This pair of legs bear Haller's organ (Fig. 16a). So long as this is present, ticks such as *Ixodes reduvius*, will turn away from oil of citronella when they are a centimetre or so from the drop[329] (Fig. 136). When its forelegs are removed, a tick will move right up to the drop being repelled only when its palps make contact with the oil. Placed in an olfactory gradient a tick will avoid parts of it until it comes to rest at one point where the concentration is optimum, for example, in a butyric acid gradient at a concentration of 1 : 3,000,000. A similar choice of an optimum is shown by cheese mites, *Tyrolichus casei*, which move towards the source of the odour until they reach an optimum position in the gradient when they circle the substance, say a crystal of skatol[239] (Fig. 137). They react in this way to minced-up caterpillar and to meat juice.

Most of the other investigations on olfaction in invertebrates have been concerned with aquatic animals. When such animals perceive chemical stimuli arising from a substance at a distance we have proposed to call this olfaction. Often a contact and a distant chemical sense are clearly distinguished, objects such as food, being recognized at a distance by the latter sense and objects tested for their edibility, for example, by the former. Favourable stimuli perceived from a distance usually cause an animal to move towards their source directing itself by one of a number of means, (see later, p. 273).

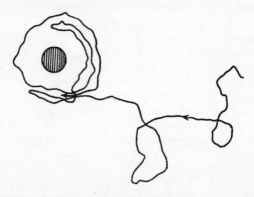

Fig. 137. Path taken by a cheese-mite, *Tyrolichus casei*, approaching a crystal of skatol (shaded). The animal was still moving at the point at which the recorded path ends (after Henschel[239]).

The first antennae of crustacea, such as *Crangon* and *Carcinus*, seem to be sensitive to chemicals in solution, while the legs and mouthparts are sensitive to chemicals on contact, though these chemicals may be those which man perceives by their odour. However, stimulation of the first antennae alone does not suffice to evince the feeding reactions though their removal affects the speed of reaction to contact chemical stimuli by increasing the latent period between stimulation and the animal's reaction.

Sense organs have been described on the wall of the gill chamber of *Astacus* (=*Potamobius*), the fresh-water crayfish, which appear to be chemosensitive to judge from their position.[524] Though their function in the crayfish is not known, the behaviour of both *Carcinus* and *Eupagurus*[345] suggest that similar organs could be found in their gill chambers. The water stream through the gill chamber of *Carcinus* passes from behind forwards. If pieces of meat are held behind the crab near the posterior opening of the chamber so that water bathing them will be drawn into the chamber, the chelae are bent round under the body and search in the direction of the food. Almost certainly there are organs in the gill chamber which are sensitive to chemicals in the water stream. Since the stream comes from a restricted area behind the animal, the source of stimulation can be located.

The surrounding water is also sampled in the process of respiration by some molluscs. Prosobranch gastropods have a mobile siphon through which the respiratory water stream is drawn and they are in many cases sensitive to chemicals carried into the mantle cavity by this stream. Thus by moving the siphon the direction from which the strongest stimulation is coming can be gauged and the animal can move towards or away from it.

Soluble starch and glycogen are perceived in solution in this way by *Nassarius reticulatus*.[240] And it also reacts positively to glucose, maltose, saccharose, glycol, aminobenzoic acid, lactic acid, and skatol. But it retreats when solutions of lactic acid stronger than 0·055 mg./100 ccs. are pipetted close to the siphon tip, though it reacts positively to lower concentrations. There is some evidence that all the substances which produce a positive reaction, except skatol, are detected by the same sense organs since they reinforce the stimulating effect of each other, but that skatol and, possibly, quinine is perceived by another set of cells. It might be expected that the salt concentration of the surroundings would be perceived by these animals, but only *Busycon* (=*Fulgur*) has been shown to retreat from 3–5% sodium chloride. Cephalopods, however, are apparently sensitive to salt concentration[206] (p. 290).

It is possible that the osphradium of the prosobranchs is in fact a collection of chemoreceptors responsible in carnivores for the detection of food. However, it is not absent altogether in browsing herbivores, like the periwinkles, *Littorina* spp., though it is better developed in a carnivore, such as the whelk, *Buccinum* and the cowrie, *Cypraea*.[590] Possibly it is a tactile organ responsible for the detection of sediment in the incoming water current, in which case chemoreceptors must be sought elsewhere, perhaps in the walls of the siphon itself, or the osphradium may serve both functions.

Distance chemoreceptors in planarian worms are arranged in

two groups one on either side of the head. Such flatworms, as *Planaria lugubris*, will find their way to a piece of food so long as the sides of the head are intact.[309] Since the receptors are arranged symmetrically this worm can make its way up a chemical gradient diffusing outwards from a piece of food by chemotropotaxis if the gradient is sufficiently steep or by klinotaxis if it is less strong (see later, p. 273).

THE BIOLOGICAL FUNCTIONS OF THE OLFACTORY SENSE

Among the activities in which olfaction plays a part in most animals are food finding and mate selection. The chemicals to which insects, for example, react positively are often ones that occur in their food, thus skatol and ammonia are attractive to dung-eating beetles of the genera, *Geotrupes*,[547] *Necrophorus*[131] and *Creophilus* as well as to flies such as *Sarcophaga* and *Lucilia*. Similarly *Drosophila* is attracted to acetic acid, and other products of rotting fruit. The attraction of particular substances which occur uniquely in one particular kind of food serves to bind a monophagous species to its food, thus the caterpillars of *Papillio ajax*[129] feed only on Umbelliferae, which contain the oil methylnonylcetone. It can be shown that this oil alone is attractive to the caterpillars. Colorado beetles, *Leptinotarsa decemlineata* will follow a trail of acetaldehyde, which occurs in the potato plant.

Female beetles, *Hylotrupes* (=*Hylophilus*) *bajulus*, are attracted by terpentine derivatives found in the pine trees on which they lay eggs.[40] There appears to be a 'wool factor' in sheep wool which is attractive to female *Lucilia sericata*, *L. cuprina*, *L. caesar* and *L. illustris*, blowflies which oviposit on the back of sheep. This factor which is particularly potent in attracting fertile females has no effect on females of *Calliphora vomitoria*.[107] When wool was mixed with odorous substances in field trials it was found that while *L. sericata* females were more attracted by mixtures containing ammonia, *L. caesar* individuals visited sulphydryl mixtures more frequently.

Honeybees are attracted to flowers from a distance by their colour, shape and movement (p. 159) but the final decision to alight is made after satisfactory olfactory stimuli have been received. A rich source of food is marked by the workers who find it and extrude their scent glands so that some of the substance secreted by the gland is left on the flower or the dish of sugar water.[454] On their return to the hive the foragers dance, communicating the direction and distance of the food source to the other workers (p. 104). The presence of scent substances, like peppermint or flower oils, in the sugar water enhance the likelihood of the bee dancing on its return.[338] Skatol on the other hand reduces it. While they dance they again expose their scent glands so that workers following them also learn the odour mark which has been put on the food place. The body of a returning worker will be covered with the scent of the flower which it has visited and the nectar which it brings in its honey stomach will also smell of the flower from which it came. The substance on the outside of the body is more easily lost on the return flight and as a result the scent of the nectar which is regurgitated to the other workers is a better preserved sign of the scent of the source of the nectar. Bees are attracted as well to flowers which bear the scent of a bee's body, that is the scent left even without exposure of the scent glands. Perhaps bees may learn to avoid flowers which bear a lot of this body scent since these must have received much attention from other bees and therefore in all probability have little food left in them. The scent characteristics of a food source are learned as the bee approaches it, as the visual characteristics are also[405] (p. 161).

Orientation towards the source of odour, be it food or mate, may be in several different ways. The sensitive cells are often arranged in two areas symmetrically placed, such as the two antennae of an insect or the head lobes of a planarian, or they are stimulated from one direction only by a water stream taken in through a siphon, for example, in molluscs, or into a respiratory chamber, as in *Carcinus*. An animal moving up a gradient with symmetrical organs can compare two areas simultaneously provided that the gradient is steep enough to permit a detectable difference in the stimulation of the two areas, in the same way that two symmetrically placed eyes are used in photo-tropotaxis. It should be noted that any difference there may be at the two points will not be enhanced by the shadowing effect of the body as it is with directional light. But when the organ is single it is necessary for comparisons to be made between successive samples taken from different places either by a moving siphon, say, or by movement of the whole animal. Such bending movements of the body must also be made by an animal with closely set paired organs when the gradient is not steep enough to produce much difference in stimulation at the two organs. In all these cases there cannot be simultaneous comparison but the environment must be sampled successively. Thus this is chemo-klinotaxis in the case of a planarian moving in the periphery of the area which contains chemical emanating from food at its centre; however, as it draws nearer the source and the gradient steepens

its behaviour may change to tropotaxis and it will cease to bend
from side to side (Fig. 138).

It seems improbable that insects are in fact reacting tropotactically when moving towards a source of chemical stimulation
for the differences between the stimulation will be so small, though
removal of one antenna does cause movements to the intact side in
Geotrupes,[547] *Tenebrio*[538] and a number of other insects when they
are placed in a diffused odour, or in a gradient—usually accepted
as evidence of tropotactic behaviour. Nevertheless many insects
can find their way to the source despite the removal of one antenna.

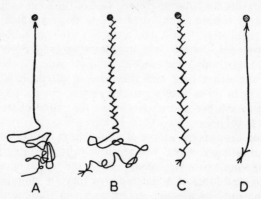

FIG. 138. Tracks of *Planaria lugubris* stimulated by chemicals emanating
from food (shaded). A and B, undirected searching at first followed
by a direct path to the food (accompanied by swinging the head
from side to side in B). C and D, direct path from the outset without
preliminary searching (Koehler[309]).

Rhodnius prolixus with only one antenna, can still locate a warmed
tube covered with fresh mouse skin[574] as can *Idechthis* (= *Nemeritis*)
canescens find its host after being operated upon.[503] And *Drosophila*
still reaches its goal though by less direct routes than with both
antennae.[163]

The odour of the place in which eggs are to be laid is also attractive to females about to lay. Dung beetles are attracted by dung
chemicals and flesh-eating flies by rotting flesh. In both cases the
eggs are laid on the food store so that the same attractive substances
draw the fly when it is hungry and when it is to lay. Pollination in
some flowers depends upon imitation of the attractive smells so that
the flies will visit the flower. The well known lords and ladies, *Arum
maculatum*, produces such a smell, in this case, of rotting flesh so
that flies land on it and become trapped in the lower part of the

spathe until the anthers have dehisced and the flies' bodies are covered with pollen when they are released. The imitation is made more complete by the spike being at a higher temperature than the surroundings. On the other hand, the various species of the orchid genus, *Ophrys*, which are each pollinated by the males of particular species of hymenopteran, attract their pollinators by a scent which is very close to, if not identical with, that of the female insect of the species. The flower bears a slight visual likeness to a female insect but this plays no part in attracting the males to the flowers from a distance[324] (see p. 324).

Many parasites find their hosts by their odour. *Idechthis canescens* is attracted to a flour moth culture from a distance of up to 800 metres.[503] Their preference for the odour of the flour moth appears to be another case of pre-imaginal conditioning.[518] While *Rhyssa persuasoria* which parasitizes the larvae of *Sirex gigas* can locate the larvae through several inches of wood. Frequently a host is parasitized during one stage in its life history and parasites are able to distinguish between hosts ripe for oviposition and others of other ages. For example, *Bracon hebetor* (= *Habrobracon juglandis*), parasitizes the caterpillar of the wax moth only just before it pupates.[229] Even if the caterpillar has begun to spin its cocoon preparatory to pupation the female parasite can distinguish through the cover between an older pupa and a caterpillar just about to pupate. It will only lay its eggs in the caterpillar.

One of the dangers of parasitism when there are more parasites than there are hosts is that one host may have so many eggs laid in it by different parasites that none can develop efficiently. However, the parasitized host may have a different odour from the unparasitized, and later parasites finding it will avoid egg-laying on this host. The eggs of *Ephestia kühniella*, a flour moth, in which *Idechthis* has laid its eggs do not invoke egg-laying by another female. For it appears the first parasite to visit them leaves traces, probably from its tarsi, which are detectable as odour to a subsequent visitor.[463] If parasitized eggs are washed clean, female wasps will attempt to oviposit in them, since the warning traces have been removed. But once the ovipositor enters, the presence of the egg of the other wasp is detected by receptors on the ovipositor and no egg is laid. *Rhyssa persuasoria* also seems to be able to perceive whether it has been forestalled by another female because the first-comer has left odour traces.

Commensalism demands accurate recognition of the correct partner, as parasitism does the correct host. Not a great deal of work has been done on the manner in which partners recognize each other,[120] but it is known that a polynoid worm, *Arctonoë*, which lives in the ambulacral groove of a starfish, *Evasterias*, chooses a current of sea-water which has passed over this starfish in preference to one that has not been in contact with a potential partner.[119] Moreover damaged starfish produce some substance which has the effect of repulsing the worm, thus it is prevented from taking up its abode on the body of a damaged and therefore ill-suited partner.[121] The material, tunicin, of which the ascidian test is constructed, seems to attract the commensal lamellibranch, *Modiolaria*, to its tunicate partner, even when present in low concentrations.[56]

Odour has a very important part to play in the courtship of many invertebrates. Its role in Salticid spider courtship has already been mentioned (p. 268). But it is probably among the insects that it is raised to its greatest importance in this activity. For example, though at first the male grayling butterfly, *Eumenis semele*, is attracted to the female by her shape and the way in which she flies (p. 134) once the pair has alighted scent becomes the dominant stimulus. The partners face each other and the male bows to the female pushing his wings forwards to grasp her antennae between them.[523] This rubs them against the scent-producing scales on the male's wing, and without this stimulation the female does not co-operate in the remainder of the courtship.

For many years it has been known that females of some species of moth can attract males from great distances. Experiments involving the release of marked males of the moth, *Actias selene*, have given 8 out of 20 successful returns to a female from 4 kilometres, and 25 from 11 kilometres,[368] while male gipsy moths, *Lymantria dispar*, returned from 3·8 kms.[103] The females of many night flying moths possess scent glands on their abdomens. In view of the numbers of different species flying at the same time it is not surprising that the scent is almost species specific. Thus in an investigation into the scents produced by a number of pyralid species it was clear that any one species odour was attractive usually only to one other species and that one a close relative[30] (Table IX).

A substance has been extracted from female *Bombyx mori* which in a concentration of 0·01 γ is attractive to males; it is neither carbohydrate, fat or protein in character.[90] Even day flying male insects can detect their females by scent, male blowflies, *Lucilia caesar*, can find females hidden from their sight.[332]

Sexual isolation between *Drosophila pseudoobscura* and *D. persimilis* seems to depend upon scent among other factors, for females of each species attempt to mate indiscriminately with males of either after their antennae have been removed (though some

TABLE IX. The effect of substances extracted from female moths on males of the same and other species (from Barth[30])

Species producing the scent	Plodia	Ephestia kuhniella	Ephestia elutella	Galleria	Achroea	Aphomia
Plodia interpunctella	S	—	—	—	—	—
Ephestia kühniella	S	S	S	—	—	—
E. elutella	S, C	S, C	S	—	—	—
Galleria mellonella	S	—	—	S	S, C	—
Achroia grisella	—	—	—	S, C	S	—
Aphomia gularis	—	—	—	—	—	S

S: Stimulated, —: no reaction, C: attempted copulation

discrimination remains even then). It has been suggested that scent from the male raises the female's state of readiness to a pitch when she will accept a male; other stimuli release copulation.[366]

Many marine animals, among them ascidians and echinoderms, discharge their gametes into the sea. The greater the concentration of gametes of both sexes the greater the chance of fertilization, therefore synchronous spawning of a number of individuals will be most advantageous. In fact the release of gametes by echinoids and asteroids stimulates others to discharge gametes as well. A similar chemical stimulus acts in ascidians but in a more roundabout way. Gametes drawn in with the water current are taken by cells of the neural gland which then releases a hormone which stimulates the discharge of the individual's own gametes and also the closing of the inhalent siphon which prevents the further intake of gametes.[92]

But apart from its functions in reproduction where it is often the badge of one of the sexes, odour is the badge of the colony carried by the individuals of insect societies. It has been demonstrated over and over again that an individual with a strange odour evokes hostile reactions from a colony whether it be of honeybees or ants. Each hive or colony has its own odour to which the members are attracted. Washing an intruder or shaking it up with dead insects from a colony may make it acceptable for a while presumably because it will have taken some of the odour of the colony. In honeybees the nest odour appears to be the result of sharing in a common food source, for radioactive food collected by six foragers was detectable in 43–60% of the colony after 27 hours.[399] Modification of the species specific odour of the abdominal scent glands by the diet may lead to a unique odour. This would not have to differ widely from that of other hives for the sensitivity of the bee's olfactory sense is such that very subtle nuances could be appreciated. A similar explanation may lie behind the odour of other insect colonies.

CHAPTER XI

THE CONTACT CHEMICAL SENSE

IT is better to discard the name taste when we are dealing with invertebrates for the word carries many human connotations which are misleading when applied to these animals. To replace it by the contact chemical sense seems more adequate since this states objectively the relationship between chemical substance and sense organ, for the main mass of the substance actually touches the sense organs.

Taste in man divides itself into four modalities, sweet, bitter, acid and salt. These have been sought, occasionally successfully, in the investigation of the invertebrate contact chemical sense as a final proof that such sensitivity is homologous with taste in man. Interesting though such a similarity would be there seems no reason to expect the occurrence of parallel modalities to these. Indeed since their very postulation in vertebrates may be a simplification,[24] or an experimental abstract from a far more complex situation, it is perhaps better not to demand a close parallel. Invertebrate chemical senses have unique characteristics of their own which in no way reduce the possibility that the basic processes of stimulation are the same as those in man.

THE CONTACT CHEMICAL SENSE IN INSECTS

The contact chemoreceptors of insects are localized in three main areas, the antennae, the mouth parts, particularly the labial palps, and the tarsi, mainly those of the forelegs. In addition, chemoreceptors are also present on the ovipositors of some ichneumonids, braconids, and crickets.[186] Insects with mouthparts which form a proboscis such as flies and butterflies respond to food by unfolding or unrolling their proboscis preparatory to feeding. This is a very useful sign that the receptors have been stimulated by an 'acceptable' substance. Since the tarsi can be stimulated alone, no stimulus need be applied to the mouthparts themselves, nor does the insect imbibe any of the test solution, so that the insect's state of hunger, for example, remains unaltered throughout the experiment. For the response is dependent upon the physiological state of the insect, great care, for instance, must be taken to see that the insects have drunk their fill so that they do in fact respond to the test substance dissolved in water and not to the water of solution. Threshold levels are affected by the state of hunger of the test animal. Non-acceptable substances may be tested by giving them in pure water to thirsty insects, their stimulating power being measured by the extent to which the desire to drink is inhibited, or they may be mixed in a standard solution of an acceptable substance of a strength that it is normally taken by the insects, so that if the non-acceptable substance is strong enough their feeding reaction is suppressed. Another indication has been used in the study of honeybees for they are known to fill their honey stomachs to an extent which depends upon the strength of the sugar solution which they are drinking and non-acceptable substances added to the solution cause the bees to take less of the sugar. Also the length of time taken to feed has been correlated in *Vanessa* (=*Pyrameis*) *atalanta*, the red admiral butterfly, with the strength of sugar solution offered.[552]

Sucrose is one of the most generally acceptable substances and it is commonly used for experiments. The threshold concentration at which sucrose is perceived in water by a number of insects is given in Table X. These figures are subject to wide variation according to the state of hunger of the insect, a reduction from 1/50 M to 1/3200 M, or even 1/102,400 M, for example, occurring in the tarsal

TABLE X. Thresholds of sucrose solutions for various insects and man

Species	Organs involved	Thresholds in molarities	Authority
Danaus plexippus	Tarsi of forelegs	$3 \times 10^{-4} - 1 \times 10^{-5}$	Anderson, 1932
Vanessa atalanta	,,	$0.1 - 1 \times 10^{-3}$ (individuals 1×10^{-4})	Minnich, 1921 Weis, 1930
Pieris rapae	Mouthparts	1.5×10^{-3}	Verlaine, 1927
Calliphora vomitoria	Tarsi of forelegs	$1 \times 10^{-4} - 3 \times 10^{-4}$	Minnich, 1929 Crow, 1932
	Mouthparts	$1 \times 10^{-2} - 2 \times 10^{-3}$	Minnich, 1932
C. erythrocephala	Tarsi of forelegs	$1.5 \times 10^{-5} - 3 \times 10^{-4}$	Crow, 1932
Lucilia sp.	,,	$5 \times 10^{-4} - 1.2 \times 10^{-3}$	Crow, 1932
Phormia regina	Tarsal hair (type B) (type C)	3.0 1.0	Dethier, 1955 ,, ,,
	Labellar hair	$1 \times 10^{-4} - 1 \times 10^{-5}$	,, ,,
	All receptors acting together	1×10^{-7}	Dethier and Rhoades, 1954
Apis mellifera	Antennae	$7 \times 10^{-2} - 1 \times 10^{-2}$ 1×10^{-4} (after training)	Kunze, 1933 Kantner, von Frisch, 1934
	Mouthparts	$6 \times 10^{-2} - 1.2 \times 10^{-1}$	von Frisch, 1934
Lasius niger	Mouthparts	5×10^{-3}	Schmidt, 1938
Myrmica rubida	Mouthparts	1×10^{-2}	Schmidt, 1938
Man	Tongue	1.1×10^{-2}	Skramlik, 1948

receptors of *Danaus plexippus* (= *D. menippe*) after 7–8 days on a water diet.[9] The threshold for *Vanessa* adults falls to 8×10^{-5} M after starvation.[379] This reduction occurs in the thresholds for both tarsal and mouthpart stimulation, the increase in sensitivity being greatest in the tarsal organs. The drop is not specific to sucrose alone but appears in the reaction to other sugars as Table XI shows.[233] These figures were obtained by testing the sensitivity of *Calliphora* adults after one and after ten days starvation.

TABLE XI. The influence of starvation on the threshold values for various sugars in *Calliphora erythrocephala* (from Haslinger[233])

Sugar	After 1 day of starvation		After 10 days of starvation		Increase in Sensitivity	
	Mouthparts	Tarsi	Mouthparts	Tarsi	Mouthparts	Tarsi
Glucose	28/100	128/100	1/25	1/8	7x	10x
Fructose	20/100	95/100	1/250	1/300	55x	286x
Saccharose	8/100	14/100	1/280	1/1500	22x	200x
Maltose	9/100	94/100	1/500	1/800	46x	700x

Insects are as sensitive to non-acceptable substances like quinine as they are to acceptable sugars. A bee, for example, will reject 1·0 M sucrose to which 8×10^{-4} M quinine has been added.[193] Sensitivity to these substances is sharpened by learning, and the threshold for rejection appears to be lowered, for individual water beetles, *Dytiscus* sp., were conditioned to respond to concentrations of quinine as low as $1·25 \times 10^{-6}$ M.[33]

Sodium chloride is rejected at a higher concentration than quinine. A bee will refuse 0·5 M sucrose with 0·24 M sodium chloride added, and acids, such as hydrochloric, are rejected at a lower threshold (in the case of hydrochloric acid, 0·001 M acid causes rejection of 1·0 M sucrose)[193].

Some experiments suggest that the contact chemical sense of some insects may be organized into modalities similar to those of man. For example, the water beetles, *Dytiscus marginalis* and *Hydrophilus* (=*Hydrous*) *piceus*, can be trained to respond positively to sucrose, but after such training they will respond to other sugars,[33] such as glucose also, since they cannot be trained to select one sugar and avoid others, all sugars are apparently alike to them though the thresholds at which they are perceived vary greatly (Table XII). They can, however, be trained to distinguish a sugar, say, sucrose, from sodium chloride, or either of these two substances from acids or quinine. But acids such as hydrochloric and tartaric were indistinguishable from each other. Other bitter substances (aloin, salicin) were indistinguishable from quinine. Thus there are apparently sweet, salt, acid and bitter taste modalities.

Another method of approach is to investigate the effect of various substances on loads taken by honeybees. Having determined a concentration of sucrose which is just sufficiently strong to be accepted by all the bees being tested, the various substances can be added and their effect determined. For example, the addition of sodium chloride in such low concentrations that none of the bees refuse to drink nevertheless causes them to take less of the solution. Other halogen salts such as lithium bromide produce similar results as does the addition of hydrochloric acid also. In fact addition of sodium chloride at too low concentration to have any effect with one of these other salts at a similar low concentration affects the load taken to the same extent as a concentration of sodium chloride equivalent to the sum of the two salts. In other words the effects of sub-liminal solutions summate which implies that the action of the two salts must be alike. Quinine, however, does not summate with any of these substances, in fact, the addition of acids with the quinine reduced its repellency. This suggests that the taste modalities of bees are sweet, acid-salt, and bitter. But since starved bees take quinine-sugar, and acid-sugar mixtures less readily than unstarved bees (at thresholds 8 times and 5 times higher respectively), and yet show as much reluctance to take salt-sugar mixtures as bees which have been fed, it may well be that the category acid-salt is in fact subdivided into acid and salt. There is also evidence that the category bitter may not be a uniform one for bees.[193]

There is some evidence that the water beetle, *Hydrophilus piceus*, detects the modalities of sweet, salt and bitter by sense organs on the maxillary palps while acids are detected by sensory endings on the tips of the labial palps.[457] But this does not agree with later work on the same species in which the reactions to sucrose remained after removal of the maxillary palps,[33] and in *Laccophilus maculosus*, another water beetle, it seems that both antennae and mouthparts are responsive to acids, salts and alcohols.[264] The individual receptors on the tarsi of the fly *Phormia regina*, seem to react to all substances, and it has been shown that they can also respond to water and mechanical bending[137].

The work on bees showed that concentrations of sugars could summate so that the same result could be produced by a mixture of sucrose and fructose, both at half threshold level, as a solution of

TABLE XII. The effect of various concentrations of different substances on Dytiscid larvae (from Bauer[33])

Sugar	Conc. M.	+	weak	no obvious
			Nos. of animals reacting	
Pentoses				
Arabinose	1	7	5	1
	1/4	7	4	2
Xylose	2	14	2	–
	1/10	5	4	5
Rhamnose	1	5	5	4
	1/3	3	2	9
Hexoses				
Glucose	2	16	–	–
	1/25	–	2	–
Fructose	2	8	–	–
	1/20	8	5	1
Mannose	2	7	1	–
	1/10	1	6	7
Galactose	1	14	–	–
	1/10	10	4	–
Di-saccharides				
Saccharose	1	16	–	–
	1/100	6	3	4
Maltose	1	12	–	–
	1/8	12	–	–
Cellobiose	1/2	2	1	–
	1/4	1	1	1
Lactose	1	10	–	–
	1/4	7	3	3
Tri-saccharides				
Melecitose	1	12	–	–
	1/20	11	3	–
Raffinose	1/2	9	3	–
	1/16	4	3	7
Polyhydric alcohols				
Mannitol	1	12	2	–
	1/10	5	6	3
Dulcitol	1/2	10	2	2
	1/10	8	2	4
Sorbitol	1	11	2	1
	1/10	8	1	5
Inositol	1	6	2	4
	1/6	1	6	7
Glycoside				
a-Methyl-glucoside	1	14	–	–
	1/20	12	1	1

K*

either sugar at threshold concentration.[193] Such summation would appear to be taking place peripherally, at the sense organs. However, the summation of the stimulation of tarsal hairs on one foreleg with that of hairs on the opposite leg which can be demonstrated in *Phormia* must occur centrally. Indeed the threshold for unilateral stimulation is higher than for bilateral stimulation.[133] Sodium chloride placed on one hair while sucrose is placed on a neighbouring one on the same foot may produce rejection, again by central summation or so it would appear. Indeed the threshold varies according to the number of hairs on the tarsus which are involved. Thus a 3 M concentration of sucrose may be required to produce proboscis extension if applied to one hair, but 1 M suffices if applied to at least four hairs, 0·5 M with 6–8 hairs and 0·1 M to 10 or more. This must result from central summation as indeed must also the inhibition of proboscis extension when one hair is stimulated with a sucrose solution of more than threshold strength and a drop of sodium chloride of the necessary concentration is placed on a neighbouring hair.[137]

There is every indication that there are two systems at work, one mediating responses to sugars and the other to non-sugar, usually repellent, substances[133] (a similar dual modality for the chemical sensitivity of *Nassarius reticulatus* may be suspected).[240] Since a sodium chloride-sucrose mixture inhibits the proboscis extension which would have occurred to the sucrose alone, both mechanisms reside in one hair. Electrophysiological studies show that there is an S fibre which carries small spike potentials when the hair is stimulated by acceptable substances (e.g. sugar and dilute sodium chloride) and an L fibre showing larger spike potentials after stimulation with substances which are avoided (e.g. strong sodium chloride solution, other salts, acids, alcohols, etc.).[266]

The sugar system is very sensitive, concentrations of sucrose as low as 1×10^{-7} M being selected in choice experiments in preference to pure water.[144] Single hairs, however, vary widely in their thresholds not only according to their position on the fly (e.g. B-type tibial hair, 3 M sucrose; hair on margin of labellum, 0·0001 M) but also from day to day. They can, in fact, be stimulated by the surface of a well desiccated crystal of sucrose which has been split and applied to the hair. This suggests that the hair may have some water on its surface, for the response is very rapid, the latent period being of the order of 0·1 sec.[137]

The reaction to sugar is highly specific. Though the essential character of a stimulating molecule of a monosaccharide is difficult to ascertain, presence of the α-D-glucopyranoside link in a compound sugar makes it a powerful stimulator; thus maltose, sucrose and turanose stimulate while lactose does not.[137] Perhaps the sugar is weakly combined with a specific receptor substance forming a complex which causes depolarization of the membrane and hence initiates an impulse in the nerve. After this the sugar is removed passively apparently without the intervention of a chemical process, such as the glycolytic cycle.[138]

Sensitivity to non-sugar substances shows some of the characteristics of olfactory stimulation, rejection thresholds of the members of a series of homologous glycols decrease with increasing chain length, for example.[140] But otherwise measurement of the threshold at which they inhibit positive responses to sucrose solutions of various concentrations reveal two main groups (Fig. 139). One set, organic compounds, such as alcohols and ketones, show only slight increases, while the others, the inorganic compounds and certain organic substances, like glycols and fatty acids, show definite increases. These inhibiting substances probably act through a chemoreceptor other than that stimulated by sugar. It should be remembered that a hair is in fact supplied with three neurones (p. 25).

The stimulating efficiency of inorganic cations is:

$$Li^+ < Na^+ \leqq K^+ < Ca^+ <<< H_3O^+$$

and of anions

$$CH_3COO' < Cl' < NO_3' <<< OH'$$

both series being tested on labellar hairs.[137] This suggests that the stimulating efficiency of the cations is correlated with their ionic mobilities,[184, 185] entering the receptor in the aqueous phase, while aliphatic compounds seem to stimulate according to their solubility particularly in the lipoid phase by which they probably gain entry into the hair.[141]

Though parallels can be drawn between the olfactory sense of man and certainly bees, among the insects, similar likenesses between the contact chemical sense and human taste are fewer. It may be that the sensitivity of insects is divided into the four modalities of human taste, but apart from that one possibility there are no general likenesses between the sensations perceived by man and those of an insect as they are demonstrated by their behaviour. For example, dulcin, a synthetic sweetening substance, appears to be distasteful to *Vanessa*, being rejected when in contact with the tarsal receptors, though solutions are sucked when they come in contact with the proboscis.[552] Sugars, such as glucose, fructose, saccharose, maltose and melicitose are sweet to man and accepted by all the insects investigated, but other sugars, such as galactose, lactose, raffinose, mannitose, and sorbitol and dulcitol are not apparently sweet to all insects (Table XIII).

TABLE XIII. Acceptability of various sugars and polyhydric alcohols to insects (from von Buddenbrock[80] with additions)

M: Mouthparts, T: tarsi

Sugar	Tastes sweet to:	Only slightly sweet or tasteless to:
Galactose	Myrmica rubra, M	Lasius niger, M
	Apis mellifera, M	Myrmica rubida, M
	Calliphora erythrocephala, M and T	Formica sanguinea, M
	Phormia regina, M and T	Vanessa atalanta, T
Lactose	Calliphora erythrocephala, M	Calliphora erythrocephala, T
		Apis mellifera, M
		Myrmica spp., M
		Lasius niger, M
		Phormia regina, M and T
Raffinose	Almost all insects, particularly Myrmica, spp., M, and Lasius niger, M	Apis mellifera, M
Sorbitol	Myrmica rubra, M	Apis mellifera, M
	Lasius niger, M	Myrmica rubida, M
		Phormia regina, M and T
Mannitol	Apis mellifera, Antennae	Apis mellifera, M
	Myrmica rubra, M	Myrmica rubra, M
	Calliphora, M and T	Lasius niger, M
		Phormia regina, M and T
Dulcitol	Calliphora, M and T	Apis mellifera, M
		Various spp. of ant, M
		Phormia regina, M and T

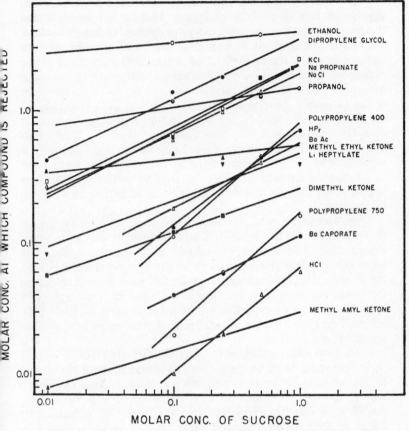

FIG. 139. Threshold concentrations at which various glycols cause rejection of sucrose solutions of different strengths (Dethier[137]).

CONTACT CHEMORECEPTION IN OTHER INVERTEBRATES

Among other land invertebrates, as well as among insects, olfaction and contact chemoreception act in concert. Olfaction often produces locomotion and even causes food to be grasped, which on contact is proved to be either edible or inedible. Even in aquatic animals there appear to be two sets of chemoreceptors, one set reacting to chemicals in solution in the water and the other to immediate contact with the substance. These two sets are used in a parallel manner to the way in which distant and contact chemoreception are co-ordinated in land animals.

Consider first arachnids, which are terrestrial and possess sensory capabilities similar to those of insects. There is a suggestion that the tarsal organs are chemoreceptors in spiders. Certainly *Araneus diadematus* reacts to oil of turpentine and clove oil either from a distance or when the oils touch the organs.[50] The reactivity of the organs on the different pairs of legs seem to vary, so that the speed of reaction is greatest to substances touching the fore pair, the spider (a female *Zelotes*) retreating one second after being stimulated, but is progressively less when the other legs are stimulated until the animal reacts only after 5 seconds when the fourth pair are touched. Since these organs react to quinine sulphate, a substance which is classified by man as a taste substance, and to oils from a distance (and, incidentally, to carbon dioxide) they appear to be able to function both as contact and distant chemoreceptors.

There appears to be a clear spatial separation of the sense organs responsible for the two types of sensitivity in some crustacea, sensitivity to distant sources seems to reside in the antennules while one set of contact chemoreceptors occur on the legs and another around the mouth. The antennal and leg receptors have been classified as the 'outer' and the mouth receptors as the 'inner' chemoreceptors.[345] Their functions do seem rather separate and it seems likely that the antennal receptors have a lower threshold than either of the other sets of organs.

When food juices are added to water in which are crabs (*Carcinus*) their antennules begin to wave about as if searching for the source of the stimulus. They then react to a current bearing chemicals, moving towards the source of the chemical. Food is, however, only picked up if the contact receptors on the chelae are stimulated.[345] Pieces of filter paper soaked in sugar solution, acids and even in alcohol or xylol are grasped and passed to the mouth where they may be rejected. However, if they are rejected, they may be picked up again by the chelae, carried to the mouth once more and again discarded. This does not go on indefinitely. Soon a substance which is unacceptable to the mouth receptors is not picked up again by the chelae, so there seems to be some central organization of these feeding movements, though the cessation might be explained if the chelae receptors become adapted to the repeated stimulus. But if grasping a piece of filter paper soaked in acetic acid has been suppressed, the same chela will still pick up a piece soaked in sucrose which might suggest central rather than peripheral inhibition, unless different receptors are in play. These receptors can be used to distinguish between sucrose and saccharine, sucrose and sodium chloride, and between sucrose and such scented substances as cumarin or vanilla. Even if the crab is walking out of water, it can follow a trail of food juice by means of the receptors on its legs. When food juice is in the water, both fore and hind pairs of legs may be lifted off the ground and waved about, moving and, perhaps, functioning like the first antennae. The presence of the antennae seems to affect the sensitivity of the contact receptors if the antennae are removed, the latent period between stimulation of the leg receptors and the commencement of feeding increases. This is reminiscent of the role of 'stimulation organs' such as some insect ocelli are believed to be.

We have seen that these contact receptors react to substances which we perceive by their scent. This renders the distinction between olfaction and contact reception even more difficult for one would like to call the recognition of these substances, olfaction. The situation is made more obscure by the strong suggestion that *Carcinus* and *Crangon*[501] can perceive glycogen, and *Carcinus* soluble starch, both of which are tasteless to ourselves. The threshold of what are to us scented substances like cumarin and vanilla is very much lower than that for 'taste' substances including starch and glycogen (Table XIV) though skatol is an exception, ranging itself in experiments with *Carcinus* with the 'taste' substances. Learning can reduce the threshold, as it does in insects. Hermit crabs, *Eupagurus*, trained to react to cumarin do so at concentrations a thousand times lower than untrained animals.[586]

TABLE XIV. Threshold concentrations (% solutions) of various substances stimulating crustacea (*Crangon*, from Spiegel[501]; *Eupagurus*, from Wrede[586] *Carcinus*, from Luther[345])

	Crangon	*Eupagurus*	*Carcinus*
Saccharose	0·1–0·05	—	0·005
Lactose	—	—	0·005
Starch	—	—	0·0005
Glycogen	0·5–0·1	—	0·001
Sodium chloride	1·3–1·5	—	—
Acetic acid	0·01	—	0·00006
Tartaric acid	—	—	0·00006
Cumarin	0·0001–0·00005	0·00005 without training 0·00000005 with training	0·0000005
Vanillin	0·0001–0·00005	—	0·000001–0·0000005
Skatol	—	0·0000001	—

The reaction of what is apparently one set of chemoreceptors only to such varied substances suggests strongly that the contact and distant sensitivity are not seated in morphologically distinct areas, if, indeed, they are not resident in the same organs. The 'scent' substances like vanilla appear to be more active stimulators.

The foot of pulmonate molluscs is extremely sensitive to chemicals. When a snail's foot touches a drop of sugar solution, the snail stops and sucks in the drop. Many pulmonates depend upon the stimulation of the end of the foot to find their food for their mouth lobes are, apparently, not sensitive to chemicals.[433] For example, a water snail, *Limnaea stagnalis*, hanging from the surface film can be fed without touching its foot, it will imbibe anything put into its mouth, even quinine, sodium chloride or pepper, which in the water nearby caused the snail to expel air violently from its mantle cavity and sink. On the other hand, when the mouth lobes of *Helix* are removed the rejection threshold of glucose, quinine sulphate, salicin and sodium chloride is doubled.[300] It is the mouth lobes which give warning of predators in *Physa fontinalis*,[315] while the hind end of the foot of *Nassarius reticulatus* is sensitive to contact with starfish which feed upon it.[551]

The skin of *Octopus vulgaris* is generally sensitive to chemicals but particularly so along the arms. The ventral side of these with their suckers is the most sensitive area. Though an *Octopus* usually hunts visually, blinded individuals can still locate their food, for they search in any area of chemical stimulation until an arm touches the source of the chemical, when the suckers grasp it and it is carried to the mouth. There is little doubt that these are reactions to chemical stimulation, for an empty crab's carapace is investigated but discarded, while a piece of porous pot soaked in fish juice is picked up and carried to the mouth where, however, it too is discarded.[206] What component of the juice causes this reaction is not known. Various substances have been tested but no clue is given by the results. The animal is indifferent to sugar, but retreats from quinine, salicin, acetic acid, skatol, and musk. The thresholds are fairly low, for example, acetic acid stimulates at 0·006%, quinine at 0·0005%, skatol at 0·0001%. Here again skatol, a 'scent' substance joins the 'taste' substances in stimulating efficiency. If the octopus is satiated the feeding reactions do not appear.

The octopus is sensitive to salt concentration, for it reacts defensively to concentrations of 6%, 5%, 2%, 1% and lower strengths but does not react to 3% or 4% salt solution. It is interesting to note that the salinity of the sea water at Naples where this work was carried out is 3·6%.[206]

An arm severed from the body will also react to the same substances but at a higher threshold than an intact animal. It curls away
from 0·01 % solutions of acetic acid or quinine, for example. The
arm will grasp food but does not bend to pass it in the direction in
which the mouth would lie were it still on the whole animal. Again
an arm from a satiated octopus which is not showing any reaction
to food, will react to stimulation by juices when it is severed from
the body. Both these observations indicate the extent of central
control over the feeding behaviour of this animal.[206]

Echinoderms also have the ability to locate food by chemoreception. Chemical stimuli will evoke typical feeding behaviour. In the
starfish, *Asterias rubens*, this consists of five stages, first, in water
containing food juices, the unattached feet bend back and forth,
then they bend to point away from the animal's mouth, and at this
stage the edge of the stomach begins to make its appearance as the
gut everts. This third stage is followed by the raising of the central
part of the body on the arms so that the starfish is raised over its
food, and finally the stomach everts completely to cover the food.[241]
These stages are the normal pattern and they appear when the
starfish is stimulated by naturally occurring foodstuffs but the
whole pattern may not be evoked if pure chemicals are used to
stimulate the starfish. As might be expected with a carnivorous
animal, carbohydrate has no effect, but amino acids and peptones
all evoke most of the stages, though the first stage never appears
and the last stage only rarely. It is interesting to compare the reaction to these 'taste' substances with that of a 'scent' substance
like skatol, in answer to which the first four stages appear strongly
marked but the last, of actually enveloping the food, is never seen.
It may be that the amino acids are stimulating one set of receptors,
by which feeding reactions are controlled to the exclusion of the
preliminary searching behaviour with the feet, while skatol acts
through organs—with a lower threshold, perhaps—which release
searching behaviour, but are unable to bring all the stages into play.

There is some evidence of the abilities of earthworms to distinguish chemical substances. Certain species (e.g. *Eisenia foetida*) are
confined to compost heaps or other places where there is much
decaying matter. Similarly worms will congregate in humus-sand
mixtures in preference to sand alone. This suggests that they can
choose their habitat by its chemical characteristics. Making use of
the earthworm's habit of drawing leaves and so forth into its burrow,
some tests have been made of their ability to distinguish chemical
stimuli. Pine needles were coated with pure gelatine and gelatine
mixed with a variety of test substances. The worms rejected quinine

and salt mixtures but were generally indifferent to saccharose though they occasionally chose this sugar.[351] Certain preferences for leaves from particular plants, thus beech leaves were often favoured, and for leaves of particular age and dryness, rotten leaves being most preferred, can be explained if their choice was based on chemicals present in them.[351]

Leeches will reject fluids which contain salt, sucrose or quinine sulphate above certain concentrations. They can be induced to attach themselves and to suck at an animal membrane stretched over a tube filled with blood. However, though they continue to suck when any of these chemicals are mixed with the blood, they stop and release when the concentration rises to 7% of sodium chloride, to 5% of sucrose or to 0·8—1% of quinine.[340] Chemical stimuli also aid leeches to find their hosts (see later, p. 295).

TABLE XV. The threshold concentrations at which various substances stimulate the tentacles and mouth of *Anemonia sulcata*, indicating the strength of the cnidae response where there is one (from Pantin and Pantin[411])

| | % dry wt. at threshold concentration. | | Relative cnida response |
	Tentacles	Mouth	
Proteins			
Soluble casein	0·1	0·005	+ +
Fat free casein	1·0	0·1	0
Egg white	1·0	0·01	+ +
Blood fibrin	0·4	0·005	+ +
Amino acids			
Tyrosine	1·0–0·1	0·001	0
Cystein	3	0·01	0
Arginine	10	0·01–0·001	0
Glutathione	1	0·1	0
Other substances			
Quinine hydrochloride	0·1	0·01	no effect
Skatol	no effect	0·05	,, ,,
Glucose	,, ,,	10	,, ,,
Methylamine chloride	,, ,,	1·0	,, ,,

Many coelenterates show by their behaviour towards chemicals and towards natural food that the distinction between edible and inedible food depends upon chemical stimuli, for their reactions are altered in the presence of certain chemicals. Substances associated with protein stimulate the tentacles and the mouth of *Anemonia sulcata*, though the mouth is more sensitive and will respond to some other substances, e.g., skatol and glucose which are without effect on the tentacles (Table XV). This is reminiscent of the 'outer' and 'inner' chemoreceptors of crustacea but in a reversed way, the mouth has a wider spectrum of acceptable substances than the more selective outer tentacles.[404] The effect of chemicals on the cilia of the oral disc of *Metridium marginatum* also play a part in feeding. They normally beat away from the mouth, but when food is near they reverse to aid in moving food to the mouth. Such reversal occurs when filter paper soaked in glycogen, peptone, deutero albumose, aspariginic acid, creatin or potassium chloride is placed on the disc, but sucrose and glucose have no effect.[422] These chemicals may be characteristic of edible and inedible food as the sea anemone is a carnivore.

But unlike the anemone, the Scyphomedusae *Aurelia aurita* and *Cyanea capillata* do not react to glycogen. Tests were made by dropping small pieces of clay soaked with various chemicals onto the amputated oral arms of *Aurelia*. These were transferred to the central groove and passed along it in the direction which would lead mouthwards in the intact animal. Carbohydrates were without effect the particles being rejected, but albumin, peptones, various amino acids and some fatty acids were accepted, as was also skatol usually considered as a 'smell substance'. The mouth lobes of *Cyanea* will also continue to react when they are separated from the body but in this case, when stimulated by suitable substances, they show a positive response by spreading out over the floor of the dish, so the area covered by them is a measure of the stimulating efficiency of the substance. Their reactions were similar to those of *Aurelia*. The Hydromedusan *Sarsia tubulosa* contracts its manubrium and extends its tentacles in response to favourable stimulation; it reacted positively to the same substances as *Aurelia* and *Sarsia*. It is somewhat surprising that these jellyfish whose food must include many animals such as copepods, rich in glycogen, should not react to this substance.[241] though, of course, it would not be released until the animal had been injured.

It has been known for some years that the nematocysts of *Hydra* require chemical substances to stimulate their release. Surface active materials alone are effective but mechanical stimulation added to the chemical produces a larger proportion of releases. It is now clear that the whole feeding reaction, at least in *Hydra littoralis*,[341] shown as writhing of the tentacles, tentacular contraction, and finally mouth opening is initiated by glutathione released from the prey when it is pierced by the penetrant nematocysts (thus edible prey can be distinguished from inedible objects not containing glutathione). The gradient of chemical diffusing from the prey directs the reactions for a *Hydra* in a 10^{-5} M solution cannot localize its prey, and, indeed, in such a solution may attempt to engulf other *Hydra* (starvation lowers the threshold to 10^{-7} M glutathione after eight days). Though the thresholds are so low as to suggest mechanisms which should be grouped as distant chemoreceptors, the origin of the chemical is close to or in contact with the animal and therefore this behaviour can be included in this chapter.

THE BIOLOGICAL FUNCTION OF THE CONTACT CHEMICAL SENSE

It is quite obvious from the examples which have already been cited that the contact chemoreceptors play a most important role in feeding behaviour in every invertebrate group. A butterfly will unroll its proboscis in response to sugars touching its tarsi, a crab will chew substances which stimulate the receptors around its mouth satisfactorily and the mouth arms of jellyfish are sensitive to food, to give but a few examples. Further the chemicals which are attractive are usually ones which occur in the normal food and in general, though not invariably, the substances accepted have nutritional value. Honeybees, for example, perceive fructose, glucose and maltose as sweet but reject lactose. The first group are capable of maintaining bees alive if fed alone, but lactose is not apparently metabolized. But bees do not react to sorbitol or xylose, both of which can be metabolized.[540] On the other hand *Calliphora* accepts fucose and cellobiose, yet these sugars have no food value.[233] Choice depends —as would be expected—upon power of stimulation rather than the nutritional value of a substance, thus a mixture of rhamnose and glucose which will support life for 8 days is preferred by blow-flies, *Phormia regina*, to a glucose solution on which a fly can live for 14 days.[142]

The strength of the sugar solutions found by foraging honeybees influence whether they will dance on their return to the hive, spring bees can only be induced to dance by 1·5–2·0 M sugar solutions, though autumn bees will dance after finding weaker solutions, e.g. 0·25 M or even 0·125 M. Bitter, salt or acid substances added to the sugar solutions reduce the proportion of dancers.[333] Indeed, the strength of the sugar solution in the worker's stomach may directly determine the form and speed of its dance, and, thus, the information conveyed, on its return to the hive. This suggestion arose from the observation that, on imbibing sugar solution, house-flies will perform circular 'dances' which show striking resemblances to the more refined dances of honeybees.[139] The strength of the sugar solution that the flies suck up affects the speed and vigour of the movements they perform.

We have seen that substances grasped by the chelae of *Carcinus* are sometimes carried to the mouth where they are accepted or rejected. The receptors on the legs seem to react to a wider range of substances than those round the mouth, which are the final arbiters in the decision whether to eat the food.

Spiders test the prey caught in their web with their forelegs before spinning it up into a bundle. A fly is touched with the palps as well before it is rolled up, but a wasp is covered first and then bitten to kill it. It would seem that the spider (*Epeira diadema*) will not come close to prey which may sting it but immobilizes the prey before biting it. A fly soaked in oil of turpentine is treated like a wasp and bundled up without being 'tasted'. Tactile stimuli are also important for odourless glass balls are spun up apparently because they present the same sort of touch stimuli as a chitin-covered insect. But the final decision on whether to eat the prey seems to rest on the result of biting it. Tactile sensation from non-chitinous material cause it to be discarded and thrown off the web. The chemical stimuli received when the bundle is bitten determine whether it is carried to the centre of the web or to the spider's lair to be sucked dry. If the prey is vibrating strongly even after being bound up it is bitten for some time the bite lasting some seconds. A glass ball covered with the flesh of *Pieris* caterpillar is carried off, but one covered with flesh and quinine is thrown off the web.[429] Similarly individuals of *Tegenaria ferruginea* (= *T. domestica*) can distinguish a pith ball soaked in the juices of a fly from one soaked in distilled water, when they bite the pith. The ability to reject flies soaked in quinine (1/36–1/60%), sodium chloride (1–3%) or tartaric acid remains when the maxillary palps and the forepart of the maxillae have been removed.[28]

Chemical stimuli are important for insect parasites in finding their prey and no doubt more evidence could be found of a similar role in other invertebrate parasites. There are, however, already some observations on the effect of chemicals on the behaviour of various leeches. We have seen the importance of vibration and other stimuli in warning a leech of the approach of its possible prey. But chemical stimuli are important in making the reaction more specific. *Hemiclepsis marginata*, a fish leech, will begin its typical searching movements when water containing mucus scraped from the body of a tench reaches it. And though a piece of filter paper moved back and forth over hungry leeches resting on the bottom does not evoke any reaction, if the paper has been rubbed on the skin of a carp, within a short time leeches swim up and attach themselves to it. As might be expected since the host range of these parasites is fairly limited this reaction is only made to a few substances. *Hemiclepsis* attaches itself to fish and certain amphibia, such as *Amblystoma*, but these leeches can be induced to attach themselves to *Rana temporaria* only with difficulty and will not attach to *R. esculenta*.[248] The duck leech, *Theromyzon tessulatum*, is stimulated to search when the secretion of the uropygial gland of a duck is added to the water.[251] Not a great deal appears to be known of the stimuli affecting host selection in trematodes, though the fact, for example, that the miracidia of *Opisthorchis felineus* attach themselves only to *Bithynia leachi* but not to *B. tentaculata*, though they are usually present with the host species and in greater numbers is suggestive that specific chemical stimuli are involved.[18]

Nothing appears to be known of the stimuli which attract parasitic crustacea, such as the great range of copepod parasites, to their hosts, it would, however, hardly be a wild conjecture that chemical stimuli are one of the means by which these parasites find their hosts. When the parasite is associated with two hosts during its life-history, the problem of whether the ability to recognize them is innate or imprinted is a fascinating one.

Animals which are preyed upon employ various devices to protect themselves and among these is an ability to perceive chemical stimuli signalling the approach of a predator. The reactions of *Pecten* to various optical stimuli have been described, these warn the scallop of the approach of the starfish which feeds upon it (p. 133). When the tentacles of the mantle edge which are sensitive to chemical stimuli are exposed, the scallop is then able to perceive whether the cause of the optical changes is in fact a potentially dangerous starfish. At this stage starfish juice added to the water provokes immediate flight. Indeed chemicals are the dominant stimulus, for the scallop will swim when stimulated with starfish juice whether it has been previously stimulated visually or not.[32]

The fresh-water pulmonates, *Physa fontinalis* and *Planorbis* sp. among others are the prey of the *Glossiphonia complanata* when the leech's usual food of *Chironomus* larvae and *Tubifex* are not available.[249] When one of these leeches touches a snail, the snail takes avoiding action, *Physa* by swinging its shell back and forth through 180° and *Planorbis* by retreating into its shell. *Bithynia tentaculata* withdraws into its shell pinching the leech's head between operculum and shell rim. The leech is perceived in these instances when it touches the mouth lobes of the snail for these are sensitive to chemical stimuli from the leech's body. Indeed a snail will react in a similar way to ground over which a leech has just crawled.

The touch of a starfish, or, merely, a tube foot torn from the body,[86] causes *Nassarius reticulatus* to make a violent escape reaction (Fig. 140). Chemoreceptors seem to localized at the hind end of the foot and they will react to many pure chemicals, such as

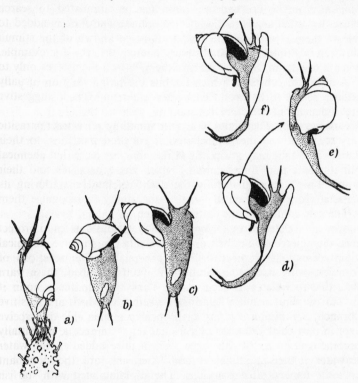

FIG. 140. Escape reaction of *Nassarius* (Weber[551]).

picric acid, alkalis and chloroform.[551] Herbivorous littoral gastropods react strongly to the touch of a carnivorous gastropod, whether it is one which they normally encounter in their particular littoral zone or not;[98a] chemical stimuli are involved. For example, a trochid, *Melagraphia aethiops*, when touched by the whelk, *Lepsia haustrum*, raised its shell and swung it violently through 180° several times before crawling away. Such a pattern of response, which might have the effect of throwing off a predator, seems not uncommon among both marine and freshwater gastropods.

When a predator attacks its prey a substance may be released which acts as a warning to other potential prey. For example, a substance is released from the body of a minnow which is being eaten by a pike, other minnows on perceiving it swim away from the area.[194] A chemical with a somewhat similar function seems to be released when one of the South American fresh-water snails, *Helisoma nigricans*, is crushed in a tank. The presence of the chemical causes the other snails to dig into the bottom, and if it persists, they release themselves from the sand to float up and crawl among the surface vegetation. Other snails bury themselves in the sandy bottom when blood from the snail reaches them.[294]

A chemical substance which inhibits the biting reaction of pedicellaria seems to be produced by sea urchins.[533] The pedicellariae are independent effectors functioning without the control of the nervous system. Their jaws will grasp anything provided the necessary chemical and mechanical stimuli are present. Clearly there is danger that they may grasp one of the tube feet on their own body, but it seems that some stimulus which has been given the name 'autodermin', is produced by the flesh which prevents the pedicellariae from closing on it.

The salt content of the water in which an animal lives has been shown to be detected by *Octopus* (p. 290). Changes in salinity influence the emergence or shell opening of other molluscs. Such behaviour seems to be protective for, in general, it prevents the animal from exposing itself to solutions of a different osmotic pressure than that to which it is accustomed. Thus, the osmotic pressure of the surrounding medium determines whether the shells of the lamellibranch, *Scrobicularia plana*, shall open or remain closed. Animals kept in particular dilutions of seawater until their tissue fluids have become isotonic with them open more readily when transferred to seawater of the same dilution than if they are put into more dilute or more concentrated solutions. The stimulus appears to be the total osmotic pressure of the solution outside the animal and may be detected by receptors, as yet undescribed, along the edge of the mantle which protrudes except on the rare occasions on which the shells are tightly shut.[181]

Similar receptors seem to be born on the cephalic tentacles as well as the mantle edge of limpets, *Patella vulgata*. After eight hours exposure in the air, a limpet will respond to being splashed with seawater by lifting its shell and extending its tentacles, but if freshwater is used its head is withdrawn further and the mantle edge contracted (within 30 seconds of splashing). Limpets from around the high water mark are particularly quick to react but may be tolerant of 50% or even 20% seawater, while animals from lower down the shore react negatively to 80% seawater. This prevents the shell from becoming flooded with water of low salinity and enables the animal to react appropriately to the potentially dangerous rain water and to seawater in which it can move about and feed.[10] Though it is unproven it is probable that the effective stimulus is once again the osmotic pressure of the medium.

Though the total osmotic pressure seems to play a part in controlling the emergence of the Japanese winkle. *Nodilittorina granularis*, from its shell, the presence of particular ions seems to increase the effectiveness of the stimulus. Thus, a solution of glucose isotonic with seawater produced full emergence responses from test animals only after the addition of a mixture of magnesium chloride and sodium chloride (isotonic with seawater). This mixture of salts was more effective than others, though its action could be imitated by isotonic lithium chloride.[402] The receptors seem to be on the operculum, though the stimulus may act in this, and the previous examples, through an alteration in the osmotic pressure of the body fluids, brought about by the new solutions outside the animal, which affects the nervous system, as such changes have been shown to do in slugs.[299]

Social insects recognize their nest mates by their odour but the chemicals produced by their companions are also perceived by contact. It was once considered that the perceptual world of the ant or bee was one of 'shapes of odour' perceived by the contact chemoreceptors on the antennae.[165] This belief arose mainly because it appeared that ants could recognize the direction in which a scent trail was running, either to the nest or to the food. This trail was supposed to be composed of the foot marks of the foragers and that the polarization of the trail could be perceived by the shape of the marks.[45] Alternatively the directional qualities of the trail were supposed to arise from the attenuation of goal odour towards the nest and nest odour in the opposite direction.[70] The trails are polarized but it is very doubtful whether this polarization is in fact recognized by the ants,[96] except in certain exceptional cases.[347]

The advancing bands of army ant raiders (*Eciton* spp.) seem to be held together by a complex of tactile and chemical stimuli, whether perceived from a distance or by contact with them is not clear, most probably the latter.[482] Ground over which a swarm advances becomes saturated with chemicals so that workers do not hesitate to advance across it only halting to turn back when they cross the boundary onto ground that has not this chemical, but before turning they in their turn deposit chemicals on some of the new ground, so that the saturated area grows ever larger.[480, 481] The ground marking is apparently done by leaving an anal secretion as is also trail marking by workers of *Lasius fuliginosus*. This ant deposits streaks of material from its anus when it leaves an abundant food supply so that its track back to the nest is marked.[94] Other foragers leaving the nest can detect and follow this trail and on their return reinforce it with more material provided that the food supply is not failing, if it is doing so, the ant will be less stimulated and will not reinforce the trail so that gradually the marking fades and attracts no more workers to follow it. Though the streaks are shaped, being drawn out in the direction in which the ant is running,[93] this shape is not perceived. The ant maintains contact with the trail as it runs by touching it occasionally with one antenna, apparently sensing it through contact receptors. Unfamiliar chemicals, like those left on the ground where a finger has been drawn across the trail, disturb it and these again are apparently perceived on contact, though they may be detected at a distance as well.

CHAPTER XII

HUMIDITY SENSITIVITY

STUDIES of humidity sensitivity have been carried out mainly on insects, though a few terrestrial arthropods have been used as well (otherwise there appears only to be a study on earthworms and one on slugs). Many of these lose water easily or relatively easily and therefore behavioural reactions which keep them in a moist atmosphere are advantageous. Dry sand seems to stimulate sand hoppers (*Talitrus saltator*) to make their way down the beach to moister parts, for example,[414] while water content, both of the earth and the air above it, is the most important restricting factor in the distribution of *Scutigerella immaculata*.[182] Aggregation in the moist side of a choice chamber often comes about because the animal moves faster in a dry atmosphere. Thus the woodlice, *Porcellio scaber*[213] (Fig. 141), *Oniscus asellus* and *Armadillidium vulgare*[544] are very active in dry air but almost motionless in a saturated atmosphere (low orthokinesis).[544] They also turn more frequently in the higher humidities (high klinokinesis). The reactions are most striking in *Oniscus asellus*, and least obvious in *Armadillidium*, which reflects the extent to which these isopods are adapted morphologically to land life, the species least well adapted has a compensating behavioural reaction which keeps its members in saturated atmospheres.

Some insects also show a preference for moister conditions. Ants will gather in the more nearly saturated end of a humidity gradient.[209] Wireworm larvae (*Agriotes* spp.), particularly susceptible to abrasion by soil particles of the waterproofing wax layer of their cuticle, show a strong preference for moist air, the nearer to saturated the air, the stronger the preference. They, too, move more in a dry atmosphere.[328] However, tortricid caterpillars (*Choristoneura fumiferana*) move faster in their preferred zone of humidity, but they turn so much more frequently, even so often and so sharply as to prevent any forward movement and confine themselves to that zone.[556]

But other insects, particularly pests of stored products, choose the drier of two atmospheres. Mealworm beetles (*Tenebrio molitor*) are motionless for four-fifths of the time in a drier atmosphere of a gradient between 94% and 100% relative humidity.[216] Adults of *Ptinus tectus* also gather in drier regions.[42] But the preference of migratory locusts (*Locusta migratoria migratorioides*) for drier conditions was unexpected since moist conditions are optimal for development.[219] They move faster and turn more frequently in moist atmospheres.[295] Such a result may stress the artificiality of such laboratory investigations, for under natural conditions some other stimulus probably serves to ensure that the locusts choose the moister areas.

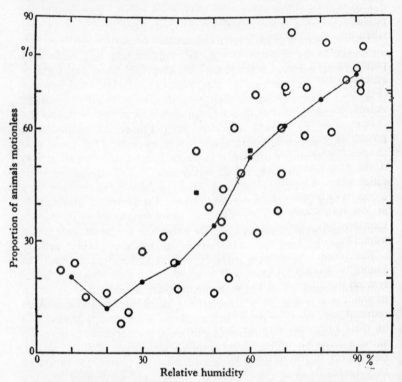

Fig. 141. Inactivity of woodlice, *Porcellio scaber*, and humidity. Each point records the proportion of individuals quite motionless during a set of observations each lasting 30 secs. and 15 mins. apart, at a given constant humidity. The humidity was controlled by H_2SO_4 solutions except in 2 cases (black squares) when P_2O_5 and KOH were used (Gunn[213]).

When locusts pass from the preferred dry side of a choice chamber across the boundary into the moist side, they turn violently (avoidance or phobic reaction). This, in despite of the fact that the boundary is not represented by a sudden change of humidity but a steep gradient. Such a violent reaction is also shown when mealworm beetles,[216] *Drosophila* larvae,[43] or *Agriotes* larvae[328] pass from the moist side to the dry, though they pass in the opposite direction without change in their behaviour. Often the avoiding reaction is quite characteristic, thus *Drosophila* larvae rear up and expose the underside of the thorax on which the receptors are probably arranged (p. 27).

This suggests that directed movements towards moist air may be possible, indeed mealworm beetles do perform antennal movements when approaching higher humidities.[216] Adult flour beetles, *Tribolium castaneum* and *T. confusum*, locate a piece of moistened filter paper, moving almost directly towards it. Removal of one or other antenna causes the beetles to move in a circular path to the paper (Fig. 142) which suggests that a reaction akin to tropotaxis is involved.[462]

It is common for sensitivity to differences in humidity to be greater at higher humidities. Thus, wireworms choose the moister chamber when the difference is as little as 0·5% relative humidity if the atmosphere approaches saturation, though at lower humidities sensitivity is much less.[328] On the other hand, beetles, *Ptinus tectus*, which prefer dry air show the greatest reaction to differences at low humidities, no reaction over the range 75%–90% relative humidity but a reaction once again between 90% and 100% relative humidity.[42]

The physiological state of the animal influences its reaction to humidity. Cockroaches, *Blatta orientalis*, which are hygronegative, reacted positively after desiccation. Since at the same time no food or water was supplied to them, clearly their body water content was reduced and this must be the factor determining the change in sign of their response.[215] After desiccation, the beetles, *Ptinus tectus*, show a reduced response to drier air and indeed at higher humidities collect in the wetter regions. After drinking water, however, they revert to their original preference for the drier conditions.[42] When unfed sheep tick nymphs, which had been kept in a saturated atmosphere, were placed in a choice chamber they tended to prefer the dry side, but, as desiccation proceeded, they gradually congregated at rest on the moist side. This took as long as six days, but showed the effect of the alteration of their physiology consequent on the reduction in their body water.[329] Similarly desiccated ticks, which have been inactivated by a short exposure to saturated air, are roused into activity when put in dry air; they fail to show avoidance of either the higher or lower humidity in choices with differences ranging up to 60% relative humidity. The water content of slugs influences their behaviour (p. 305).

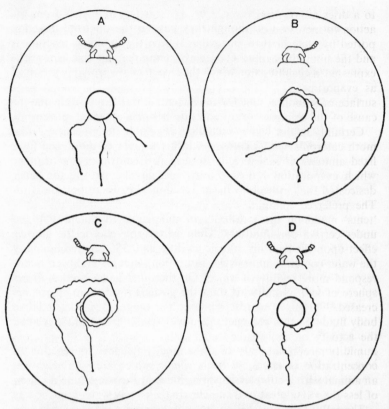

FIG. 142. Paths taken by operated and unoperated adults of the flour
beetle, *Tribolium castaneum*, reacting to a disc of moist filter paper
in a closed Petri dish. Diagrams of heads indicate conditions of the
insect's antennae. A, normal; B, left antenna amputated; C, right
antenna amputated; D, 11th segment of right antenna removed. All
insects were starved and desiccated at 0% R.H. for 5 days prior to
the test (Roth and Willis[462]).

And in the opposite sense humidity affects the reactions of some
animals towards other stimuli, thus, as water loss increases, woodlice (*Oniscus asellus*) become positively instead of negatively phototactic.[544] Should their dark hiding places dry out they leave them
and avoid desiccation.

THE MODE OF ACTION OF THE SENSE ORGANS

The way in which the receptors function remains a matter for argument. The avoidance reaction shown when crossing from a moist

to a drier atmosphere by *Agriotes* larvae suggests that this is a re-action to increased evaporation from the sense organ. This is sup-ported by a closer correlation between the sensitivity of the insects and the humidity expressed as saturation deficiency than when it is expressed as relative humidity. Thus, the receptors may be acting as evaporimeters.[328] Indeed loss of water from the whole body surface of woodlice, which reduces the body fluids, is probably the cause of the changes in response of these animals after desiccation.

Certainly rate of water loss determines the preferences of tortricid moth caterpillars, *C. fumiferana*, in a temperature gradient with a fixed amount of moisture. The larvae choose the temperature at which evaporation rate is lowest, so that as they become more desiccated they move into the lower temperature ranges (Fig. 143). The preferred humidities are close to those found in the silken 'tents' made by these caterpillars and in which they congregate under certain conditions. This would be supposed to be a direct effect upon the nervous system, producing undirected activity when the water content had been decreased. Slugs (*Agriolimax reticulatus*) respond more readily to stimuli when they have been in an atmo-sphere of low humidity, in fact, when their water content has de-creased.[117] This, of course, increases the osmotic pressure of their body fluids. Such a change in the fluid bathing it is known to affect the activity of an isolated pedal ganglion of a slug,[299] and thus humidity reception in the slug may be through the alteration in the concentration of the body fluids which must quickly follow when an animal with a completely permeable skin is placed in atmosphere of less than 100% relative humidity.

The cells of the prostomium of earthworms are perhaps stimulated by loss of water and this initiates avoidance of dry places in these animals. They do not seek moist conditions but rather shun dry ones, for instance, if they are crawling over a dry filter paper which has been moistened in patches, they stop immediately their anterior end comes over a dry patch and bend their bodies from side to side. On contacting moist paper once again they go forward in the new direction.[423]

Humidity affects the spinning activity of first instar larvae of the spruce budworm (*C. fumiferana*), for construction of hibernacula is initiated most quickly in an atmosphere where the evaporation rate is the same as that in which these caterpillars aggregate (Fig. 143). Again, the sixth instar caterpillars make webs and tunnels over the foliage upon which they are feeding. Within these the evap-oration rate is equivalent to that found in the laboratory to be the one preferred by caterpillars of this age. They remain relatively

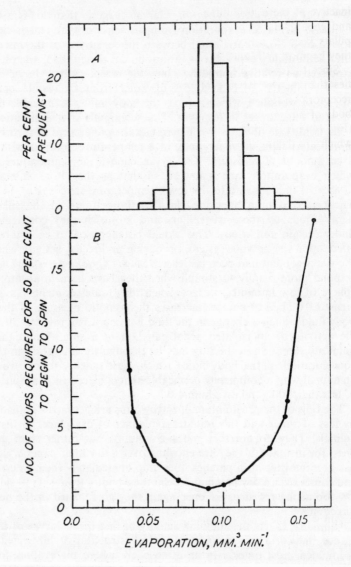

FIG. 143. Time required for first instar larvae of *Choristoneura fumiferana* to begin to spin hibernacula at different constant rates of evaporation and the rate of evaporation at which larvae aggregate in a moisture gradient. A, frequency distribution of larvae in the gradient. B, time required for 50% of a group of larvae to spin at various rates of evaporation (Wellington[555]).

inactive at these humidities but when they have fed heavily, holes and gaps in the web cause the evaporation rate to rise, the caterpillars become active and move on to other feeding places where they begin to spin once again.[557]

Since the detectable difference is larger between two low humidities than between two higher ones, it has been argued that the receptors on the ventral side of the thorax and the hind end of the body of *Drosophila melanogaster* larvae must be *dryness* receptors[43] (Fig. 144). It is supposed that when stimulation is greatest, two stimuli which are distinguished must differ more than when stimulation is

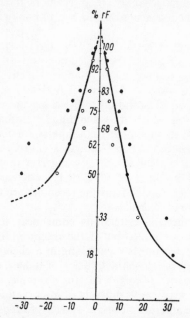

← Decrease in R.H.   Increase in R.H. →

FIG. 144. Results of tests on the sensitivity of larvae of *Drosophila melanogaster* to differences in relative humidity. Ordinate, relative humidity in which the larva starts the experiment. Abscissa, relative humidity in the chosen part; to the left, less humid, to the right, more humid. ●, difference detected, ○, difference not detected (Benz[43]).

less intense. Certainly these larvae, as well as those of *Musca domestica*,[218] react strongly when entering a drier atmosphere. Avoidance of moister atmospheres by mealworm beetles might suggest that their receptors are *moisture* receptors which absorb water hygroscopically, in which case one supposes the hygroscopic material is

L

able to absorb more water for a small increase in humidity in a moist atmosphere than in a dry one as the sensitivity of these receptors is greatest in the more humid atmospheres.

Removal of up to five terminal segments of the antennae of *Ptinus tectus* does not affect the beetle's reaction to humidities, but when only one or more of the basal three segments remain, the reactions to humidity are reversed so that a beetle behaves like a desiccated one. Perhaps there exist two sorts of receptor on the antennae of these beetles.[42] Removal of all but a few peg organs on the antennae of *Tribolium confusum* leaves its ability to differentiate between 0% and 100% R.H. unaffected.[462] These receptors appear to serve for a wet or a dry reaction according to the physiological state of the insect.[463]

The chemoreceptive hairs on the labellum of *Phormia regina* are sensitive to water,[137] as are the coeloconic pegs on the antennae of *Melanoplus m. mexicanus*, a grasshopper which can detect water drops from as far away as 40 cms.[497] A thirsty butterfly (*Vanessa atalanta*) will unroll its proboscis in moist air and attempt to probe dry filter paper on which it is standing.[552] Probably the chemoreceptive hairs on its tarsi or its mouthparts are acting as humidity receptors. On the other hand blowflies (*Lucilia sericata* and *L. cuprina*) deprived of their antennae wander at random in a choice chamber with a gradient of 20% R.H. whereas intact animals remain on the drier side.[107] Thus the receptors are on the antennae, as indeed they are in *Pediculus*.[573]

But none of these investigations come near to explaining the ultimate process of stimulation of the receptor. It is unlikely, that water affects the receptor by partaking in a chemical reaction but it may alter the physical characteristics of a hair or peg, producing movement of it. It might be, for example, that absorption or loss of water may cause differences in curvature of the hairs of the sensilla of the anterior pit on the foreleg of *Ixodes reduvius* which stimulate the nerve endings by stretching them, though such alterations have not been detected with certainty under the microscope.[329]

CHAPTER XIII

WHOLE PATTERNS OF BEHAVIOUR

IF one must classify the different behaviour patterns of invertebrates, the kineses and taxis displayed in response to sources of simple stimuli, such as lamps and so forth in the analytical experiments, must be called reflex rather than instinctive since they involve simple stimuli. Further they often depend upon balanced stimulation as in the tropotactic reactions of animals to two lights. The reaction, is, however, deceptively simple in that movement of an insect, or a worm for that matter, demands a complex set of interactions of motor patterns. Thus reflex used in this sense is far from the least complicated, classical, reflex arc where the stimulus is simple and the reaction usually involves only one set of muscles.

Because the reactions in these patterns of behaviour are complex it is difficult to separate them from instinctive acts. Both types of behaviour have the striking common feature of being innate in all members of a species and are shown by them all under the same circumstances. However, it is usual for the instinctive acts, such as courtship and so forth, to be released by complex—often configurational—stimuli, and also to be themselves a complex set of motor patterns. But complexity is a relative matter. For example, the chemical stimulus which releases grasping in a *Philanthus* which is near a bee appears to be a simple stimulus and the motor patterns involved are on the face of it no more complex than those involved when an *Eristalis* with one eye blackened makes its way to a light. It would seem more logical to suppose that the simplest reflex behaviour and the most complex instinctive act represent two ends of a continuous spectrum, though it must be admitted that those reactions which we have chosen to call reflex usually cease when the stimulus is removed, while an instinctive act only requires to be triggered off and continues without the releaser taking any further part. Again this is not an absolute distinction, for there are many cases of insects moving towards a light which on removal of the light continue in the same direction.

But in addition there is abundant evidence that an ability to learn exists in members of nearly all the invertebrate groups, its role being most plainly evident in the learning of landmarks by foraging honeybees, ants and solitary wasps. But this whole subject has been reviewed critically and in great detail recently,[515] therefore this point will not be developed further here. However, learning is one source of variability in behaviour and it is the demonstration of this variability, not only among individuals but also in one individual at different times, that has shown invertebrate behaviour to be less rigid than was previously supposed.

An essential of efficient behaviour—if by efficient we mean that which leads to the survival of the animal—is that the reactions should be variable. Without such variability many animals would be trapped by the formality of their own behaviour, passing their time, for example, unable to move from a place where a certain momentarily favourable set of conditions holds good. The place which serves as a refuge from predators or where water loss is at a minimum may not be the best place for finding food or mating. At some time or other animals must be released from the strictures of their automatic-response.

VARIABILITY IN REACTION

Though such variability is common not all of it can be attributed to learning. We are inclined to take variability as a mark of intelligent behaviour, as indeed it is, but it can arise from other sources. For like each individual internal process in the body, the expression of nerve impulses is under the influence of the other processes which make up the total physiological state of an animal. Changes in this physiological state bring with them changes in the pattern of the nervous conduction and, therefore, in the response to a stimulus. The past history of an animal to a large extent determines the reaction at the present because it also determines the present physiology of its body. The changes occur in the nervous system and the body as a result of a number of factors which we can classify conveniently under three headings: adaptation to a constant stimulus; the effect of the environment, that is temperature, intensity of illumination and so forth; and the effect of bodily changes—developmental age and whether the animal is well fed or starving are examples of this last group. In addition to these factors whose effect varies, there may be stable differences between different parts of the nervous system so that when these parts are used in different sequences the resultant response may be varied. We shall consider the sources of variation in behaviour under these headings.

Adaptation

Adaptation occurs when the intensity of the response to a stimulus decreases under continued stimulation at the same intensity. This diminution of response can arise from several causes. The receptor itself may become insensitive or the muscles producing the action be unable to respond to further stimulation through fatigue. In this case any change in the intensity of the stimulation would still fail to produce a reaction. But in fact the reduction may occur independently of fatigue. The electrical responses in the optic nerve of *Limulus*, for example, decrease under continued stimulation of the eye.[548] This might appear to be evidence of fatigue in the receptor, but if the intensity is suddenly increased the responses also increase to decline once again under continued stimulation at the new level. The eye has retained its ability to respond. Such adaptation of a sense organ is sensory adaptation and may occur, one suspects, in any receptor organ of invertebrates, touch receptors adapting particularly quickly.

On the other hand negative adaptation may occur centrally when the animal learns not to react. Though this is termed negative adaptation to distinguish it from sensory adaptation in most cases there is no clear proof that sensory adaptation has not also occurred. However, where the adaptation effect is long lived lasting over a period of days, for example, it is difficult to believe that sensory adaptation is involved. This type of adaptation seems to be a central process, which can from an observational point of view, at least, be considered as a form of learning (habituation). This does not necessarily imply that the mechanisms of this and other types of learning are identical.

Alarm reaction may occur in response to stimuli which are not in fact harmful but merely strange (supernormal). When the harmless stimuli are repeated a number of times consecutively the animal will gradually cease to show its alarm behaviour. Its reaction becomes progressively less violent until finally it does not occur at all. A classic example which demonstrates this is the experiment in which a snail (*Helix albolabris*) was placed on a wooden platform which could be jerked back and forth.[276] As soon as a snail was crawling across the platform, the board was jerked at regular intervals. Generally at the first jerk the snail would withdraw its tentacles even withdrawing totally into its shell for fourteen seconds in one case. At subsequent jerks the reaction diminished until a long series of, say, fifty to sixty produced no response. Now a period was allowed in which the animal was not stimulated; at first the full reaction would return at the first new jerk after a rest of about half a minute. But this time for recovery of the original reaction became longer as the experiment was continued. If in the middle of one of these rest periods a steel ball was dropped on the platform and the jerks recommenced immediately afterwards, the snail reacted maximally although the recovery period was incomplete. This shows that the recovery period was not a period of rest from fatigue, for the muscles and nerves effecting the reaction were still capable of working to the full. Thus the process must have been a central change whose action was eliminated by a period of rest or overcome by a new stronger stimulus.

This is a method by which useless movement can be eliminated, that is, movement unwarranted by the results of the stimulus. An animal could not carry out its life activities efficiently if it reacted to every strange stimulus as if it were harmful, thus spending its time performing alarm behaviour. This negative adaptation or habituation has been defined as 'an instance of the living system's power of establishing a conservative equilibrium to change of external conditions'. In more modern parlance it is analogous to negative feedback controlling the motor output of the nervous system.

The process is akin to acclimatization, though here a behavioural response is not necessarily involved but a temporary physiological change. Protozoa become acclimatized to living under conditions of acidity, or increased temperature, because their shock reactions tending to drive them out of acid or warm areas are gradually eliminated. This is a behavioural change. On the other hand insects may die when they are placed in temperatures of 40° C or more, yet if they are gradually warmed to these temperatures with periods at intermediate stages, they may survive. Here a behavioural change is not obvious but a physiological change is occurring with no outward sign apart from the insect's ability to survive. No doubt, the disappearance of overt behavioural responses is a sign of physiological change.

The effect of environmental changes

The essential difference between the examples in this group and those described as adaptation is that unlike the process of adaptation when a response wanes under constant stimulation, here, as a result of the environmental conditions, the response when first evoked differs markedly and may often be different in sign from those obtaining under other environmental conditions.

Many animals which are photopositive in weak light become photonegative in strong light. In both cases the response is to light but the level of its intensity determines whether the animal shall move towards or away from the source. This may on occasion be a protective change since continuous strong light is often liable to cause damage to the animal as a whole or to its light receptors in particular. Again the responses may depend upon the recent activities of the animal, the earthworm, *Lumbricus terrestris*, for example, reacts positively to weak light after it has been kept in darkness, but if it is taken from the dark and strongly illuminated it crawls away from the light.[262] If a worm which has been kept in dim light is suddenly lit intensely the reaction is not so clear, and there may be no change at all.

A change in light intensity may bring with it a change in the direction of the animals reactions to other stimuli, such as gravity. Ciliates (*Paramecium* sp.), swim downwards to the bottom of a test tube when suitably illuminated. Since it does not matter from which direction the light is coming they must be reacting geopositively. In darkness, however, they swim upwards, reversing their reaction to gravity.[166] Though this is a change in their reaction under natural conditions it has the effect of altering the lighting conditions to which they are submitted for they will move downwards from the well illuminated upper layers of a pond into the lower less well lit parts. Though these movements may have the appearance of direct reactions to light intensity, analysis shows that they are only secondarily coupled with the lighting conditions. Changes in the temperature of the surroundings may also alter the responses of animals to light. Various moth and sawfly larvae (e.g. *Malacosoma disstria*, *Choristoneura fumiferana* and *Neodiprion banksianae*) remain in the diffusely illuminated part of a light–dark chamber, but if they are warmed they move into the dark part when a critical temperature is passed (*Malacosoma* at 35·5° C, *Choristoneura* at 37·9° C and *Neodiprion* at 36·5° C). Similarly though the larvae crawl towards a point source of light, they react negatively to it after these temperatures have been reached. It has been found that the body, as well as the head, must be warmed to produce these changes.[560]

The chemical nature of the surroundings influences the animal's responses to other stimuli, not necessarily chemical ones. Thus, *Daphnia* in a lighted tank will either be indifferent in their response to light or show variable responses fluctuating between approach to the light source and retreat from it. But as soon as water containing carbon dioxide is added to the tank, the animals all show a striking positive response moving in a band towards the light. Another crustacean, *Hyalella*, which is usually negatively phototactic will become positive when certain chemicals are added to the water in which it is living. Small increases in the concentration of the chemicals permit adaptation to take place but even at the point at which the concentration becomes lethal the response changes to positive momentarily before the animal dies. Chemicals from the host may alter the reactions of parasites, without the resulting behaviour being directed by the chemical. The mites (*Unionicola* sp.) found in various species of the fresh-water mussel, *Anodonta*, are positively phototactic when tested in the laboratory but if material from the host species, particularly mucus from the gills, is added to the water they become negatively phototactic.[564]

Current responses of some animals are only evoked if the current bears with it chemicals which stimulate the animal, thus *Nassarius reticulatus* is indifferent to currents unless the water contains albumin, say, when it becomes positively rheotactic.[240] The current response adds a directional quality to the diffuse non-directional chemical stimulus.

Evidence that it is the internal physiological state of some animals which determines whether they are attracted or repelled by water is given by experiments on cockroaches, *Blatta orientalis*. These insects are hygronegative when fully fed and kept in moist air. However, kept in dry air and prevented from drinking or eating, they become attracted to water.[215] Obviously the dry air is not acting directly upon the nervous system to produce its effect, but it may well be acting through desiccation of the body which occurs when the insects cannot feed and yet lose water to their surroundings. It may or may not be that heat, light or chemicals have a direct effect on the nervous system producing a change in response, it could be so in protozoa where because of the small size of the body these might influence the irritable part of the cell directly, but in metazoa the nervous system is usually screened from the stimuli of the environment except where its receptors 'look out' on the surroundings. With these animals the effect of the environment is caused secondarily through a change in the physiological conditions in which the nervous system exists.

The effect of bodily changes

But these changes in physiology may also be produced by alterations which take place relatively independently of the environment, such as, growth, aging, starvation and satiation, or sexual maturity. The speed of growth is often correlated with the temperature of the surroundings of the young animal and so is not completely independent of the environment. Again hunger is satisfied by food obtained from around the animal. But a distinction can be drawn between the factors we have dealt with in the last section when variation arises from what may be the direct effect of the environmental conditions on the nervous system and the changes in physiology produced by the conditions which are at least initiated within the animal.

The behaviour of animals usually alters during their development; thus, at the beginning of the third, fourth and fifth instars of the hawk moth, *Smerinthus ocellatus*, the caterpillars are consistently more photopositive than photonegative, but towards the end of the instar they become increasingly photonegative.[465] Behaviour differences are most obvious when the larval form and habitat differ from that of the adult, and most strikingly when there may be several different stages in the larval life differing from each other, for example, the stages in the life histories of some parasitic copepods and platyhelminthes, or of almost all marine invertebrates. Very often no comparison at all has been made between the behaviour in these stages of parasitic life but there is some information about the reactions of insects of various stages in their life histories. An obvious example is that of the blowfly. The larva is negatively phototactic while the adult is positively phototactic.

But even during larval life the reactions may change, the older stages of the caterpillar of *Choristoneura fumiferana* become photonegative, though during the earlier stages the caterpillars crawl towards a source of light. This change is not a sudden one, the photonegative response is strongest in the last instars.[560]

A reaction which leads a hungry animal to its food may be reversed when the animal is satiated. A hungry sheep tick crawls to the tip of a grass blade and 'quests' when its host comes near (p. 192).[329] But when it has had a blood meal it descends into the grass. Similarly a leech no longer moves towards shadows above it when it is fully fed.[248] The tick which moved down the blade is protected in its new position for at the tip of the grass it was exposed to water loss which in the humid atmosphere at the grass base is reduced. Since the time between meals is long it is better passed where dehydration is less likely to occur. Without this change in behaviour, a hungry tick would be less likely to encounter its host.

Again the place most suitable for the eggs and early stages of an animal may not be the same as that in which the adult normally lives. To find the requisite place the normal behaviour has to be altered. Thus planarian worms about to lay eggs react positively to a current moving upstream to where the water temperature is lower and egg development is most successful. After the eggs are laid, the worms' reaction returns to a negative rheotaxis so that they move downstream again[38].

A greater variety of different connections can be made in a complex nervous system than in a simple one. The range of variability

L*

of their responses in many of the lower animals is limited therefore by the very structure of their nervous systems. However, all parts of such a simple system may not have the same physiological properties though there may be no anatomical distinction. This introduces a factor which aids in variability for by these differences parts of an apparently homogenous system become differentiated. The relative complexity of the responses of a sea anemone compared with the repertory of behaviour of, say, *Hydra*, demonstrate this, for both animals have what appear to be morphologically the same sort of nervous system. In fact, close study of the nervous system of *Calliactis parasitica* has shown that impulses are carried at speeds in different parts of the nerve net,[409] for there the synapses are fewer as the cells are larger.

THE INTERPLAY OF REACTIONS TO STIMULI FROM VARIOUS SOURCES

Laboratory investigations are essentially analytical. They concern themselves with the parts of the whole so that by elegant measurement and ingenious experimentation they reveal something of the nature of the units and hence of the whole. The essence of the controlled experiment is the elimination of all factors other than the one under investigation. The observations made under these artificial conditions can go far towards explaining the behaviour of an animal in nature when all manner of stimuli may be impinging upon it though it is rare, if not impossible, for an animal under natural conditions to comport itself with reference to one kind of stimulus alone, ignoring all others. Thus the natural behaviour unlike that under some experimental conditions is the result of the interplay of reactions to many stimuli, both physical and chemical.

Relatively few whole patterns of invertebrate behaviour have been analysed in detail, but those that have show clearly how complex is the set of stimuli to which the animal pays attention.

A simple example of such interplay of factors is given by the behaviour of *Lepidochitona cinera*.[159] This mollusc lives amongst stones in the upper part of the tidal zone. When the stones are exposed by the retreating tide, the chitons are found on the undersides, the upper surfaces being dried by the sun and wind. But when the stones are covered the chitons move round to the upper surfaces. They cannot withstand desiccation, thus after twenty-four hours in a dry chamber all of a batch of fourteen chitons were dead. In their position on the underside of stones they have the benefit of the position of maximum humidity and coupled with this, the advantage of a position where the intensity of light is low. The movements of a chiton are in fact governed by its responses to gravity and to light. Chitons on a vertical glass plate immersed in water move in all directions, but when the moistened sheet stands in air they all move downwards reacting positively to gravity (Fig. 145). They move faster in strong light than in darkness, thus in sunlight they covered about 8·17 cms. in ten minutes, in artificial light about 5·10 cms. and in the dark 1·38 cms. in the same space of time. They moved faster on moist surfaces that were exposed than

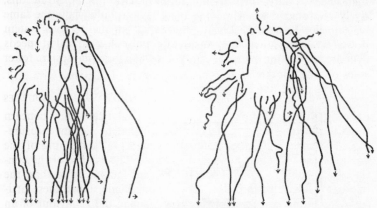

FIG. 145. Movement of chitons placed on a moistened glass sheet held vertically in air. A, on plain glass, B, on roughened glass. The results indicate that the downwards movements are not due to slipping on the smooth surface, but are directed (Evans[159]).

on the same surfaces when they were immersed in sea water. They ceased to move at all on a dry surface. They did not appear to exhibit any response to dorsal contact.

The migrations of the chitons on the stones are the result of these simple patterns of behaviour. When the stones are exposed, the animals become positively geotactic and move downwards, their progress being hastened by the accelerating effect of the sunlight. Once beneath the stone their rate of movement decreases and they come to rest. When the tide rises once again the chitons become negatively geotactic when they are covered by the water. They move upwards around the stone. When the stones are beneath the surface the light intensities at various points on the stones differ less than when they are exposed so that the animals' speeds are fairly constant wherever they are, therefore they do not tend to congregate by a simple orthokinetic response as they do when the stones are exposed. Thus, unfettered from their previous responses, they are now able to feed and to travel over the stone in all directions.

In rather a similar manner the position of winkles, *Littorina neritoides*, on the shore might be explained in terms of the animals' simple reactions to light and gravity.[168] They are found on rock-faces, etc., just above the high water mark in crevices. In the laboratory they can be shown to be negatively geotactic, for in a horizontal circular dish rotated about its centre they move against the centrifugal force towards the axis of rotation. Their reaction to light depends upon their orientation to gravity, thus they are negatively phototactic when moving on a horizontal surface the right way up but become positively phototactic when they hang upside down. This is shown very neatly by their movements within a cylinder, or by the path they follow in glass vessels laid on their sides on one another (Fig. 146). This change of response with position takes place, however, only when the winkles are submerged.

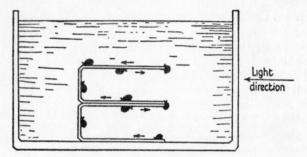

Light direction

FIG. 146. Behaviour of *Littorina neritoides*, see text (Fraenkel[168]).

With these reactions in mind it is possible to suggest reasons for the movement of a winkle from the bottom below the sea, through the water surface to its normal exposed position on the rock face. First it would crawl along the bottom towards the rock which is darker and where, therefore, the light intensity is lower than in the direction of the open sea. This would be a negatively phototactic response. On reaching the rock face, being negatively geotactic it will crawl up it. On its way it may encounter a crevice which it enters crawling along the floor away from the light. But ultimately as it goes deeper into the crevice it will turn over and crawl in an upside down position along the upper wall of the crack. Since we are supposing that the winkle is still immersed, we can suppose that its phototactic response now changes to positive and it crawls out of the crevice. This is repeated as it crawls higher up the rock until finally it emerges from the water onto the rock surface when it continues its march upwards under the influence of negative geotaxis until it reaches another crevice. It enters this but since it is no longer submerged its phototactic response does not now alter with its position and so it crawls into the crevice and remains there. The alteration of phototactic response when the winkle is under the water has the advantage that without this variability it might be trapped in any crevice into which it entered. On this theoretical plan it is not clear how the winkle feeds for it would appear to be trapped in the crevice. Possibly when the winkle is in such a place and out of the water it may feed there or it may possibly emerge at night to feed on the moist surface of the neighbouring rock.

The diurnal movements of planktonic animals are in all probability the result of a complex of adjustments to various stimuli, some of which like light intensity increase and decrease during the day–night cycle and others like pressure which remain constant throughout. It has already been stated that planktonic animals are sensitive to pressure changes and that these changes produce appropriate activity or quiescence as the case may be (p. 215). However, since the optimum level for many planktonic larvae, for example, apparently changes during the day, if pressure is to be the controlling stimulus, either there is a daily cycle of different preferences innate in the animal, or the effect of another changing stimulus is to alter the animal's pressure preferendum. There seems little doubt that light plays a major, but not exclusive, role in determining the distribution of planktonic animals. An analysis has been carried out on *Daphnia magna* which though not a marine planktonic animal is sufficiently closely related to many marine cladocerans for the results to be suggestive at least.[226] These animals do perform daily migrations and will continue to do so in a tank if the changing light conditions alone are simulated. There appear to be three reactions to light at work, they show, firstly, a dorsal light response, secondly, a phototactic response, either negative or positive, by tilting the body so that they move down or up respectively, and thirdly, a photokinetic response by increased activity in dim light which produces a rise ('dawn rise') which is stopped by inhibition of antennal movement at higher light intensities. The effects of these responses can be clearly demonstrated when eyeless *Daphnia* are lit from below by a light whose intensity increases, remains constant for a time and then wanes. At first in dim light, the animals move down under the influence of the dorsal light response and negative photokinesis until, as the light increases and they reach the bottom, their swimming movements cease and they remain more or less motionless. If they had been lit from above, it is at this point that they would have sunk

320   THE BEHAVIOUR OF INVERTEBRATES

downward passively only to recommence activity as the intensity
of the light fell as they sank downwards. On moving upwards again
they are inhibited once again. After each alteration they are adapted
to a higher light intensity but a point probably comes when the
light adaptation balances the dark adaptation. In the reversed
position as the light wanes activity recommences but the animals
rise in the tank (Fig. 147).[226] Thus some sort of explanation of planktonic movements could be derived, though, doubtless, light is not
the only stimulus involved.

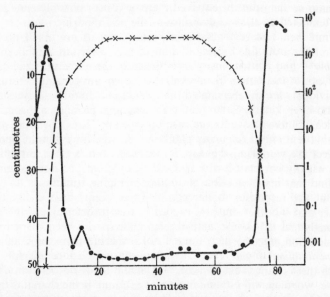

FIG. 147. Effect of fluctuating illumination from below on a population
of 60 eyeless *Daphnia magna*. Dashed line indicates the intensity of
illumination in lux at the bottom of the tank; the ordinate on the
right refers to this dashed line (Harris and Mason[226]).

The advantages which some animals obtain, if indeed they obtain
any, from living in the places they are found are far from clear. It
is generally concluded and surely correctly, that where animals
aggregate naturally they also find their optimal conditions of life,
though what these conditions may be are not always known. Studies
of the various mosquitoes found in tropical forests, for example,
have shown that different species may occur at the same place but
that each has its own particular height which it favours for flight.[217]
The selection of this flight level seems to be the result of a variety

of factors, among them the different intensities of light near to and far from the canopy, and the differing humidities at various heights above the forest floor.

There is no doubt that humidity is a potent factor in determining the habitat of an animal. This is particularly so among the invertebrates for few of them, outside the insects, have any system of conserving water developed to any extent. Many of the woodlice are capable of imbibing water through their mouths or their anuses.[500] In general the terrestrial isopods seek moist places and remain in them but the behaviour which ties them to moisture must be tempered to allow distribution of the individuals over areas and permit them to feed.[155] The behavioural mechanisms utilized in the search for a suitable habitat are quite simple. Individuals of *Porcellio scaber*[213] and *Oniscus murarius*[284] certainly move more quickly in a dry atmosphere than in a wet one, and a greater proportion of individuals are on the move in the dry areas than in the wet. This ortho-hygrokinesis is supported in *Porcellio* by a klinokinesis by which it increases the amount of turning in the dry atmosphere. Both these effects, on speed and on rate of turning, will tend to collect the woodlice in moist surroundings. Since moist conditions are usually correlated with low light intensity, it is not surprising to find that many woodlice are normally photonegative.

But the responses to light and humidity are modified by each other and by other conditions. *Porcellio*, for example, shows a less strongly marked photonegative reaction after it has been in dry air.[213] Desiccation reverses the reaction to light on *Oniscus asellus*[544] and *Armadillidium vulgare* (= *A.cinereum*)[238] from negative to positive. Both these changes could mean that should the dark places in which these woodlice find themselves dry up, the behavioural trap is opened and they are free to wander away in search of other places which are still moist.

Temperature, also, has its influence. The change to a photopositive response may be brought about in *A. vulgare* by an increase in temperature.[238] The increase in activity at 9 a.m., which is followed by a decline after mid-day, has been explained as due to more positive phototactic behaviour with the increase in air temperature in the morning, and a decrease with the decreasing temperatures after mid-day.[99, 100] Reaction to temperature itself may also be influenced by the humidity conditions for individuals of *Hemilepistus reaumurii*, a North African species, dig holes in which they hide when the temperature reaches 35° C if the soil in which they dig is dry. But the temperature at which they dig is raised if the soil is wet and they may not begin to excavate until the air temperature reaches 45° C, though when they have been operated on so that the water loss from their bodies is increased they dig at a lower temperature even if the earth is moist.[539]

Some woodlice (*Oniscus asellus*) can be found widely distributed during the night though during the day they hide beneath stones and so forth.[100] It is difficult to explain this reversal of their tendency to hide, though it is obvious that this behaviour allows them to seek food and new hiding places. It has been suggested that an explanation may be found in a composite scheme of behavioural patterns each of which is known to occur in isolation in various woodlouse species. There appears to be a reduction in the strength of the positive hygrokinesis in the dark so that animals no longer tend to aggregate strongly in moist places. This allows them to wander in drier places. Their tendency to be photonegative also increases, so that as soon as first light appears animals caught outside hiding places flee from the light into dark places. Thus animals which are in well lighted places, which will also probably be dry, will save themselves from desiccation by going into the dark and usually damp places. On occasion their daytime shelters may dry up, in which event their photonegative response reverses so that they are attracted by light and leave their retreats. As soon as they enter a moist place, the damp air has the effect of altering their photoresponse once again, so that they remain there.[100]

FOOD SELECTION

Some invertebrates have very restricted food preferences and are highly selective in their choice of what they eat. Though food is recognized as such by odour mainly (p. 272), in the process of food finding and capture other stimuli are also involved.

An excellent example of the complexity of hunting manoeuvres is given by the result of an analysis of the hunting behaviour of the bee-killer wasp, *Philanthus triangulum*, whose orientation capabilities have already been discussed (p. 166). This wasp recognizes its prey at some distance, grasps it in flight and stings it, carrying the dead body of the bee back to the hole it has dug as a place in which to lay an egg and store food for the larva which will emerge. There are three behavioural stages involved.[520] First the prey is recognized by sight from a distance. This is not completely specific for the wasp will be attracted by any insect like a hover fly, which has the appearance of a bee. It flies towards it but will only proceed with the second stage, grasping the prey, if the chemical stimuli arising from the other insect are satisfactory. These it perceives as it flies close to the supposed prey. Thus though it will not normally grasp a hover fly though attracted to it at first, if the fly has been shaken up in a tube with honeybees and is well coated with bee odour, the wasp will grasp it. Odours which are attractive in this phase have no effect in the first stage. A wasp which is endeavouring to locate prey is not therefore attracted by a tube in which bees have been kept. The final stage is that of stinging the prey and is only initiated if the prey feels like a bee, thus the hover fly covered with bee odour is grasped but not stung for the feel of the captive is wrong.

We have already mentioned that bees are attracted by certain colours and that flowers of these colours are more attractive if they are moving in the wind so that the bee's eyes are stimulated to a maximum. But bees will not alight on artificial flowers which satisfy all these conditions unless they have a flower scent or contain honey which the bee can smell. In other words, final acceptance of the flower only comes about if it is scented. Indeed the forager which has returned to the hive and is dancing to inform other foragers of the place of its success has got flower scent all over its body which the outgoing bees sense and this aids them to distinguish the actual flowers which the forager had visited in the general area which is indicated by the other features of the dance. Foragers may also mark food sources with their own body scent which further aids the other foragers in identifying the food source.[454]

SELECTION OF MATES

Just as a particular food preference restricts choice, and involves discriminatory behaviour, so also mating which involves a choice of a sexual partner restricted to the same species and the opposite sex requires accurate recognition of that possible partner. Physical and chemical characteristics of the partner may be unique and the choice is made after the necessary mixture of characteristics has been perceived.

The male grayling recognizes the female by her flight and flies up to join her (p. 134). The two butterflies alight and the male moves round to face the female.[523] Here he 'bows' bringing his wings forward over his head. He does this once or twice and then does a deeper 'bow' so that he grasps the female's antennae between his wings. From this position he draws his wings back so that they rub over the surface of the female's antennae and since the position of the antennae coincides with the position of the male's scent scales on his forewings, the female is stimulated chemically as well as visually and tactually. At this stage chemical stimulation is of paramount importance. If the female is sufficiently stimulated chemically she allows the male to move round and mate with her.

In a similar manner the final judgement of the recognition of some female Salticid spiders by males, and of males by females, also depends upon odour. For, though the appearance of a dried spider may evoke courtship display in the other partner, the culminating copulation never occurs[110] (p. 268).

The attraction of male insects to flowers emitting scents like those of the female has already been mentioned (p. 175). Pollination does not occur in the orchids, *Ophrys* spp., unless the male hymen-opteran makes copulatory movements after settling on the labellum of the flower. Such movements are not released unless the hairs on this lower lip are of the right length, pliability, and density, copying the pilosity on the abdomen of the particular female. In various species of *Ophrys* not only the scent but also the hairs on the labellum are appropriate for the imitation of the female of the particular species of insect.[324] This is an excellent case of the parasitism by a plant on the behaviour of an insect.[20]

ORIENTATION AS THE RESULT OF THE REACTION TO VARIOUS STIMULI

The process of following a route, whether by a man or an insect, consists of picking out a series of landmarks which have in the past led the animal home successfully or which it perceived as it journeyed out. A flying animal can usually fly directly to its goal and its route is rarely interrupted by obstructions unless it is in a mountainous or a hilly district, and provided that it is flying at a fair height. A small animal moving along the ground, however, is constantly meeting obstacles which necessitate detours. Further-more frequently various sources of stimuli are temporarily masked, as, for example, when the sky and the sun's position is cut off from the vision of an ant making its way among grass blades. It is not surprising to find that social insects returning to their nests along the ground employ both physical and chemical guide posts as a double insurance that the temporary disappearance of one shall not upset their accurate orientation.

Among the various species of ant, one method of navigation, such as the use of polarized light or a scent trail, may be dominant in each species. This method may be the only one which appears under laboratory conditions. Yet there are in many of the experiments indications that other methods are also possible. For example, though it is clear that ants of the species, *Lasius niger*, find their way mainly by vision, a disturbance of the background of familiar scents produces a disturbance in their orientation.[94] Thus when an ant was retrieving larvae from the middle of an arena, cleaning the ground over which it ran did not prevent it ultimately finding its way out of the arena but increased the distance it wandered before doing so. Yet in this case there was no demonstrable scent trail as such; the disturbance seems to have been due merely to the removal of the general odour of the surroundings to which the ant was accustomed. The recently emerged workers of *Formica rufa* show an unmodified positive phototaxis on leaving the nest and a negative one on returning. Also they show a rigid light compass orientation. However, as they become more experienced in foraging, this behaviour becomes modified and they learn to guide themselves by polarized light from the sky or by landmarks; but in the absence of landmarks, beneath a completely clouded sky, they may revert to a light compass reaction towards the sun's position provided that there is a greater intensity of light in that part of the sky.[284a]

Again under different experimental conditions the same species may show quite different capabilities. Foraging ants of *Myrmica ruginodis* appear to be dependent under natural conditions, and in certain laboratory arrangements, on guiding themselves by polarized light,[541] yet under other conditions, in different sorts of arena, they appeared to be using a scent trail which could be distinguished by blinded ants.[347] Undoubtedly in nature these different sources of stimuli are utilized at the appropriate times. More recently it has been shown that there is transposition of the orientation in terms of one source of directional stimulation to a similar orientation in relation to directional stimuli of a different nature. *Myrmica rubra* workers running at an angle to a beam of light will take up a similar angle to gravity if the light is extinguished and the board upon which they are running is turned to the vertical,[542] though the angle may be to the left or right of the vertical and heading up or down, so that the ant does not maintain the exact relationship between direction of stimulation and its course. Oddly enough the beetle, *Geotrupes stercorosus* (= *G. sylvaticus*), seems to be able to transpose stimuli more accurately, for when it is running on the vertical board the relationship between the direction of gravity and the course is almost exactly the same as that between the light beam and the course[48] (Fig. 148). This is strange, for this highly developed ability appears to play no part in the normal behaviour of the beetle. Another striking example of this change of coding, as it were, is seen in the dance of the honeybee, where the direction of the sun to which it has been orientating on its return journey is symbolized by gravity when a worker dances on the vertical face of a comb.[196]

Again a locust flying against the wind maintains its direction by flying in such a way that the images of objects on the ground are travelling at a preferred speed from the front to the back of its retina

(p. 139). But the higher it flies the slower the images will move and the less easily distinguished are small objects.[298] Another method of maintaining an upwind direction must then enter into play. Undoubtedly the pressure sensibility of a locust (p. 254) and also possibly some method of orientating with respect to the sun must play their part in holding the locust on its course.

These few examples show that the whole pattern of a particular activity, even in these so-called simple animals, results from the

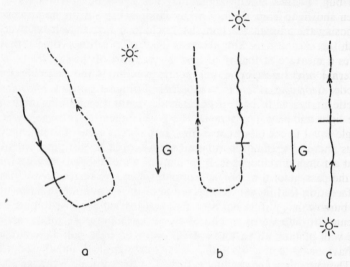

FIG. 148. Orientation of *Geotrupes silvaticus* to light and gravity. In each case the beetle was moving on a horizontal board in light at first but at the point marked by a line across the path, the board was tipped to the vertical and the light switched out. The beetle maintained the angle to the source of stimulation, now the direction of gravity, which it had held previously to the light. (Birukow[48]).

complex interplay of a number of reactions to different stimuli, each of which may sometimes be separately analysed and investigated under controlled conditions in the laboratory.

It will be freely confessed, however, that in addition to these patterns in which we have some idea of the stimuli which initiate the behaviour, there is much behaviour which begins apparently spontaneously. Often it is rhythmic, occurring at definite periods, echoing natural periodicities such as the day–night sequence or tidal cycles, the rhythm continuing under uniform conditions.[222a] Often these appear to be controlled by a temperature-independent internal 'clock',[65, 434] which is sometimes set right by a short exposure to the external conditions. The nymphs of the mayfly, *Ecdyonurus torrentis*, require to experience only one day–night sequence,[221] that is twenty-four hours exposure, for their rhythm to remain correctly in phase. In general the rhythm may be of endogenous origin though with external control of the phase.[222] Similar internal time markers are essential if an animal is navigating by the sun and compensates for the sun's movement, thus *Talitrus saltator*,[417] *Apis mellifera*,[199] the bug, *Velia currens*[49] and the spider *Arctosa perita*[412] have all been shown to have timing mechanisms, which can be affected by exposing the animals to changes of light and darkness out of phase with the natural one. The height of the sun at any one time of day gives a measure of that time, and a primitive sort of clock (but an external one) based upon this indicator seems to be found in the beetle, *Geotrupes silvaticus*. The angle which the course run by this beetle makes with a lamp depends upon the angular elevation of the light and may be to right or left of the original course by an angle equal to the elevation of the lamp. Time of day has no effect; thus there is apparently no internal clock, but one can suppose that a rough sun clock, based upon the height of the sun as a measure of the passage of time, might be used. Other cyclic activity, like the defaecation-feeding movements of the worm, *Arenicola marina*, in its burrow may not have a periodicity connected with environmental events. In the case of the worm there seems to be a pacemaker in the wall of the fore-part of the gut which sets off and controls the behaviour.[582]

The systems which in invertebrates lie between the receptor and effector are deceptively simple when compared with those of vertebrates. Interest has centred on the function of the central nervous system of vertebrates in initiating and modifying reactions while the study of invertebrate behaviour has largely been one of sensory abilities. Work on cephalopods and insects has shown that the history of the nerve impulse, from the time that it leaves the receptor to the time when motor impulses emerge from the central nervous system, may be more complex than had been suspected. The demonstration of cyclic activity, apparently internally controlled, adds another central modifying influence on behaviour. Though much remains to be found out about the function of invertebrate sense organs, attention has now begun to shift to the central processes at work in invertebrate behaviour.

BIBLIOGRAPHY

1 ALEXANDROWICZ, J. S., 1955. *J. mar. biol. Ass. U.K.*, **34**, 47–53.
Innervation of the heart of *Praunus flexuosus*.

2 ALEXANDROWICZ, J. S. and WHITEAR, M., 1957. *J. mar. biol. Ass. U.K.*, **36**, 603–628.
Receptor elements in the coxal region of Decapod Crustacea.

3 ALLEE, W. C., 1951. *Co-operation among animals*. London: Pitman.

4 ALLEE, W. C., EMERSON, A. E., PARK, O., PARK, T., and SCHMIDT, K. P., 1949.
Principles of animal ecology. Philadelphia: W. B. Saunders.

5 ALVERDES, F., 1926. *Z. vergl. Physiol.*, **4**, 699–765.
Stato-, Photo- und Tangoreaktionen bei zwei Garneelenarten.

6 ALVERDES, F., 1928. *Z. wiss. Zool.*, **132**, 135–170.
Lichtsinn, Gleichgewichtsinn, Tastsinn und ihre Interferenzen bei Garneelen.

7 ALVERDES, F., 1930. *Z. wiss. Zool.*, **137**, 403–475.
Tierpsychologische Analyse der intracentralen Vorgange welche bei decapoden Krebsen die locomotorischen Reaktionen auf Helligkeit und Dunkelheit bestimmen.

8 AMELN, P., 1930. *Zool. Jb., Abt. allg. Zool. Physiol. Tier.*, **47**, 685–722.
Der Lichtsinn von *Nereis diversicolor*.

9 ANDERSON, A. L., 1932. *J. exp. Zool.*, **63**, 235–259.
The sensitivity of the legs of common butterflies to sugars.

10 ARNOLD, D. C., 1957. *J. mar. biol. Ass. U.K.*, **36**, 121–128.
The response of the limpet, *Patella vulgata*, to waters of different salinities.

11 AUTRUM, H., no date, in SCHÖNE, H.[487]

12 AUTRUM, H., 1940. *Z. vergl. Physiol.*, **28**, 326–352.
Uber Lautäusserungen und Schallwahrenehmung bei Arthropoden. II. Das Richtungshören von *Locusta* und Versuch einer Hörtheorie für Tympanalorgane von Locustidentyp.

13 AUTRUM, H., 1941. *Z. vergl. Physiol.*, **28**, 580–637.
Uber Gehör und Erschütterungssinn bei Locustiden.

14 AUTRUM, H., 1949. *Experientia*, **5**, 271–277.
Neue Versuche zum optischen Auflösungsvermogen fliegender Insekten.

15 AUTRUM, H., 1955. *Ann. Épiphyt. (C)*, 338–355.
Analyse physiologique de la réception des sons chez les Orthoptères.

16 AUTRUM, H., and SCHNEIDER, W., 1948. *Z. vergl. Physiol.*, **31**, 77–88.
Vergleichende Untersuchungen über den Erschutterungsinn der Insekten.

17 AUTRUM, H., and STUMPF, H. 1950. *Z. Naturf.* **5**, 116–122.
Das Bienenaugen als Analysator für polarisiertes Licht.

18 BAER, J., 1951. *Ecology of animal parasites.* Urbana: University of Illinois.

19 BAERENDS, G. P., 1941. *Tijdschr. Ent.*, **84**, 71–275.
Fortpflanzungsverhalten und Orientierung der Grabwespe, *Ammophila campestris*.

20 BAERENDS, G. P., 1950. *Symp. Soc. exp. Biol.*, **4**, 337–360.
Specialization in organs and movements with a releasing function.

21 BAINBRIDGE, R., and WATERMAN, T. H., 1957. *J. exp. Biol.*, **34**, 342–364.
Polarized light and the orientation of two marine crustacea.

21a BAINBRIDGE, R. and WATERMAN, T. H. 1958, *J. Exp. Biol.* 35
Turbidity and the polarized light orientation of the crustacean, *Mysidium*.

22 BALDUS, K., 1926. *Z. vergl. Physiol.*, **3**, 475–505.
Experimentelle Untersuchungen über die Entfernungslokalization der Libellen, (*Aeschna cyanea*).

23 BALTZER, F., 1930. *Rev. suisse Zool.*, **37**, 363–369.
Uber die Orientierung des Trichterspinne *Agalena labyrinthica* nach der Spannung des Netzes.

24 BARADI, A. F., and BOURNE, G. H., 1953. *Int. Rev. Cytol.*, **2**, 289–330.
Gustatory and olfactory epithelia.

25 BARBER, S. B., 1951. *Anat. Rec.*, **111**, 561–562.
Contact chemoreception in *Limulus* (Abstract).

26 BARLOW, H. B., 1952. *J. exp. Biol.* **29**, 667–674.
The size of ommatidia in apposition eyes.

27 BARTELS, M., 1929. *Z. vergl. Physiol.*, **10**, 527–593.
Sinnesphysiologie und psychologische Untersuchungen an der Trichterspinne *Agalena labyrinthica*.

28 BARTELS, M., 1930. *Rev. suisse Zool.*, **37**, 1–42.
Uber den Fressmechanismus und den chemischen Sinn einiger Netzspinnen.

29 BARTELS, M. and BALTZER, F., 1928. *Rev. suisse Zool.*, **35**, 247–258.
Uber Orientierung und Gedächtnis der Netzspinne, *Agalena labrinthica*

[30] BARTH, R., 1937. *Zool.Jb., Abt. allg.Zool. Physiol.*, **58**, 297–329.
Herkunft Wirkung und Eigenschaften des weiblichen Sexual-
duftstoffes einiger Pyraliden.

[31] BAUER, V., 1910. *Z. allg. Physiol.*, **10**, 231–248.
Die anscheinend nervöse Regulierung des Flimmerbewegung
bei den Rippenquallen.

[32] BAUER, V., 1912. *Zool. Jb., Abt. allg. Zool. Physiol.*, **33**, 127–150.
Zur Kenntnis der Lebensweise von *Pecten jacobeus*.

[33] BAUER, L., 1938. *Z. vergl. Physiol.*, **26**, 107–120.
Geschmacksphysiologische Untersuchungen an Wasserkäfern.

[34] BAUMGARTNER, H., 1928. *Z. vergl. Physiol.*, **7**, 56–143.
Der Formensinn und die Sehschärfe der Bienen.

[35] BAUNACKE, W., 1912. *Zool. Jb., Abt. allg. Zool. Physiol.*, **34**,
179–346.
Statische Sinnesorgane bei den Nepiden.

[36] BAUNACKE, W., 1913. *Biol. Zbl.*, **33**, 427–452.
Studien zur Frage nach der Statocysten Funktion.

[37] BAYLOR, E. R. and SMITH, F. E., 1953. *Amer. Nat.*, **87**, 97–101.
The orientation of Cladocera to polarized light.

[38] BEAUCHAMP, R. S. A., 1933. *J. exp. Biol.*, **10**, 113–129.
Rheotaxis in *Planaria alpina*.

[39] BEAUCHAMP, R. S. A., 1937. *J. exp. Biol.*, **14**, 104–116.
Rate of movement and rheotaxis in *Planaria alpina*.

[40] BECKER, C., 1942. *Naturwissenschaften*, **30**, 253–256.
Die Sinnesphysiologie des Hausbockkäfers.

[41] BEGG, M. and HOGBEN, L., 1946. *Proc. roy. Soc., B.*, **133**, 1–19.
Chemoreceptivity of *Drosophila melanogaster*.

[42] BENTLEY, E. W., 1944., *J. exp. Biol.*, **20**, 152–158.
The biology and behaviour of *Ptinus tectus*. V. Humidity
reactions.

[43] BENZ, G., 1956. *Experientia*, **12**, 297–298.
Der Trockenheitsinn bei Larven von *Drosophila melanogaster*.

[44] BERTHOLF, L. M., 1932. *J. Agric. Res.*, **42**, 379–419.
Reactions of the honeybee to light.

[45] BETHE, A., 1898. *Pflüg. Arch. ges. Physiol.*, **70**, 15–100.
Durfen wir den Ameisen und Bienen psychische Qualitaten
zuschreiben?

[46] BEUSEKOM, G. V., 1948. *Behaviour*, **1**, 195–225.
Some experiments on the optical orientation in *Philanthus
triangulum*.

[47] BIERENS de HAAN, J. A., 1921. *Biol. Zbl.*, **41**, 395–413.
Phototaktischen Bewegungen von Tieren bei doppelten
Reizquelle.

[48] BIRUKOW, G., 1953. *Rev. suisse Zool.*, **60**, 535–540.
Photo-menotaxische transpositionen bei *Geotrupes silvaticus*.

[49] BIRUKOW, G., 1957. *Z. Tierpsychol.*, **13**, 463–484.
Lichtkompassorientierung beim Wasserläufer, *Velia currens*, am Tage und Nachtzeit. 1. Herbst- und Winterversuche.

[49a] BIRUKOW, G. and BUSCH, E., 1957. *Z. vergl. Physiol.*, **14**, 184–203.
Lichtkompassorientierung beim Wässerlaufer, *Velia currens*, (Heteroptera) am Tage und zur Nachtzeit. II. Orientierungsrhythmik in verscheiden Lichtbedingungen.

[49a] BIRUKOW, G. and DE VALOIS, R. L., 1955. *Naturwissenschaften*, **11**, 349–350.
Uber den Einfluss der Hohe einer Lichtquelle auf die Lichtkompassorientierung des Mistkafers *Geotrupes silvaticus*.

[50] BLUMENTHAL, H., 1935. *Z. Morph. Okol. Tiere.*, **29**, 667–719.
Untersuchungen über das 'Tarsalorgan' der Spinnen.

[51] BODINE, J. H., 1921. *J. exp. Zool.*, **32**, 137–164.
Factors influencing the water content and the rate of metabolism of certain Orthoptera.

[52] BODINE, J. H., 1923. *J. exp. Zool.*, **37**, 457–476.
Hibernation in Orthoptera. I. Physiological changes during hibernation in certain Orthoptera.

[53] BOLIN, L., 1926. *Int. Rev. Hydrobiol.*, **16**, 125–129.
Der Geotropismus von *Psammechinus miliaris*.

[54] BOLWIG, N., 1945. *Viden. Medd. Dansk. Nat. For., Kob.*, **109**, 81–217.
Senses and sense organs of the anterior end of the house fly larva.

[55] BORING, E. G., 1912. *J. Anim. Behav.*, **2**, 229–248.
Note on the negative reaction under light-adaptation in a planarian.

[56] BOURDILLON, A., 1950. *Bull. Lab. Arago.*, **1**, 198–199.
Note sur le commensalisme des *Modiolaria* et des Ascidies.

[57] BOYCOTT, B. B. and YOUNG, J. Z., 1955. *Pubbl. Staz. zool. Napoli*, **27**, 232–249.
Memories controlling attacks on food objects by *Octopus vulgaris*.

[58] BOYCOTT, B. B. and YOUNG J. Z., 1956. *Proc. zool. Soc. Lond.*, **126**, 491–547.
Reactions to shape in *Octopus vulgaris*.

[59] BOZLER, E., 1925. *Z. vergl. Physiol.*, **3**, 145–182.
Experimentelle Untersuchungen über die Funktion der Stirnaugen der Insekten.

[60] BOZLER, E., 1926. *Z. vergl. Physiol.*, **4**, 37–80.
Sinnes- und Nervenphysiologische Untersuchungen an Scyphomedusen.

[61] BRANDT, H., 1934. *Z. vergl. Physiol.*, **20**, 646–673.
Die Lichtorientierung der Mehlmotte, *Ephestia kühniella*.

[62] BRECHER, G., 1929. *Z. vergl. Physiol.*, **10**, 495–526.
Beitrag zur Raumorientierung des Schabe, *Periplaneta americana*.

[63] BRETNALL, G. H., 1927. *Science*, **66**, 427.
Earthworms and spectral colours.

[64] BROCK, F., 1930. *Z. vergl. Physiol.*, **11**, 774–790.
Das Verhalten der ersten Antennen von Brachyuren und Anomuren in Bezug auf das umgebende Medium.

[65] BROWN, F. A. and WEBB, H. M., 1948. *Physiol. Zoöl.*, **21**, 271–281.
Temperature relations of an endogenous daily rhythmicity on the fiddler crab, *Uca*.

[66] BROWN, L. A., 1929. *Amer. Nat.*, **63**, 248–264.
The natural history of cladocerans in relation to temperature. I. Distribution and the temperature limits for vital activities.

[67] BROWNING, I., 1947. *Anat. Rec.*, **99**, 605–606.
Touch response in the ciliate protozoan, *Tetrahymenea geleii*.

[68] BRUES, C. T., 1939. *Proc. Amer. Acad. Arts. Sci.*, **73**, 71–95.
Studies on the fauna of some thermal springs in the Dutch East Indies.

[69] BRUES., C. T. 1941. *Proc. Amer. Acad. Arts Sci.*, **74**, 281–285.
Photographic evidence on the visibility of colour patterns in butterflies to the human and insect eye.

[69a] BRUIN G. H. P. de and CRISP, D. J., 1957. *J. exp. Biol.*, **34**, 447–463.
The influence of pigment migration on vision of higher crustacea.

[70] BRUN, R., 1914. *Die Raumorientierung der Ameisen.* Jena: Fischer.

[71] BUDDENBROCK, W. von., 1912. *Biol. Zbl.*, **32**, 564–585.
Die Funktion der Statocysten im Sande grabender Meerestiere.

[72] BUDDENBROCK, W. von., 1913. *Zool. Jb., Abt. allg. Zool. Physiol.*, **33**, 441–482.
Die Funktion der Statocysten im Sande grabender Meerestiere. II.

[73] BUDDENBROCK, W. von., 1914. *Zool. Jb., Abt. allg. Zool. Physiol.*, **34**, 479–514.
Uber die Orientierung der Krebse im Raum.

74 BUDDENBROCK, W. von., 1917. *S. B. heidelberg. Akad. Wiss. Math.-Nat. Kl.*, **8B**, 1–26.
Die Lichtkompassbewegungen bei Insekten, insbesondere den Schmetterlingsraupen.

75 BUDDENBROCK, W. von., 1919. *Zool. Jb., Abt. allg. Zool. Physiol.*, **37**, 313–360.
Versuch einer Analyse der Lichtreaktionen der Heliciden.

76 BUDDENBROCK, W. von., 1922. *Wiss. Meeresuntersuch. N. F., Abt. Helgoland.*, **15**, 1–19.
Die Untersuchungen über den Mechanismus der phototropen Bewegungen.

77 BUDDENBROCK, W. von., 1934. *Biologe*, **3**, 231–233.
Einige Beobachtungen über die Funktion der einfachsten Facettenaugen.

78 BUDDENBROCK, W. von., 1935. *Naturwissenschaften.*, **23**, 98–100.
Eine neue Methode zur Erforschung des Formensehens der Insekten.

79 BUDDENBROCK, W. von., 1937. *Grundriss des vergleichende Physiologie.* Berlin: Borntraeger.

80 BUDDENBROCK, W. von., 1952. *Vergleichende Physiologie. Band I. Sinnesphysiologie.* Basel: Birkhäuser.

81 BUDDENBROCK, W. von., and FRIEDRICH, H., 1932. *Zool. Jb., Abt. allg. Zool. Physiol.*, **51**, 131–148.
Uber Fallreflexe bei Arthropoden.

82 BUDDENBROCK, W. von. and FRIEDRICH, H., 1933. *Z. vergl. Physiol.*, **19**, 747–761.
Neue Beobachtungen über die Kompensatorischen Augenbewegungen und den Farbensinn des Taschenkrabben (*Carcinus maenas*).

83 BUDDENBROCK, W. von and MOLLER-RACKE, I., 1953. *Pubbl. Staz. zool. Napoli.*, **24**, 217–245.
Uber den Lichtsinn von *Pecten.*

84 BUDDENBROCK, W. von. and SCHULZ, E., 1933. *Zool. Jb., Abt. allg. Zool. Physiol.*, **52**, 513–536.
Beiträge zur Kenntnis der Lichtkompassorientierungsbewegung und der Adaptation des Insektenauges.

85 BULLINGTON, W. E., 1930. *J. exp. Zool.*, **56**, 423–449.
A further study of spiralling in the ciliate *Paramecium*, with a note on morphology and taxonomy.

86 BULLOCK, T. H., 1953. *Behaviour*, **5**, 130–140.
Predator recognition and escape responses of some intertidal gastropods in presence of starfish.

[86a] BURDON-JONES, C. and CHARLES, G. H., 1958. Nature, **181**, 129–131.
Light reactions of littoral gastropods.

[87] BURKHARDT, D. and SCHNEIDER, G., 1957. *Z. Naturforsch.* **12b**, 139–143.
Die Antennen von *Calliphora* als Anzeiger der Fluggeschwindkeit.

[88] BURTT, E. T. and CATTON, W. T., 1954. *J. Physiol.*, **125**, 566–580.
Visual perception of movement in the locust.

[89] BUSNEL, R. G., 1955. *C. R. Acad. Sci. Paris.*, **240**, 1477–1479.
Mise en évidence d'un caractère physique réactogène essentiel de signaux acoustique synthétique déclenchant les phonotropismes dans le regne animal.

[90] BUTENANDT, A., 1939. *Jb. Preuss. Akad. Wiss.*, **1939**, 97–98.
Zur Kenntnis des Sexuallockstoffe des Insekten.

[91] BUTLER, C. G., 1945. *J. roy. Soc. Arts.*, **93**, 501–511.
The behaviour of bees when foraging.

[92] CARLISLE, D. B., 1951. *J. exp. Biol.*, **28**, 463–472.
On the hormonal and neural control of the release of gametes in Ascidians.

[93] CARTHY, J. D., 1950. *Nature*, **166**, 154.
Odour trails of *Acanthomyops fuliginosus*.

[94] CARTHY, J. D., 1951. *Behaviour*, **3**, 275–303, 304–318.
The orientation of two allied species of British ant. I. Visual direction finding in *Acanthomyops niger*. II. Odour trail laying and following in *Acanthomyops fuliginosus*.

[95] CHAUVIN, R., 1947. *Ann. Épiphyt.*, **13**, 5–17.
Observations et experiences sur les facteurs qui controlent le deplacement des bandes larvaires du Cricquet morocain *Dociostaurus maroccanus*.

[96] CHAUVIN, R., 1948. *L'Année Psychol.*
Sur l'experience de Bethe.

[97] CLARK., L. B., 1928. *J. exp. Zool.*, **51**, 37–50.
Adaptation versus experience as an explanation of modification in certain types of behaviour.

[98] CLARK, L. B., 1931. *J. exp. Zool.*, **58**, 31–41.
Reactions of insects to changes in luminous intensity.

[98a] CLARK, W. C., 1958. *Nature.* **181**, 137–138
Escape responses of herbivorous gastropods when stimulated by carnivorous gastropods.

[99] CLOUDSLEY-THOMPSON, J. L., 1951. *Ent. mon. Mag.*, **87**, 275–278.
Rhythmicity in the woodlouse. *Armadillidium vulgare.*

100 CLOUDSLEY-THOMPSON, J. L., 1952. *J. exp. Biol.*, **29**, 295–303.
Studies in diurnal rhythms. II. Changes in the physiological responses of the wood louse, *Oniscus asellus*, to environmental stimuli.

101 COHEN, M. J., KATSUKI, Y. and BULLOCK, T. H., 1953. *Experientia*, **9**, 434–435.
Oscillographic analysis of equilibrium receptors in crustacea.

102 COLE, W. H., 1923. *J. gen. Physiol.*, **5**, 417–426.
Circus movements of *Limulus* and the tropism theory.

103 COLLINS, C. W. and POTTS, S. F., 1932. *U.S. Dept. Agr. Tech. Bull.*, **336**, 1–43.
Attractants for the flying gipsy moth as an aid in locating infestations.

104 COOK, W. C., 1926. *J. Agric. Res.*, **32**, 347–358.
The effectiveness of certain paraffin derivatives in attracting flies.

105 CORNETZ, V., 1911. *Z. wiss. Insektbiol.*, **7**, 347–350.
Das Problem des Ruckkehr zum Nest der forschenden Ameise.

106 CRAGG, J. B., 1956. *Ann. appl. Biol.*, **44**, 467–477.
The olfactory behaviour of *Lucilia* species under natural conditions.

107 CRAGG, J. B. and COLE, P., 1956. *Ann. appl. Biol.*, **44**, 478–491.
Laboratory studies on the chemosensory reactions of blowflies.

108 CRANE, J., 1943. *Zoologica*, **28**, 217–223.
Display, breeding and relationships of fiddler crabs (Brachyura, genus *Uca*) in the N.E. United States.

109 CRANE, J., 1949. *Zoologica*, **34**, 31–52.
Comparative biology of salticid spiders at Rancho Grande, Venezuela.
III. Systematics and behaviour in representative species.

110 CRANE, J., 1949. *Zoologica*, **34**, 159–214.
Comparative biology of salticid spiders at Rancho Grande, Venezuela. IV. An analysis of display.

111 CRANE, J., 1957. *Zoologica*, **42**, 69–82.
Basic patterns of display in fiddler crabs.

112 CRISP, D. J. and STUBBINGS, H. G., 1957. *J. Anim. Ecol.*, **26**, 179–196.
The orientation of barnacles to water currents.

113 CROMBIE, A. C. and DARRAH, J. H., 1947. *J. exp. Biol.*, **24**, 95–109.
The chemoreceptors of the wireworm.

114 CROW, S., 1932. *Physiol. Zoöl.*, **5**, 16–35.
The sensitivity of the legs of certain calliphorids to saccharose.

[115] CROZIER, W. J., 1935. *J. gen. Physiol.*, **18**, 729-738.
The geotropic response in *Asterina*.

[116] CROZIER, W. J. and NAVEZ, A. E., 1930. *J. gen. Physiol.*, **3**, 3-37.
The geotropic orientation of gastropods.

[117] DAINTON, B. A., 1954. *J. exp. Biol.*, **31**, 165-187, 188-197.
The activity of slugs. I and II.

[118] DANGEARD, P. A., 1928. *Ann. Protist.*, **1**, 3-10.
Le determinisme des mouvements chez les organismes in-
ferieurs.

[119] DAVENPORT, D., 1950. *Biol. Bull.*, **98**, 81-92.
Studies in the physiology of commensalism. 1. The polynoid
genus *Arctonöe*.

[120] DAVENPORT, D., 1955. *Q. Rev. Biol.*, **30**, 29-46.
Specificity and behaviour in symbiosis.

[121] DAVENPORT, D. and HICKOK, J. F., *Biol. Bull.*, **100**, 71-83.
Studies in the physiology of commensalism. 2. The polynoid
genera *Arctonöe* and *Halosydna*.

[122] DEBAISIEUX, P., 1934. *Ann. Soc. Sci.*, Bruxelles, **54**, 86-91.
Scolopidia des pattes chez les insectes neuroptères.

[123] DEBAISIEUX, P., 1935. *La Cellule*, **44**, 273-314.
Organes scolopidiaux des pattes d'insectes. I. Lepidoptères et
Trichoptères.

[124] DEBAISIEUX, P., 1938. *La Cellule*, **47**, 79-202.
Organes scolopidiaux des pattes d'insectes. II.

[125] DELAGE, Y., 1902. *C. R. Acad. Sci.*, *Paris*, **134**, 1030-1033.
Sur les fonctions des sphéridies des oursins.

[126] DEMBOWSKI, J., 1931. *Arch. Protistenk.*, **66**, 104-132.
Die Vertikalbewegungen von *Paramecium caudatum*. I. Die
Lage des Gleichgewichtscentrums im Korper des Infusors.

[127] DEMBOWSKI, J., 1931. *Arch. Protistenk.*, **74**, 153-187.
Die Vertikalbewegungen von *Paramecium caudatum*. III.
Polemisches und Experimentelles.

[128] DENZER-MALBRANDT, U., 1935. *Zool. Jb.*, *Abt. allg. Zool. Physiol.*,
55, 525-562.
Helligkeits- und Farbensinn bei deutschen Süsswasseregeln.

[129] DETHIER, V. G., 1941. *Biol. Bull.*, **80**, 403-414.
The function of the antennal receptors of lepidopterous larvae.

[130] DETHIER, V. G., 1943. *J. cell. comp. Physiol.*, **22**, 115-126.
The dioptric apparatus of lateral ocelli. II. Visual capacities
of the ocellus.

[131] DETHIER, V. G., 1947. *J. N. Y. ent. Soc.*, **55**, 285-293.
The role of the antennae in the orientation of carrion beetles
to odors.

132 DETHIER, V. G., 1952. *Biol. Bull.*, **102**, 111–117.
The relation between olfactory response and receptor population in the blowfly.

133 DETHIER, V. G., 1953. *Biol. Bull.*, **105**, 257–268.
Summation and inhibition following contralateral stimulation of the tarsal chemoreceptors of the blowfly.

134 DETHIER, V. G., 1954. *J. gen. Physiol.*, **37**, 743–751.
Olfactory responses of blowflies to aliphatic aldehydes.

135 DETHIER, V. G., 1954. *Ann. N.Y. Acad. Sci.*, **58**, 139–157.
The physiology of olfaction in insects.

136 DETHIER, V. G., 1955. *Proc. R. ent. Soc. Lond.* (A), **30**, 87–90.
The tarsal chemoreceptors of the housefly.

137 DETHIER, V. G., 1955. *Q. Rev. Biol.*, **30**, 348–371.
The physiology and histology of the contact chemoreceptors of the blowfly.

138 DETHIER, V. G., 1956. Chemoreceptor mechanisms. in: *Molecular Structure and Functional Activity of Nerve Cells* (Pubn. No. 1, American Institute of Biological Sciences).

139 DETHIER, V. G., 1957. *Science*, **125**, 331–336.
Communication by insects: physiology of dancing.

140 DETHIER, V. G. and CHADWICK, L. E., 1947. *Physiol. Rev.*, **28**, 220–254.
Chemoreception in insects.

141 DETHIER, V. G. and CHADWICK, L. E., 1950. *J. gen. Physiol.*, **33**, 589–599.
An analysis of the relationship between solubility and stimulating effect in tarsal chemoreception.

142 DETHIER, V. G., EVANS, D. R. and RHOADES, M., 1956. *Biol. Bull.*, **111**, 204–222.
Some factors controlling the ingestion of carbohydrates by the blowfly.

143 DETHIER, V. G., HACKLEY, B. E. Jr., and WAGNER-JUAREGG, T., 1952. *Science*, **115**, 141–142.
Attraction of flies by iso-valeraldehyde.

144 DETHIER, V. G. and RHOADES, M. V., 1954. *J. exp. Zool.*, **126**, 177–204.
Sugar preference-aversion functions for the blowfly.

145 DETHIER, V. G. and YOST, M. Y., 1952. *J. gen. Physiol.*, **35**, 823–839.
Olfactory stimulation of blowflies by homologous alcohols.

146 DIAKANOFF, A., 1936. *Arch. néerl. Physiol.*, **21**, 104–129.
Contributions to the knowledge of the fly reflexes and the static sense in *Periplaneta americana*.

[147] DIETRICH, W., 1931. *Z. wiss. Zool.*, **138**, 187–232.
Die lokomotorischen Reaktionen der Landasseln auf Licht und Dunkelheit.

[148] DIJKGRAAF, S., 1955. *Experientia*, **11**, 407–409.
Rotationssinn nach den Bodengangsprinzip bei Crustacean.

[149] DODWELL, P. C., 1957. *Brit. J. Physiol.*, **48**, 221–229.
Shape recognition in rats.

[150] DOFLEIN, F., 1910. *Festschrift zum 60 Geburtstag Rich. Hartwigs*, **3**.
Lebensgewohnheiten und Anpassungen bei dekapoden Krebsen.

[151] DOFLEIN, I., 1926. *Z. vergl. Physiol.*, **3**, 62–112.
Chemotaxis und Rheotaxis bei den Planarien. Ein Beitrag zur Reizphysiologie und Biologie der Süsswassertricladen.

[152] DOLLEY, W. L. and WIERDA, J. L., 1929. *J. exp. Zool.*, **53**, 129–139.
Relative sensitivity to light of different parts of the compound eye of *Eristalis tenax*.

[153] DREES, O., 1952. *Z. Tierpsychol.*, **9**, 169–207.
Untersuchungen über die angeborenen Verhaltensweisen bei Springspinnen.

[154] DUYM, M. and OYEN, G. M. van, 1948. *De Levende Natuur*, **51**, 81–87.
Het sjirpen van de zadelsprinkhaan.

[155] EDNEY, E. B., 1954. *Biol. Rev.*, **29**, 185–219.
Woodlice and the land habitat.

[156] EGGERS, F., 1919. *Zool. Jb., Abt. Anat. Ontogen.*, **41**, 273–376.
Das thoracale bitympanale Organ einer Gruppe der Lepidopteren Heterocera.

[157] EGGERS, F., 1926. *Zool. Anz.*, **68**, 184–192.
Die mutmassliche Funktion des Johnstonschen Sinnesorgans bei *Gyrinus*.

[158] ENGELMANN, T. W., 1882. *Pflüg. Arch. ges. Physiol.*, **27**, 387–400.
Uber Licht- und Farbenperception niederster Organismen.

[159] EVANS, F. G. C., 1951. *J. Anim. Ecol.*, **20**, 1–10.
An analysis of the behaviour of *Lepidochitona cinereus* in response to certain physical features of the environment.

[160] FABER, A., 1929. *Z. Morph. Ökol. Tiere*, **13**, 745–803.
Die Lautäusserungen der Orthopteren I.

[161] FABER, A., 1932. *Z. Morph. Ökol. Tiere*, **26**, 1–93.
Die Lautäusserungen der Orthopteren II.

[162] FERNANDEZ-MORAN, H., 1956. *Nature*, **177**, 742–743.
Fine structure of the insect retinula as revealed by electron microscopy.

163 FLÜGGF, C., 1934. *Z. vergl. Physiol.*, **20**, 463–500.
Geruchliche Raumorientierung von *Drosophila melanogaster*.

164 FOH, H., 1932. *Zool. Jb., Abt. allg. Zool. Physiol.*, **52**, 1–78.
Der Schattenreflex bei *Helix pomatia* nebst Bemerkungen über den Schattenreflex bei *Mytilus edulis, Limnaea stagnalis* and *Testudo iberea*.

165 FOREL, A., 1886. *Ann. Soc. ent. Belg.*, **30**, 131–215.
Études myrmecologiques.

166 FOX, H. M., 1925. *Proc. Camb. philos. Soc., biol. Sci.*, **1**, 219–224.
The effect of light on the vertical movement of aquatic organisms.

167 FRAENKEL, G., 1925. *Z. vergl. Physiol.*, **2**, 658–690.
Der statische Sinn der Medusen.

168 FRAENKEL, G., 1927. *Z. vergl. Physiol.*, **5**, 585–597.
Beiträge zur Geotaxis und Phototaxis von *Littorina*.

169 FRAENKEL, G., 1927. *Z. vergl. Physiol.*, **6**, 167–220.
Die Grabsbewegungen der Soleniden.

170 FRAENKEL, G., 1927. *Z. vergl. Physiol.*, **6**, 385–401.
Die Photomenotaxis von *Elysia viridis*.

171 FRAENKEL, G., 1928. *Z. vergl. Physiol.*, **7**, 365–377.
Uber den Auslösungsreiz des Umdrehreflexes bei Seesternen und Schlangensternen.

172 FRAENKEL, G., 1929. *Biol. Zbl.*, **49**, 657–680.
Sinnesphysiologie der Larven des Wanderheuschrecke, *Schistocerca gregaria*.

173 FRAENKEL, G., 1929. *Z. vergl. Physiol.*, **10**, 237–247.
Uber die Geotaxis von *Convoluta roscoffensis*.

174 FRAENKEL, G., 1930. *Z. vergl. Physiol.*, **13**, 300–313.
Die Orientierung von *Schistocerca gregaria* zu strahlender Warme.

175 FRAENKEL, G., 1931. *Biol. Rev.*, **6**, 36–87.
Die Mechanik der Orientierung der Tiere im Raum.

176 FRAENKEL, G., 1932. *Z. vergl. Physiol.*, **16**, 371–393.
Die Flugreflexe der Insekten und ihre Koordination.

177 FRAENKEL, G. and GUNN, D. L., 1940. *The orientation of animals*.
Oxford: *Monogr. Anim. Behav.*

178 FRAENKEL, G. and PRINGLE, J. W. S., 1938. *Nature*, **141**, 919–920.
Halteres of flies as gyroscopic organs of equilibrium.

179 FRANZ, V., 1911. *Int. Rev. Hydrobiol.*, **3**, 1–23.
Weitere Phototaxisstudien.

180 FREE, J. B. and BUTLER, C. G., 1955. *Behaviour*, **7**, 304–316.
An analysis of the factors involved in the formation of a cluster of honeybees (*Apis mellifica*).

M

[181] FREEMAN, R. F. H. and RIGLER, F. H., 1957. *J. mar. biol. Ass. U.K.*, **36**, 553–567.
The responses of *Scrobicularia plana* to osmotic pressure changes.

[182] FRIEDEL, H., 1928. *Z. Morph. Ökol.*, **10**, 738–797.
Okologische und physiologische Untersuchungen an *Scutigerella immaculata*.

[183] FRIEDRICH, H., 1932. *Z. vergl. Physiol.*, **16**, 345–361.
Studien uber die Gleichgewichtserhaltung und Bewegungsphysiologie bei *Pterotrachea*.

[184] FRINGS, H., 1946. *Z. exp. Zool.*, **102**, 23–50.
Gustatory thresholds for sucrose and electrolytes for the cockroach, *Periplaneta americana*.

[185] FRINGS, H., 1948. *J. comp. physiol. Psychol.*, **41**, 25–34.
A contribution to the comparative physiology of contact chemoreception.

[186] FRINGS, H. and FRINGS, M., 1949. *Amer. mid. Nat.*, **41**, 602–658.
The loci of contact chemoreceptors in insects.

[187] FRINGS, H. and FRINGS, M., 1956. *Biol. Bull.*, 92–100.
The location of contact chemoreceptors sensitive to sucrose solutions in adult Trichoptera.

[188] FRISCH, K. von, 1915. *Zool. Jb., Abt. allg. Zool. Physiol.*, **35**, 1–182.
Der Farbensinn und Formensinn der Biene.

[189] FRISCH, K. von, 1919. *Zool. Jb., Abt. allg. Zool. Physiol.*, **37**, 1–238.
Uber den Geruchsinn der Bienen und seine blutenbiologische Bedeutung.

[190] FRISCH, K. von, 1921. *Zool. Jb., Abt. allg. Zool. Physiol.*, **38**, 1–68.
Uber den Sitz des Geruchsinnes bei Insekten.

[191] FRISCH, K. von, 1923. *Zool. Jb., Abt. allg. Zool. Physiol.*, **40**, 1–186.
Uber die Sprache der Bienen.

[192] FRISCH, K. von, 1924. *Naturwissenschaften*, **12**, 981–987.
Sinnesphysiologie und 'Sprache' des Bienen.

[193] FRISCH, K. von, 1934. *Z. vergl. Physiol.*, **21**, 1–156.
Uber den Geschmackssinn der Biene. Eine Beitrag vor vergleichenden Physiologie des Geschmacks.

[194] FRISCH, K. von, 1941. *Naturwissenschaften*, **29**, 321–333.
Die Bedeutung des Geruchssinnes im Leben der Fische.

[195] FRISCH, K. von, 1943. *Naturwissenschaften*, **31**, 445–460.
Versuche uber die Lenkung des Bienefluges durch Duftstoffe.

196 FRISCH, K. von, 1946. *Osterreich. Zool. Zeit.*, **1**, 1–48.
Die Tanze der Bienen.
197 FRISCH, K. von, 1948. *Naturwissenschaften*, **35**, 12–23, 38–43.
Gelöste und ungelöste Ratsel der Bienensprache.
198 FRISCH, K. von, 1949. *Experientia*, **5**, 142–148.
Die Polarisation des Himmelslichtes als orientierender Faktor
bei den Tanzen der Bienen.
199 FRISCH, K. von, 1950. *Experientia*, **6**, 210–221.
Die Sonne als Kompass im Leben der Bienen.
200 FRISCH, K. von, 1951. *Naturwissenschaften*, **38**, 105–112.
Orientierungsvermögen und Sprache der Bienen.
201 FRISCH, K. von, 1956. *Proc., Amer. phil. Soc.*, **100**, 515–519.
The 'language' and orientation of bees.
202 FRISCH, K. von and JANDER, R., 1957. *Z. vergl. Physiol.*, **40**,
239–263.
Uber den Schwänzeltanz der Bienen.
203 FRISCH, K. von, and KUPELWEISER, H., 1913. *Biol. Zbl.*, **33**,
517–552.
Uber den Einfluss der Lichtfarbe auf die phototaktischen
Reaktionen niederer Krebse.
204 FROHLICH, W., 1914. *Z. Sinnesphysiol.*, **48**, 28–164.
Beiträge zur allgemeinen Physiologie des Sinnesorgane.
205 GAFFRON, M., 1934. *Z. vergl. Physiol.*, **20**, 299–337.
Untersuchungen über das Bewegungssehen bei Libellenlarven,
Fliegen und Fischen.
206 GIERSBURG, H., 1926. *Z. vergl. Physiol.*, **3**, 827–838.
Uber den chemischen Sinn von *Octopus vulgaris*.
207 GOLDSMITH, M., 1917. *Bull. Inst. gen. psychol.*, **17**, 25–44.
Quelques reactions du poulpe.
208 GOLDSMITH, M., 1918. *C.R. Acad. Sci. Paris*, **166**, 967–970.
Les perceptions sensorielles chez le pagure (*Eupagurus bernhardus*).
209 GOSSWALD, K., 1941. *Z. wiss. Zool.*, **154**, 247–272.
Uber der Einfluss von verscheidener Temperatur und Luft-
feuchtigkeit auf die Lebensausseringen der Ameisen. II.
210 GOTHLIN, G. F., 1920. *J. exp. Zool.*, **31**, 403–441.
Inhibition of the ciliary movement in *Beröe*.
211 GRABER, V., 1883. *Sitz. Ber. Akad. Wiss. Wien*, **87**, 201–236.
Fundamentalversuche uber die Helligkeits- und Farbenemp-
findlichkeit augenloser und geblendeter Tiere.
212 GUNN, D. L., 1934. *Z. vergl. Physiol.*, **20**, 617–625.
Temperature and humidity relations of the cockroach. II.
Temperature preference.

[213] GUNN, D. L., 1937. *J. exp. Biol.*, **14**, 178–186.
The humidity reactions of the woodlouse, *Porcellio scaber*.

[214] GUNN, D. L., 1940. in: FRAENKEL, G. and GUNN, D. L.[177]

[215] GUNN, D. L. and COSWAY, C. A., 1938. *J. exp. Biol.*, **15**, 555–563.
Temperature and humidity relations of the cockroach. V. Humidity preference of *Blatta orientalis*.

[216] GUNN, D. L. and PIELOU, D. P., 1940. *J. exp. Biol.*, **17**, 307–316.
The humidity behaviour of the mealworm beetle, *Tenebrio molitor*. III. The mechanism of the reaction.

[217] HADDOW, A. J., GILLETT, J. D. and HIGHTON, R. B., 1947. *Bull. ent. Res.*, **37**, 301–330.
The mosquitoes of the Bwamba County, Uganda. V. The vertical distribution and biting cycles of mosquitoes in rainforest.

[218] HAFEZ, M., 1950. *Parasitology*, **40**, 215–236.
On the behaviour and sensory physiology of the housefly larva, *Musca domestica*. I. Feeding stage.

[219] HAMILTON, A. G., 1936. *Trans. R. ent. Soc., Lond.*, **85**, 1–60.
The relation of humidity and temperature to the development of three species of African locusts.

[220] HARDY, A. C. and BAINBRIDGE, R., 1951. *Nature*, **167**, 354–355.
Effect of pressure on the behaviour of decapod larvae.

[221] HARKER, J. E., 1953. *J. exp. Biol.*, **30**, 525–528.
The diurnal rhythm of activity of mayfly nymphs.

[222] HARKER, J. E., 1956. *J. exp. Biol.*, **33**, 224–234.
Factors controlling the diurnal rhythm of activity of *Periplaneta americana*.

[222a] HARKER, J. E., 1958. *Biol. Rev.*, **33**, 1–52.
Diurnal rhythms in the animal kingdom.

[223] HARMS, J. W., 1929. *Z. wiss. Zool.*, **133**, 211–397.
Die Realisation der Gene und die consecutive Adaptation I.

[224] HARMS, J. W., 1932. *Z. wiss. Zool.*, **140**, 167–290.
Die Realisation der Gene und die consecutive Adaptation II.

[225] HARPER, E. H., 1911. *J. Morph. Physiol.*, **22**, 993–1000.
The geotropism of *Paramecium*.

[226] HARRIS, J. E. and MASON, P., 1956. *Proc. roy. Soc.*, **B, 145**, 280–290.
Vertical migration in eyeless *Daphnia*.

[227] HARRINGTON, N. R. and LEAMING, E., 1900. *Amer. J. Physiol.*, **3**, 9–16.
The reaction of *Amoeba* to light of different colours.

228 HARTLINE, H. K. AND GRAHAM, C. H., 1938. *J. cell. comp. Physiol.*, **11.**
The discharge of impulses in the optic nerve of *Pecten* in response to illumination of the eye.

229 HASE, A., 1923. *Naturwissenschaften*, **11**, 801–806.
Uber die Morphologie und Polyphagie der Schmarotzwespen, ein Beitrag zur Kenntnis des Geruchssinnes der Insekten.

230 HASKELL, P. T., 1953. *Brit. J. anim. Behav.*, **1**, 120–121.
The stridulation behaviour of the domestic cricket.

231 HASKELL, P. T., 1956. *J. exp. Biol.*, **33**, 756–766, 767–776.
Hearing in certain Orthoptera, I and II.

232 HASKELL, P. T. and BELTON, P., 1956. *Nature*, **177**, 139–140.
Electrical responses of certain lepidopterous tympanal organs.

233 HASLINGER, F., 1935. *Z. vergl. Physiol.*, **22**, 614–640.
Uber den Geschmackssinn von *Calliphora erythrocephala* und über die Verwertung von zucker und zuckeralkoholen durch diese Fliege.

233a HASSENSTEIN, B., 1951. *Z. vergl. Physiol.*, **33**, 301–326.
Ommatidienraster und afferente Bewegungsintegration.

234 HECHT, S., 1918. *J. gen. Physiol.*, **1**, 545–558.
Sensory equilibrium and dark-adaptation in *Mya arenaria*.

235 HECHT, S., 1925. *J. gen. Physiol.*, **8**, 291–301.
The effect of the exposure period and temperature on the photo-sensory process in *Ciona*.

236 HECHT, S. and WOLF, E., 1929. *J. gen. Physiol.*, **12**, 727–760.
The visual acuity of the honeybee.

237 HEIDERMANNS, C., 1928. *Zool. Jb., Abt. allg. Zool. Physiol.*, **45**, 609–650.
Messende untersuchungen über das Formensehen des Cephalopoden und ihre optischen Orientierung im Raume.

238 HENKE, K., 1930. *Z. vergl. Physiol.*, **13**, 534–625.
Die Lichtorientierung und die Bedingungen der Lichtstimmung bei der Rollassel, *Armadillidium cinereum*.

239 HENSCHEL, J., 1929. *Z. vergl. Physiol.*, **9**, 802–837.
Reizphysiologische Untersuchungen an der Kasemilbe, *Tyrolichus casei*.

240 HENSCHEL, J., 1932. *Wiss. Meeresunters., Abt. Kiel.*, **21**, 133–158.
Untersuchungen über den chemischen Sinn von *Nassa reticulata*.

[241] HENSCHEL, J., 1936. *Wiss. Meeresuntersuch., Abt. Kiel.*, **22**, 21–42.
Untersuchungen über den chemischen Sinn der Scyphomedusen *Aurelia aurita* und *Cyanea capillata* und der Hydromeduse *Sarsia tubulosa*.

[242] HENSCHEL, J., 1936. in VON BUDDENBROCK.[80]

[243] HENSEN, V., 1863. *Z. wiss. Zool.*, **13**, 319–412.
Studien über das Gehörorgan der Decapoden.

[244] HERAN, H., 1952. *Z. vergl. Physiol.*, **34**, 179–206.
Untersuchungen uber den Temperatursinn der Honigbiene (*Apis mellifica*) unter besonderer Berucksichtigung der Wahrenehmung strahlender Wärme.

[245] HERMS, W. B., 1911. *J. exp. Zool.*, **10**, 167–226.
The photic reactions of *Lucilia caesar* and *Calliphora vomitoria*.

[246] HERTEL, E., 1904. *Z. allg. Physiol.*, **4**, 1–43.
Uber Beeinflussung des Organismus durch Licht, speziell durch die chemisch wirksamen Strahlen.

[247] HERTER, K., 1927. *Z. vergl. Physiol.*, **5**, 283–370.
Reizphysiologische Untersuchungen an der Karpfenlaus, *Argulus foliaceus*.

[248] HERTER, K., 1928. *Z. vergl. Physiol.*, **8**, 391–444.
Reizphysiologie und Wirtsfindung des Fischegels, *Hemiclepsis marginata*.

[249] HERTER, K., 1929. *Z. vergl. Physiol.*, **9**, 145–177.
Vergleichende Bewegungsphysiologische Studien an Deutschen Egeln.

[250] HERTER, K., 1929. *Z. vergl. Physiol.*, **10**, 248–271.
Temperaturversuche mit Egeln.

[251] HERTER, K., 1929. *Z. vergl. Physiol.*, **10**, 272–308.
Riezphysiologisches verhalten und parasitismus des Entenegels, *Protoclepsis tesselata*.

[252] HERTWECK, H., 1931. *Z. wiss. Zool.*, **139**, 559–663.
Anatomie und Variabilität des Nervensystems und der Sinnesorgane von *Drosophila melanogaster*.

[253] HERTZ, M., 1929. *Z. vergl. Physiol.*, **8**, 693–748.
Die Organisation des optischen Feldes bei der Biene I.

[254] HERTZ, M., 1930. *Z. vergl. Physiol.*, **11**, 107–145.
Die Organisation des optischen Feldes bei der Biene II.

[255] HERTZ, M., 1931. *Z. vergl. Physiol.*, **14**, 629–674.
Die Organisation des optischen Feldes bei der Biene III.

256 HERTZ, M., 1933. *Biol. Zbl.*, **53**, 10–40.
Uber figurale Intensitäten und Qualitäten in der optischen Wahrenehmung der Biene.

257 HERTZ, M., 1934. *Z. vergl. Physiol.*, **21**, 604–615.
Zur Physiologie des Formen und Bewegungssehens. III. Figurale Unterscheidung und reziproke Dressuren bei der Biene.

258 HERTZ, M., 1939. *J. exp. Biol.*, **16**, 1–8.
New experiments on colour vision in bees.

259 HESS, C. von., 1909. *Arch. Augenheilk.*, **64.** Erg. Heft.
Die Akkomodation des Cephalopoden.

260 HESS, C. von, 1913. *Zool. Jb., Abt. allg. Zool. Physiol.*, **33,** 387–440.
Neue Untersuchungen zur vergleichenden Physiologie des Gesichtsinnes.

261 HESS, C. von., 1918. *Pflüg. Arch. ges. Physiol.*, **172,** 448–466.
Die Akkomodation des Alciopiden, nebst Beiträgen zur Morphologie des Alciopidenauges.

262 HESS, W. N., 1924. *J. Morph. Physiol.*, **39**, 515–542.
Reactions to light in the earthworm, *Lumbricus terrestris.*

263 HESSE, R., 1896. *Z. wiss. Zool.*, **61**, 393–419.
Untersuchungen uber die Organe der Lichtempfindungen bei niederen Thieren. I. Die Organe der Lichtempfindungen bei den Lumbriciden.

263a HESSE, R., 1900. *Z. wiss. Zool.* **68**, 379–477.
Die Augen einiger Mollusken.

264 HODGSON., E. S., 1951. *Physiol. Zoöl.*, **24**, 133–140
Reaction thresholds of an aquatic beetle, *Laccophilus maculosus*, to salts and alcohols.

265 HODGSON, E. S., LETTVIN, J. Y. and ROEDER, K. D., 1955. *Science*, **122,** 417–418.
The physiology of a primary chemoreceptor.

266 HODGSON, E. S. and ROEDER, K. D., 1956. *J. cell. comp. Physiol.*, **48,** 51–75.
Electrophysiological studies of arthropod chemoreception. I. General properties of the labellar chemoreceptors of Diptera.

267 HOFFMANN, H., 1929. *Verh. dtsch. zool. Ges.*, 33, 112–118.
Uber den Fluchtreflex bei *Nassa*.

268 HOLLICK, F. S. J., 1940. *Phil. Trans. roy. Soc., B.*, **230**, 357–390.
The flight of the dipterous fly, *Muscina stabulans*.

269 HOLMES, S. J., 1901. *Biol. Bull.*, **2**, 165–193.
Habits of *Ampithöe longimana*.

270 HOLST, E. von., 1954. *Brit. J. anim. Behav.*, **2**, 89–94.
Relations between the central nervous system and the peripheral organs.

271 HOMANN, H., 1928. *Z. vergl. Physiol.*, **7**, 201–268.
Beitrage zur Physiologie des Spinnenaugen I and II.

272 HOMP, R., 1938. *Z. vergl. Physiol.*, **26**, 1–34.
Wärmeorientierung von *Pediculus vestimenti*.

273 HOPF, H. S., 1940. *Biochem. J.*, **34**, 1396–1403.
The physiological action of abnormally high temperatures on poikilothermic animals. 3. Some changes occurring in the phosphorus distribution of the haemolymph of insects under the influence of abnormally high temperature.

274 HOWLETT, F. M., 1912. *Trans. ent. Soc. Lond.*, **1912**, 412–418.
The effect of oil of citronella on two species of *Dacus*.

275 HUBER, F., 1952. *Verh. dtsch. zool. Ges. Freiburg.*, 138–149.
Verhaltensstudien am Mannchen der Feldgrille (*Gryllus campestris*) nach Eingriffen am Zentralnervensystem.

276 HUMPHREY, G., 1933. *The nature of learning in its relation to the living system*. London: Kegan Paul.

277 HUNDERTMARK, A., 1937. *Z. vergl. Physiol.*, **24**, 563–582.
Das Formunterscheidungsvermögen des Eiraupen des Nonne (*Lymantria monacha*).

278 IERSEL, J. van, 1950. *Tijd. Ent.*, **93**, 64–69.
Over de orientate van *Bembex rostrata*.

279 ILSE, D., 1929. *Z. vergl. Physiol.*, **8**, 658–692.
Uber den Farbensinn der Tagfalter.

280 ILSE, D., 1932. *Z. vergl. Physiol.*, **17**, 537–556.
Zur 'Formwahrnehmung' der Tagfalter.

281 ILSE, D., 1937. *Nature*, **140**, 544–545.
New observations on responses to colours in egglaying butterflies.

232 ILSE, D., 1949. *Nature*, **163**, 255–256.
Colour discrimination in the dronefly, *Eristalis tenax*.

283 JAGER, H., 1932. *Zool. Jb., Abt. allg. Zool. Physiol.*, **51**, 289–320.
Untersuchungen uber die geotaktischen Reaktionen verscheidener Evertebraten aufer schiefer Ebene.

284 JANDA, V. and LANG, J., 1939. *Mém. Soc. zool. tchécosl.*, **7**, 260–267.
Beiträge zur Kenntnis der durch den Feuchtigkeitsgehalt des Mediums ausgelösten Bewegungsreaktionen bei *Oniscus murarius*, *Porcellio scaber*, and *Glomeris hexasticha*.

284a JANDER, R., 1957. *Z. vergl. Physiol.*, **40**, 162–238.
Die optische Richtungsorientierung der roten Waldameise
(*Formica rufa*).

285 JENNINGS, H. S., 1904. *Carn. Instn. Publ. No. 16.* pp. 130–234.
Reactions to light in ciliates and flagellates.

286 JENNINGS, H. S., 1923. *The behaviour of the lower organisms.*
New York: Columbia Univ.

287 KALABUCHOV, N. I., 1934. *Zool. Jb., Abt. allg. Zool. Physiol.* **53**,
567–602.
Beiträge zur Kenntnis des Kaltestarre bei der Biene (*Apis
mellifera*).

288 KALMUS, H., 1929. *Z. vergl. Physiol.*, **9**, 703–733.
Die Bewegungen des Seesterne, *Asterina gibbosa*.

289 KALMUS, H., 1937, *Z. vergl. Physiol.*, **24**, 644–655.
Photohorotaxis, eine neue reaktionsart gefunden an den
Eilarven von *Dixippus*.

290 KALMUS, H., 1943. *J. Genet.*, **45**, 206–213.
The optomotor response of some eye mutants of *Drosophila*.

291 KALMUS, H., 1956. *J. exp. Biol.*, **33**, 554–565.
Sun navigation of *Apis mellifica* in the southern hemisphere.

292 KALMUS, H. and RIBBANDS, C. R., 1952. *Proc. roy. Soc., B.,*
140, 50–59.
The origin of the odours by which honeybees distinguish
their companions.

293 KELLOGG, V. L., 1907. *Biol. Bull.*, **12**, 152–154.
Some silkworm moth reflexes.

294 KEMPENDORFF, W., 1942. *Arch. Mollusk.*, **74**, 1–27.
Uber das Fluchtphänomen und die Chemorezeption von
Helisoma nigricans.

295 KENNEDY, J. S., 1937. *J. exp. Biol.*, **14**, 187–197.
The humidity reactions of the African migratory locust,
Locusta migratoria migratorioides, gregarious phase.

296 KENNEDY, J. S., 1940. *Proc. zool. Soc. Lond. A.*, **109**, 221–242.
The visual responses of flying mosquitoes.

297 KENNEDY, J. S., 1945. *Trans. R. ent. Soc. Lond.*, **95**, 247–262.
Observations on the mass migration of desert locust hoppers.

298 KENNEDY, J. S., 1951. *Phil. Trans. roy. Soc., B.*, **235**, 163–290.
The migration of the desert locust (*Schistocerca gregaria*).

299 KERKUT, G. A. and TAYLOR, B. J. R., 1956. *J. exp. Biol.*, **33**,
493–501.
The sensitivity of the pedal ganglion of the slug to osmotic
pressure changes.

M*

[299a] KERKUT, G. A. and TAYLOR, B. J. R., 1957. *J. exp. Biol.*, **34**, 486–493.
A temperature receptor in the tarsus of the cockroach, *Periplaneta americana*.

[300] KIECKEBUSCH, no date, in VON BUDDENBROCK.[80]

[300a] KITCHING, J. A., 1957. *J. exp. Biol.*, **34**, 494–510.
Effects of high hydrostatic pressures on the activity of flagellates and ciliates.

[301] KLEIN, K., 1934. *Z. wiss. Zool.* **145**, 1–38.
Uber die Helligkeitsreaktionen einiger Arthropoden.

[302] KNIGHT-JONES, E. W., 1954. *J. exp. Biol.*, **30**, 584–598.
Laboratory experiments on gregariousness during settling in *Balanus balanoides* and other barnacles.

[303] KNIGHT-JONES, E. W. and QASIM, S. Z., 1955. *Nature*, **175**, 941.
Responses of some marine plankton animals to changes in hydrostatic pressure.

[304] KNOLL, F., 1921–1926. *Insekten und Blumen*, 3 vols. Vienna: Zoologisch-botanischen Gesellschaft.

[305] KNOLL, F., 1925. *Z. vergl. Physiol.*, **2**, 329–380.
Lichtsinn und Blütenbesuch des Falters von *Deilephila livornica*.

[306] KOEHLER, O., 1922. *Arch. Protistenk*, **45**, 1–94.
Uber die Geotaxis von *Paramecium*.

[307] KOEHLER, O., 1930. *Arch. Protistenk*, **70**, 279–307.
Uber die Geotaxis von *Paramecium*.

[308] KOEHLER, O., 1924. *Z. vergl. Physiol.*, **1**, 84–174.
Uber das Farbensehen von *Daphnia magna*.

[309] KOEHLER, O., 1932. *Z. vergl. Physiol.*, **16**, 606–756.
Sinnesphysiologie der Süsswasserplanarien.

[310] KOLLER, G., 1928. *Z. vergl. Physiol.*, **8**, 337–353.
Versuche über den Farbensinn der Eupaguriden.

[311] KOLLER, G. and STUDNITZ, G. von, 1934. *Z. vergl. Physiol.*, **20**, 388–404.
Uber den Licht- und Schattenreflex von *Mya arenaria*.

[312] KREIDL, A., 1892. *S. B. Akad. Wiss. Math.-Nat. Kl. Wien.*, **102**, 149–174.
Physiologie des Ohrlabyrinthes. II. Versuche an Krebsen.

[313] KRIJGSMANN, B. J., 1930. *Z. vergl. Physiol.*, **11**, 702–729.
Reizphysiologische Untersuchungen an blutsaugenden Arthropoden im Zusammenhang mit ihrer Nahrungswahl. I. *Stomoxys calcitrans*.

314 KRIJGSMANN, B. J. and WINDRED, G. L., 1930. *Z. vergl. Physiol.*, 13, 61–73.
Riezphysiologische Untersuchungen an blutsaugenden Arthropoden im Zusammenhang mit ihrer Nahrungswahl. II. *Lyperosia exigua.*

315 KRUMBACH, T., 1917. *Zool. Anz.*, 49, 96–123.
Napfschnecken in der Gezeitenwelle und der Brandungszone der Karstkuste.

316 KUGLER, H., 1936. *Planta*, 25, 346–363.
Zur Nahanlockung von Neulingen — Versuche mit der Schmarotzer-hummel *Psithyrus rupestris*—zum Rotfarben sinn der Hummeln.

317 KÜHN, A., 1914. *Verh. dtsch. zool. Ges.*, 24, 262–277.
Die reflektorische Erhaltung des Gleichgewichtes bei Krebsen.

318 KÜHN, A., 1924. *Nachr. Ges. Wiss. Gottingen*, 1924, 66–71.
Versuche uber das Unterscheidungsvermögen des Bienen und Fische fur Spektrallichter.

319 KÜHN, A., 1927. *Z. vergl. Physiol.*, 5, 762–800.
Uber den Farbensinn der Bienen.

320 KÜHN, A., 1933. *Nachr. Ges. Wiss. Gottingen*, 1933, 10–16.
Uber Farbensinn und Anpassung des Korperfarben an die Umgebung bei Tintenfischen.

321 KÜHN, A., 1950. *Z. vergl. Physiol.*, 32, 572–598.
Uber Farbwechsel und Farbensinn von Cephalopoden.

322 KÜHN, A. and FRAENKEL, G., 1927. *Nachr. Ges. Wiss. Gottingen*, 1927, 330–335.
Uber das Unterscheidungsvermögen des Bienen für Wellenlangen im Spektrum.

323 KÜHN, A. and POHL, R., 1921. *Naturwissenschaften*, 9, 738–740.
Dressurfahigkeit des Bienen auf Spektrallinien.

324 KULLENBERG, B., 1952. *Bull. Soc. Hist. nat., Afr. Nord.*, 43, 53–62.
Recherches sur la biologie florale des *Ophrys.*

325 KUNZE, G., 1933. *Zool. Jb., Abt. allg. Zool. Physiol.*, 52, 465–512.
Einige Versuche über den Antennengeschmackssinn der Honigbiene.

326 LAMMERT, A., 1925. *Z. vergl. Physiol.*, 3, 225–278.
Uber Pigmentwanderung im Punktauge der Insekten, sowie über Licht- und Schwerkraftreaktionen von Schmetterlingsraupen.

327 LANGENBUCH, R., 1928. *Zool. Jb., Abt. allg. Zool. Physiol.*, 44, 575–622.
Uber die Statocysten einiger Crustaceen.

[328] LEES, A. D., 1943. *J. exp. Biol.*, **20**, 43–53.
On the behaviour of wireworms of the genus *Agriotes*. I.
Reactions to humidity.

[329] LEES, A. D., 1948. *J. exp. Biol.*, **25**, 145–207.
The sensory physiology of the sheep tick, *Ixodes ricinus*.

[330] LEHMANN, C., 1923. *Zool. Jb., Abt. allg. Zool. Physiol.*, **39**,
321–394.
Untersuchungen über die Sinnesorgane der Medusen.

[331] LICHE, H., 1934. *Bull. Int. Acad. polon.*, **1934**, 233–249.
Uber die photischen Reaktionen bei des Schlammschnecke
Limnaea stagnalis.

[332] LIEBERMANN, A., 1926. *Z. Morph. Ökol. Tiere.*, **5**, 1–97.
Correlation zwischen den antennalen Geruchsorganen und
der Biologie der Musciden.

[333] LINDAUER, M., 1948. *Z. vergl. Physiol.*, **31**, 348–412.
Uber die Einwirkung von Duft- und Geschmacksstoffen sowie
anderer Faktoren auf die Tanze des Bienen.

[334] LINDAUER, M., 1955. *Z. vergl. Physiol.*, **37**, 263–324.
Schwarmbienen auf Wohnungssuche.

[335] LINDAUER, M., 1957. *Bee World*, **38**, 3–14, 34–39.
Communication among the honeybees and stingless bees of
India.

[336] LISSMANN, H. W., 1951. *Nature*, **167**, 201–202.
Continuous electrical signals from the tail of a fish, *Gymnarcus
niloticus*.

[337] LOEB, J., 1890. *Der Heliotropismus der Thiere und seine Ueberein-
stimmung mit dem Heliotropismus der Pflanzen.* Würzburg:
Hertz.

[338] LOEB, J., 1891. *Pflüg. Arch. ges. Physiol.*, **49**, 175–189.
Ueber Geotropismus bei Thieren.

[339] LOEB, J., 1918. *Forced movements, tropisms and animal conduct.*
Philadelphia: Lippincott.

[340] LOHNER, L., 1915. *Biol. Zbl.*, **1915**, 385–393.
Uber kunstliche Futterung und Verdauungsversuche mit
Blutegeln.

[341] LOOMIS, W. F., 1955. *Ann. N.Y. Acad. Sci.*, **62**, 209–228.
Glutathione control of the specific feeding reactions of *Hydra*.

[342] LOTMAR, R., 1933. *Z. vergl. Physiol.*, **19**, 673–723.
Neue Untersuchungen über den Farbensinn des Bienen, mit
besonderer Berücksichtigung des Ultravioletts.

[343] LUDTKE, H., 1935. *Z. vergl. Physiol.*, **22**, 67–118.
Die Funktion waagerecht liegender Augenteile des Rücken-
schwimmer.

344 LUDWIG, W., 1934. *Z. wiss. Zool.* **146**, 193–235.
Seitenstetigkeit niederer Tiere. II. Menotaxis.

345 LUTHER, W., 1930. *Z. vergl. Physiol.*, **12**, 177–205.
Versuche über die Chemorezeption der Brachyuren.

346 MACARTHUR, J. W. and BAILLIE, W. H. T., 1929. *J. exp. Zool.*,
53, 243–268.
Metabolic activity and duration of life.

347 MACGREGOR, E. G., 1948. *Behaviour*, **1**, 267–296.
Odour as a basis for orientated movement in ants.

348 MCINDOO, N. E., 1929. *Smithson. Misc. Coll.*, **81**, 1–59.
Tropisms and sense organs of Lepidoptera.

349 MAGNUS, D., 1954. *Verh. dtsch. Zool.*, *Ges. Tubingen*, **1954**,
317–325.
Zum Problem der 'überoptimalen' Schlusselreize.

350 MANGOLD, E., 1921. *Pflüg. Arch. ges. Physiol.*, **189**, 73–98.
Der Umdrehreflex bei Seesternen und Schlangensternen.

351 MANGOLD, O., 1951. *Zool. Jb.*, *Abt. allg. Zool. Physiol.*, **62**,
441–512.
Experimente zur Analyse des chemischen Sinns des Regen-
wurms. I. Methode und Verhalten zu Blattern von Pflanzen.

352 MANNING, A., 1956. *Behaviour*, **9**, 114–139.
The effect of honey-guides.

353 MANNING, A., 1957. *Proc. R. phys. Soc. Edinb.*, **25**, 67–71.
Some evolutionary aspects of the flower constancy of bees.

354 MARCHAL, P., 1910. *Richet's Dictionaire de Physiologie*, **9**,
273–386. Insectes.

355 MAST, S. O., 1906. *Z. exp. Zool.*, **3**, 359–399.
Light reactions in lower organisms. I. *Stentor coeruleus*.

356 MAST, S. O., 1910. *Carneg. Inst. Yearbook*, **9**, 131–133.
Reactions to light in marine turbellaria.

357 MAST, S. O., 1910. *J. exp.. Zool.*, **9**, 265–278.
Reactions in *Amoeba* to light.

358 MAST, S. O., 1911. *Light and the behaviour of organisms*. New
York: Wiley.

359 MAST, S. O., 1912. *J. Anim. Behav.*, **2**, 256–272.
Behaviour of fireflies (*Photinus pyralis*?) with special reference
to the problem of orientation.

360 MAST, S. O., 1917. *J. exp. Zool.*, **22**, 472–528.
The relation between spectral colour and stimulation in lower
organisms.

352 THE BEHAVIOUR OF INVERTEBRATES

361 MAST, S. O., 1921. *J. exp. Zool.*, **34**, 149–187.
Reactions to light in the larvae of the ascidians *Amaroucium constellatum* and *A. pellucidum*, with special reference to photic orientation.

362 MAST, S. O., 1923. *J. exp. Zool.*, **38**, 109–205.
Photic orientation in insects with special reference to the drone fly, *Eristalis tenax*, and the robber fly, *Erax rufibarbis*.

363 MAST, S. O., 1938. *Biol. Rev.*, **13**, 186–224.
Factors involved in the process of orientation of lower animals to light.

364 MAXWELL, S. S., 1897. *Pflüg. Arch. ges. Physiol.*, **67**, 263–297.
Beiträge zur Gehirnphysiologie der Anneliden.

365 MAYER, A. G., 1914. *Carneg. Inst. Pub. No. 183*, 30p.
The relation between the degree of concentration of the electrolytes of sea water and the rate of nerve conduction in *Cassiopea*.

366 MAYR, E., 1950. *Evolution*, **4**, 149–154.
The role of the antennae in the mating behaviour of female *Drosophila*.

367 MEILLON, de, no date, in FRAENKEL, G. and GUNN, D. L. [177]

368 MELL, R., 1922. *Biologie und Systematik der chinesischen Sphingiden.* Berlin: Friedlander.

369 MELLANBY, K., 1932. *J. exp. Biol.*, **9**, 222–231.
The influence of atmospheric humidity on the thermal death point of a number of insects.

370 MENDELSSOHN, M., 1895. *Pflüg. Arch. ges. Physiol.*, **60**, 1–27.
Uber den Thermotropismus einzelliger Organismen.

371 MENDELSSOHN, M., 1902. *J. physiol. Path. gen.*, **4**, 393–409.
Recherche sur la thermotaxie des organismes unicellulaire.

372 MENZER, G. and STOCKHAMMER, K., 1951. *Naturwissenschaften*, **38**, 190–191.
Zur Polarisationsoptik der Facettenaugen von Insekten.

373 MERKER, E., 1929. *Zool. Jb., Abt. allg. Zool. Physiol.*, **46**, 297–374.
Die Pigmentverschiebungen im Netzauge der Insekten unter dem Einfluss von ultravioletten Licht.

374 MILLER, H. M., 1928. *Science*, **68**, 117–118.
Variety of behaviour of larval trematodes.

375 MILLOTT, N., 1954. *Phil. Trans. R. Soc. Lond. B.*, **238**, 187–220.
Sensitivity to light and the reactions to changes in light intensity of the echinoid, *Diadema antillarum*.

376 MILLOTT, N., 1956. *J. exp. Biol.*, **33**, 508–523.
The covering reaction of sea-urchins. I. A preliminary account of covering in the tropical echinoid *Lytechinus variegatus*, and its relation to light.

377 MILLOTT, N., 1957. *Endeavour*, **16**, 19–28.
Animal photosensitivity with special reference to eyeless forms.

378 MINNICH, D. E., 1919. *J. exp. Zool.*, **29**, 343–425.
The photic reactions of the honey-bee, *Apis mellifera*.

379 MINNICH, D. E., 1921. *J. exp. Zool.*, **33**, 173–203.
An experimental study of the tarsal chemoreceptors of two nymphalid butterflies.

380 MINNICH, D. E., 1925. *J. exp. Zool.*, **42**, 443–469.
The reactions of the larvae of *Vanessa antiopa* to sounds.

381 MINNICH, D. E., 1929. *Z. vergl. Physiol.*, **11**, 1–55.
The chemical sensitivity of the legs of the blowfly, *Calliphora vomitoria* to various sugars.

882 MINNICH, D. E., 1931. *J. exp. Zool.*, **60**, 121–139.
The sensitivity of the oral lobes of the proboscis of the blowfly, *Calliphora vomitoria*, to various sugars.

383 MINNICH, D. E., 1936. *J. exp. Zool.*, **72**, 439–453.
The responses of caterpillars to sounds.

384 MITTELSTAEDT, H., 1949. *Naturwissenschaften*, **3**, 90.
Telotaxis und Optomotorik von *Eristalis* bei Augeninversion.

385 MITTELSTAEDT, H., 1950. *Z. vergl. Physiol.*, **32**, 422–463.
Physiologie des Gleichgewichtssinnes bei fliegenden Libellen.

386 MOLLER-RACKE, I., 1949. *Verh. dtsch. Zool. Ges. Mainz.*, **1949**, 205–208.
Farbensinn und Farbenblindheit bie Insekten.

387 MOLLER-RACKE, I., 1952, in VON BUDDENBROCK.[80]

388 MONCRIEFF, R. W., 1946. *The chemical senses.* London: Hill.

389 MOORE, M. M., 1924. *J. gen. Physiol.*, **6**, 385–393.
Tropistic reactions of *Cerianthus membranaceus*.

390 MÜLLER, A., 1926. *Z. vergl. Physiol.*, **3**, 113–144.
Uber Lichtreaktionen von Landasseln.

391 MÜLLER, E., 1931. *Z. vergl. Physiol.*, **14**, 348–384.
Experimentelle Untersuchungen an Bienen und Ameisen über die Funktionsweise der Stirnocellen.

392 MULLINS, L. J., 1955. *Ann. N.Y. Acad. Sci.*, **62**, 247–276.
Olfaction.

393 MURBACH, L., 1903. *Amer. J. Physiol.*, **10**, 201–210.
The static function in *Gonionemus*.

394 MURBACH, L., 1907. *Biol. Bull.*, **14**, 1–8.
On the light receptive function of the marginal papillae of *Gonionemus*.

395 MURBACH, L., 1909. *Biol. Bull.*, **17**, 354–369.
Some light reactions of the medusa, *Gonionemus*.

396 NEWELL, G. E., 1957, personal communication.

396a NEWELL, G. E., 1958. *J. mar. biol. Ass.*, *U.K.*, **37**, 241–266.
An experimental analysis of the behaviour of *Littorina littorea* (L.) under natural conditions and in the laboratory.

397 NICHOLSON, A. J., 1934. *Bull. ent. Res.*, **25**, 85–99.
Influence of temperature on the activity of sheep blowflies.

398 NICOL, J. A. C., 1950. *J. mar. biol. Ass.*, *U.K.*, **29**, 303–320.
Responses of *Branchiomma vesiculosum* to photic stimulation.

399 NIXON, H. L. and RIBBANDS, C. R., 1952. *Proc. R. Soc., Lond. B.*, **140**, 43–50.
Food transmission within the honeybee community.

400 NIESCHULZ, O., 1933. *Z. Parasitenk.*, **6**, 220–242.
Uber die Temperaturbegrenzung der Aktivitätsstufen von *Stomoxys calcitrans*.

401 NIESCHULZ, O., 1935. *Zool. Anz.*, **110**, 225–233.
Uber die Temperaturabhangigkeit der Aktivität und die Vorzugstemperatur von *Musca domestica* und *Fannia cannicularis*

402 OHSAWA, W. and TSUKUDA, H., 1955. *J. Inst. Polytechnics, Osaka City Univ.*, (D), **6**, 71–96.
Extruding response of the periwinkle, *Nodilittorina granularis*.

403 OLMSTED, J. M. D., 1917. *J. exp. Zool.*, **24**, 333–379.
The comparative physiology of *Synaptula hydriformis*.

404 OPFINGER, E., 1931. *Z. vergl. Physiol.*, **15**, 431–487.
Uber die Orientierung des Biene an der Futterquelle.

405 OPFINGER, E., 1949. *Z. vergl. Physiol.*, **31**, 441–453.
Zur Physiologie des Duftdressuren bei Bienen.

406 ORLOV, J., 1924. *Z. wiss. Zool.*, **122**, 425–502.
Die Innervation des Darmes der Insekten.

407 OSSIANNILSSON, F., 1949. *Opuscula Entomologica, Suppl.*, **10**, 1–145.
Insect drummers.

408 PALMGREN, P., 1936 *Acta. Zool. Fenn.*, **19**, 1–28
Experimentelle Untersuchungen über Funktion der Trichobothrien bei *Tegenaria derhami*.

409 PANTIN, C. F. A., 1935. *J. exp. Biol.*, **12**, 139–155.
The nerve net of the Actinozoa. II. The plan of the nerve net.

410 PANTIN, C. F. A., 1942. *J. exp. Biol.*, **19**, 294–310.
The excitation of nematocysts.

411 PANTIN, C. F. A. and PANTIN, A. M. P., 1944. *J. exp. Biol.*, **20**, 6–13.
The stimulus to feeding in *Anemonia sulcata*.

412 PAPI, F., 1955. *Pubbl. Staz. zool.*, *Napoli.* **27**, 76–103.
Richerche sull'orientamento astronomico di *Arctosa perita*.

413 PAPI, F., 1955. *Experientia*, **11**, 201.
Experiments on the sense of time in *Talitrus saltator*.

414 PAPI, F. and PARDI, L., 1953. *Z. vergl. Physiol.*, **35**, 490–518.
Richerche sull'orientamento di *Talitrus saltator*. II. Sui fattori che regolano la variazione dell'angelo di orientamento nel corso del giorno. L'orientamento do notte. L'orientamento diurno do altre popolazioni.

415 PAPI, F., SERRETTI, L. and PARRINI, S., 1957. *Z. vergl. Physiol.*, **39**, 531–561.
Nuove richerche sull'orientamento e il senso del tempo di *Arctosa perita*.

416 PARDI, L. and GRASSI, M., 1955. *Experientia*, **11**, 202.
Experimental modification of direction finding in *Talitrus saltator* and *Talorchestia deshayei*.

417 PARDI, L. and PAPI, F., 1952. *Naturwissenschaften*, **39**, 262–263.
Die Sonne als Compass bei *Talitrus saltator*.

418 PARDI, L. and PAPI, F., 1953. *Z. vergl. Physiol.*, **35**, 459–489.
Richerche sull'orientamento do *Talitrus saltator*. I. L'orientamento durante il giorno in una popolazione del littorale Tirrenico.

419 PARKER, G. H., 1917. *J. exp. Zool.*, **22**, 94–110.
The movements of tentacles in actinians.

420 PARKER, G. H., 1922. *Proc. Amer. phil. Soc.*, **61**, 107–116.
The relations of the retinal image to animal reactions.

421 PARKER, G. H., 1927. *Amer. J. Physiol.*, **39**, 167–180.
Locomotion and righting movements in echinoderms, especially *Echinarachnius*.

422 PARKER, G. H., 1928. *Proc. nat. Acad. Sci.*, **14**, 713–714.
Glycogen as a means of ciliary reversal.

423 PARKER, G. H. and PARSHLEV, H. M., 1911. *J. exp. Zool.*, **11**, 361–364.
The reaction of earthworms to dry and to moist surfaces.

424 PATTEN, B. M., 1914. *J. exp. Zool.*, **17**, 213–280.
A quantitative determination of the orienting reaction of the blowfly, *Calliphora erythrocephala*.

425 PATTEN, B. M., 1917. *J. exp. Zool.*, **23**, 251–275.
Reactions of the whiptail scorpion to light.

426 PEARSE, A. S., 1908. *Biol. Bull.*, **62**, 195–200.
Observations on the behaviour of the holothurian, *Thyone briareus*.

427 PENARD, E., 1917. *Rev. suisse. Zool.*, **25**, 453–489.
Le genre *Loxodes*.

428 PETER, K., 1912. *Biol. Zbl.*, **32**, 724–731.
Versuche über das Hörvermögen eines Schmetterlings (*Endrosa var. ramosa*).

429 PETERS, H., 1931. *Z. vergl. Physiol.*, **15**, 693–748.
Die Fanghandlung der Kreuzspinne (*Epeira diademata*).

430 PFLUGSTADT, H., 1912. *Z. wiss. Zool.*, **100**, 1–59.
Die Halteren der Dipteren.

431 PIELOU, D. P., 1940. *J. exp. Biol.*, **17**, 295–306.
The humidity behaviour of the mealworm beetle, *Tenebrio molitor*. II. The humidity receptors.

432 PIELOU, D. P. and GUNN, D. L., 1940. *J. exp. Biol.*, **17**, 286–294.
The humidity behaviour of the mealworm beetle, *Tenebrio molitor*. I, The reaction to differences of humidity.

433 PIERON, H., 1908. *C. R. Acad. Sci. Paris*, **147**, 279–280.
La localisation du sens de discrimination alimentaire chez les Limnées.

434 PITTENDRIGH, C. S., 1954. *Proc. nat. Acad. Sci.*, **40**, 1018–1029.
On temperature independence in the clock system controlling emergence time in *Drosophila*.

435 PRINGLE, J. W. S., 1938. *J. exp. Biol.*, **15**, 101–113, 114–131, 467–473.
Proprioception in insects I, II and III.

436 PRINGLE, J. W. S., 1948. *Phil. Trans. R. Soc., Lond. B.*, **233**, 347–384.
The gyroscopic mechanism of the halteres of Diptera.

437 PRINGLE, J. W. S., 1954. *J. exp. Biol.*, **31**, 525–560.
A physiological analysis of cicada song.

438 PUMPHREY, R. J., 1936. *J. Physiol.*, **87**, 6–7.
Slow adaptation of a tactile receptor in the leg of the common cockroach.

439 PUMPHREY, R. J., 1940. *Biol. Rev.*, **15**, 107–132.
Hearing in insects.

440 PUMPHREY, R. J., 1950. *Symp. Soc. exp. Biol.*, **4**, 3–18.
Hearing.

441 PUMPHREY, R. J. and RAWDON-SMITH, A. F., 1936. *Nature*, 137, 990.
Sensitivity of insects to sound.

442 PUMPHREY, R. J. and RAWDON-SMITH, A. F., 1936. *J. Physiol.*, 87, 4–5.
Synchronized action potentials in the cercal nerve of the cockroach in response to auditory stimuli.

443 PUMPHREY, R. J. and RAWDON-SMITH, A. F., 1936. *Proc. R. Soc.*, *Lond. B.*, 121, 18–27.
Hearing in insects: The nature of the response of certain receptors to auditory stimuli.

444 PUMPHREY, R. J. and RAWDON-SMITH, A. F., 1939. *Nature*, 143, 806.
'Frequency discrimination' in insects: A new theory.

445 RABE, W., 1953. *Z. vergl. Physiol.*, 35, 300–325.
Beiträge zum Orientierungsproblem der Wasserwanzen.

446 RAHM, P. G., 1922. *Z. allg. Physiol.*, 20, 1–34.
Biologische und physiologische Beiträge zur Kenntnis des Moosfauna.

447 RAIGNIER, A., 1948. *La Cellule*, 51, 281–368.
L'economie thermique d'une colonie polycalique de la fourmi des bois.

448 REGEN, J., 1912. *Zool. Anz.*, 40, 305–316.
Experimentelle Untersuchungen über das Gehör von *Liogryllus campestris*.

449 REGEN, J., 1913. *Pflüg. Arch. ges. Physiol.*, 155, 193–200.
Uber die Anlockung des Weibchens von *Gryllus campestris* durch telephonisch ubertragene Stridulationslaute des Mannchens.

450 REGEN, J., 1914. *S. B. Akad. wiss. Math. Nat. Kl.*, *Wien*, 123, 853–892.
Untersuchungen über die Stridulation und das Gehör von *Thamnotrizon apterus*.

451 REGEN, J., 1923. *S. B. Akad. wiss. Mat. Nat. Kl.*, *Wien*, 132, 81–88.
Uber die Orientierung des Weibchens von *Liogryllus campestris* nach dem Stridulationsschall des Mannchens.

452 REGEN, J., 1926. *S. B. Akad. wiss. Mat. Nat. Kl.*, *Wien*, 135, 329–368.
Uber die Beeinflussung des Stridulation von *Thamnotrizon apterus* durch künstlich erzeugte Tone und Verscheidenartige Gerausche.

453 RIBBANDS, C. R., 1949. *J. Anim. Ecol.*, **18**, 47–66.
The foraging method of individual honeybees.

454 RIBBANDS, C. R., 1955. *Proc. R. Soc., Lond. B.*, **143**, 367–379.
The scent perception of the honeybee.

455 RIBBANDS, C. R. and SPEIRS, N., 1953. *Brit. J. anim. Behav.*, **1**, 59–66.
The adaptability of the homecoming honeybee.

456 RICHARD, G., 1951. *Thèse à la Faculté des Sciences de l'université de Paris.*
Le phototropisme des termites en rapport avec leur anatomie sensorielle.

457 RITTER, E., 1936. *Z. vergl. Physiol.*, **23**, 543–570.
Untersuchungen über den chemischen Sinn beim schwarzen Kolbenwasserkafer, *Hydrous piceus*.

458 ROEDER, K. D. and TREAT, A. E., 1957. *J. exp. Zool.*, **134**, 127–157.
Ultrasonic reception by the tympanic organ of noctuid moths.

459 ROKOHL, R., 1942. *Z. vergl. Physiol.*, **29**, 638–676.
Uber die regionale Verscheidenheit des Farbentuchtigkeit im zusammengesetzen Auge von *Notonecta glauca*.

460 ROMANES, G. J., 1885. *Jellyfish, starfish and sea-urchins.* London: Kegan Paul.

461 ROTH, L. M., 1948. *Amer. Mid. Nat.*, **40**, 265–352.
A study of mosquito behaviour. An experimental laboratory study of the sexual behaviour of *Aedes aegypti*.

462 ROTH, L. M. and WILLIS, E. R., 1951. *J. exp. Zool.*, **116**, 527–570.
Hygroreceptors in adults of *Tribolium*.

463 ROTH, L. M. and WILLIS, E. R., 1951. *J. exp. Zool.*, **117**, 451–488.
Hygroreceptors in Coleoptera.

464 RUITER, L. de, 1955. *Arch. néerl. Zool.*, **11**, 285–341.
Countershading in caterpillars.

465 RUITER, L. de, and HORN, Ij. van, der 1957. *Nature*, **179**, 1027.
Changes in phototaxis during the larval life of the eyed hawk moth.

466 RUSSELL HUNTER, W., 1953. *Proc. roy. Soc. Edinb. B.*, **65**, 143–165.
The condition of the mantle cavity in two pulmonate snails living in Loch Lomond.

467 SALT, G., 1937. *Proc. roy. Soc. B.*, **122**, 57–75
The sense used by *Trichogramma* to distinguish between parasitized and unparasitized hosts.

468 SALT, R. W. and MAIL, G. A., 1943. *J. econ. Ent.*, **36**, 126–127.
The freezing of insects. A criticism and an explanation.

469 SANTSCHI, F., 1911. *Rev. suisse. Zool.*, **19**, 303–338.
Observations et remarques critiques sur le mécanisme de l'orientation chez les fourmis.

470 SANTSCHI, F., 1914. *Bull. Soc. Hist. nat., Afr. Nord.*, **5**, 206–212.
Recherches sur l'orientation celeste des fourmis.

471 SCHAEFFER, A. A., 1916. *J. exp. Zool.*, **20**, 529–584.
On the feeding habits of *Amoeba*.

472 SCHAEFFER, A. A., 1917. *Biol. Bull.*, **32**, 45–74.
Reactions of *Amoeba* to light and the effect of light on feeding.

473 SCHALLER, F. and TIMM, C., 1950. *Z. vergl. Physiol.*, **32**, 468–481.
Das Hörvermögen der Nachtschmetterlinge.

474 SCHALLER, F., 1951. *Z. vergl. Physiol.*, **33**, 476–486.
Lauterzeugung und Hörvermögen von *Corixa*.

475 SCHLEGTENDAL, A., 1934. *Z. vergl. Physiol.*, **20**, 545–581.
Beitrag zum Farbensinn des Arthropoden.

476 SCHLIEPER, C., 1928. *Z. vergl. Physiol.*, **8**, 281–288.
Uber die Helligkeitsverteilung im Spektrum bei verscheidenen Insekten.

477 SCHLÜTER, E., 1933. *Z. wiss. Zool.*, **143**, 538–593.
Die Bedeutung des Centralnervensystems von *Hirudo medicinalis* für Locomotion und Raumorientierung.

478 SCHMID, B., 1911. *Biol. Zbl.*, **31**, 538–539.
Uber den Heliotropismus von *Cereactis aurantiaca*.

479 SCHMIDT, A., 1938. *Z. vergl. Physiol.*, **25**, 351–378.
Geschmacksphysiologische Untersuchungen an Ameisen.

480 SCHNEIRLA, T. C., 1933. *J. comp. Psychol.*, **15**, 267–299.
Studies on army-ants in Panama.

481 SCHNEIRLA, T. C., 1940. *J. comp. Psychol.*, **29**, 401–460.
Further studies on the army-ant behaviour pattern. Mass organisation in the swarm raiders.

482 SCHNEIRLA, T. C., 1944. *Amer. Mus. Nov.*, **1253**, 1–26.
A unique case of circular milling in ants.

483 SCHÖNE, H., 1951. *Z. vergl. Physiol.*, **33**, 63–98.
Die Lichtorientierung des Larven von *Acilius sulcatus und Dytiscus marginalis*.

484 SCHÖNE, H., 1951. *Verh. dtsch. Ges. Wilhelmshaven*, **1951**, 157–162.
Die statische Gleichgewichtsorientierung dekapoder Crustacean.

485 SCHÖNE, H., 1952. *Naturwissenschaften*, **23**, 552–553.
Zur optischen Lageorientierung (Lichtrückenorientierung) von Dekapoden.

[486] SCHÖNE, H., 1954. *Z. vergl. Physiol.*, **36**, 241–260.
Statozystenfunktion und Statische Lageorientierung bei Dekapoder Krebsen.

[487] SCHÖNE, H., 1955. *Verh. dtsch. Ges. Erlangen*, **1955**, 52–58.
Uber den optischen Lageapparat des Krebse.

[488] SCHÖNE, H., 1957. *Z. vergl. Physiol.*, **39**, 235–240.
Kurssteuerung mittels des Statocysten (Messungén an Krebsen).

[489] SCHULZ, W., 1931. *Z. vergl. Physiol.*, **14**, 392–404.
Die Orientierung des Ruckenschwimmers zum Licht und zur Strömung.

[490] SEIFERT, R., 1930. *Z. vergl. Physiol.*, **11**, 386–436.
Sinnesphysiologische Untersuchungen am Kiemenfuss, *Triops cancriformis*.

[491] SEIFERT, R., 1932. *Z. vergl. Physiol.*, **16**, 111–184.
Raumorientierung und Phototaxis des Anostraken Euphyllopoden (*Chirocephalus* und *Artemia*).

[492] SKRAMLIK, E. von, 1948. *Pflüg. Arch. ges. Physiol.*, **249**, 702–716.
Uber die zur normalen Erregung des menschlichen Geruchs- und Geschmackssinns notwendigen Molekulmengen.

[493] SLIFER, E. H., 1951. *Proc. roy. Soc. B.*, **138**, 414–437.
Some unusual structures in *Locusta migratoria migratorioides* and their probable functions as thermoreceptors.

[494] SLIFER, E. H., 1953. *Trans. Amer. ent. Soc.*, **79**, 37–68, 69–97.
The pattern of specialized heat-sensitive areas on the surface of the body of Acrididae. I. The males. II. The females.

[495] SLIFER, E. H., 1954. *Biol. Bull.* **106**, 122–128.
The permeability of the sensory pegs on the antennae of the grasshopper.

[496] SLIFER, E. H., 1954. *Proc. R. ent. Soc. Lond.* (*A*), **29**, 177–179.
The reaction of a grasshopper to an odorous material held near one of its feet.

[497] SLIFER, E. H., 1955. *J. exp. Zool.*, **130**, 301–317.
The detection of odors and water vapor by grasshoppers and some new evidence concerning the sense organs which may be involved.

[498] SLIFER, E. H. and FINLAYSON, L. H., 1956. *Q. J. Micro. Sci.*, **97**, 617–620.
Muscle receptor organs in grasshoppers and locusts.

[499] SMITH, F. E. and BAYLOR, E. R., *Amer. Nat.* **87**, 49–55.
Colour responses in the cladocera and their ecological significance.

500 SPENCER, J. O. and EDNEY, E. B., 1954. *J. exp. Biol.*, **31**, 491–496.
The absorption of water by woodlice.

501 SPIEGEL, A., 1927. *Z. vergl. Physiol.*, **6**, 688–730.
Uber die Chemorezeption von *Crangon vulgaris*.

502 SPOONER, G. M., 1933. *J. mar. biol. Ass. U.K.*, **19**, 385–438.
The reactions of marine plankton to light.

503 STEIN-BELING, J. von, 1934. *Biol. Zbl.*, **54**, 147–168.
Uber den Ausflug der Schlupfwespen *Nemeritis canescens* und
über die Bedeutung des Geruchssinns bei der Rückkehr
zum Wirt.

504 STEINER, A., 1930. *Z. vergl. Physiol.*, **11**, 461–502.
Die Temperaturregulierung im Nest des Feldwespe.

505 STEPHENS, G. C., FINGERMAN, M. and BROWN, F. A. Jr., 1953.
Ann. ent. Soc. Amer., **46**, 75–83.
The orientation of *Drosophila* to plane polarised light.

506 STRIDE, G. O., 1956. *Brit. J. anim. Behav.*, **4**, 52–68.
On the courtship behaviour of *Hypolimnas misippus* with
notes on the mimetic association with *Danaus chrysippus*.

506a STRIDE, G. O., 1957. *Brit. J. Anim. Behav.*, **5**, 153–167.
Investigations into the courtship behaviour of the male of
Hypolimnas misippus with special reference to the role of
visual stimuli.

507 STUDNITZ, G. von, 1932. *Zool. Jb., Abt. allg. Zool. Physiol.*, **50**,
313–478.
Die statische Funktion des sogenannten 'pelotaktischen'
Organe des Limnobiidenlarven.

508 SUFFERT, F., 1932. *Z. Morph. Ökol. Tiere*, **26**, 147–316.
Phanomene visueller Anpassung, I, II and III.

509 TALIAFERRO, W. H., 1920. *J. exp. Zool.*, **31**, 59–116.
Reactions to light in *Planaria maculata* with especial reference
to the function and structure of the eyes.

510 THOMSEN, E. and THOMSEN, M., 1937. *Z. vergl. Physiol.*, **24**,
343–380.
Uber das Thermopräferendum der Larven einiger Fliegenarten.

511 THOMSEN, M., 1938. *Stueflen og Stikfluen*. Copenhagen: Bangs.

512 THORNTON, I. W. B., 1956. *Brit. J. anim. Behav.*, **4**, 143–146.
Diurnal migrations of the echinoid *Diadema setosum*.

513 THORPE, W. H., 1939. *Proc. roy. Soc., B.*, **127**, 424–433.
Further studies on pre-imaginal olfactory conditioning in
insects.

514 THORPE, W. H., 1950. *Behaviour*, **2**, 257–263.
A note on detour experiments with *Ammophila pubescens*.

515 THORPE, W. H., 1956. *Learning and Instinct in Animals*. London: Methuen.

516 THORPE, W. H. and CAUDLE, H. B., 1938. *Parasitology*, **30**, 523–528.
A study of the olfactory responses of insect parasites to the food plant of their host.

517 THORPE, W. H. and CRISP, D., 1947. *J. exp. Biol.*, **24**, 310–328.
Studies on plastron respiration. III.

518 THORPE, W. H. and JONES, F. G., 1937. *Proc. roy. Soc. B.*, **124**, 56–81.
Olfactory conditioning in a parasitic insect and its relation to the problem of host selection.

519 TINBERGEN, N., 1932. *Z. vergl. Physiol.*, **16**, 305–334.
Uber des Orientierung des Bienenwolfes.

520 TINBERGEN, N., 1935. *Z. vergl. Physiol.*, **21**, 699–716.
Uber des Orientierung des Bienenwolfles II. Die Bienenjagd.

521 TINBERGEN, N., 1951. *The study of instinct*. Oxford: University Press.

522 TINBERGEN, N. and KRUYT, 1938. *Z. vergl. Physiol.*, **25**, 292–334.
Uber die Orientierung des Bienenwolfes (*Philanthus triangulum*).

523 TINBERGEN, N., MEEUSE, B. J. D., BOEREMA, L. K. and VAROSSIEAU, W. W., 1942. *Z. Tierpsychol.*, **5**, 182–226.
Die Balz des Samtfalters, *Eumenis* (=*Satyrus*) *semele*.

524 TONNER, F., 1933. *Z. Zellforsch.*, **20**, 423–426.
Uber Chemorezeptoren in der Kiemenhohle des Flusskrebses.

525 TONNER, F., 1935. *Z. vergl. Physiol.*, **22**, 517–523.
Schwimmreflex und Zentrenfunktion bei *Aeschna* larven.

526 TONNER, F., 1938. *Z. vergl. Physiol.*, **25**, 427–454.
Halsreflexe und Bewegungssehen bei Arthropoden.

527 TORREY, H. B., 1904. *J. exp. Zool.*, 395–422.
Biological studies on *Corymorpha*. I. *C. palma* and its environment.

528 TOTZE, R., 1933. *Z. vergl. Physiol.*, **19**, 110–161.
Beiträge zur Sinnesphysiologie des Zecken.

529 TREAT, A. E., 1955. *Ann. ent. Soc. Amer.*, **48**, 272–284.
The response to sound in certain Lepidoptera.

530 TURNER, C. H., 1907. *J. comp. Neur. Psych.*, **17**, 367–434.
The homing of ants.

531 TURNER, C. H., 1914. *Biol. Bull.*, **27**, 275–293.
An experimental study of the auditory powers of the giant silkworm moths.

[532] TURNER, C. H. and SCHWARZ, E., 1914. *Biol. Bull.*, **27**, 325–332.
Auditory powers of the *Catocala* moths; an experimental field study.

[533] UEXKÜLL, J. von, 1899. *Z. Biol.*, **37**, 334–403.
Die Physiologie der Pedicellarien.

[534] UEXKÜLL, J. von, 1912. *Z. Biol.*, **58**, 305–332.
Studien über den Tonus. 6. Die Pilgermuschel.

[535] UEXKÜLL, J. von, and BROCK, F., 1927. *Z. vergl. Physiol.*, **5**, 167–178.
Atlas zur Bestimmung der Otte in den Sehrauemen der Tiere.

[536] ULLYOTT, P., 1936. *J. exp. Biol.*, **13**, 253–264, 265–278.
The behaviour of *Dendrocoelum lacteum*, I and II.

[537] URBAN, F., 1932. *Z. wiss. Zool.*, **140**, 291–355.
Der Lauf der entflugelten Honigbiene, *Apis mellifica*, zum Licht.

[538] VALENTINE, J. M., 1931. *J. exp. Zool.*, **58**, 165–220.
The olfactory sense of the adult meal-worm beetle, *Tenebrio molitor*.

[539] VERRIER, M. L., 1932. *Bull. biol.*, **66**, 200–231.
Étude des rapports de la forme, de l'habitat et du comportement de quelques Crustaces Isopodes.

[540] VOGEL, B., 1931. *Z. vergl. Physiol.*, **14**, 273–347.
Uber die Beziehungen zwischen Süssgeschmack und Nahrwert von Zucken und Zuckeralkoholen bei der Honigbiene.

[541] VOWLES, D. M., 1950. *Nature*, **164**, 282.
Sensitivity of ants to polarized light.

[542] VOWLES, D. M., 1954. *J. exp. Biol.*, **31**, 341–355, 356–375.
The orientation of ants. I. The substitution of stimuli. II. Orientation to light, gravity and polarized light.

[542a] WALD, G., 1955. *Amer. J. Opthalm.*, **40**, 18–41.
The photoreceptor process in vision.

[543] WALD, G. and HUBBARD, R., 1957. *Nature*, **180**, 278–280.
Visual pigment of a decapod crustacean—the lobster.

[544] WALOFF, N., 1941. *J. exp. Biol.*, **18**, 115–135.
The mechanism of humidity reactions of terrestrial isopods.

[545] WALTER, H. E., 1907. *J. exp. Zool.*, **5**, 35–162.
The reactions of planarians to light.

[546] WALTON, W. R., 1927. *Science*, **66**, 132.
Earthworms and light.

[547] WARNKE, G., 1931. *Z. vergl. Physiol.*, **14**, 121–199.
Experimentelle Untersuchungen über den Geruchssinn von *Geotrupes sylvaticus* and *Geotrupes vernalis*.

548 WATERMAN, T. H., 1950. *Science*, **111**, 252–254.
A light polarization analyser in the compound eye of *Limulus*.

549 WATERMAN, T. H., 1954. *Science*, **120**, 927–932.
Polarization patterns in submarine illumination.

550 WATERMAN, T. H., 1954. *Proc. nat. Acad. Sci.*, **40**, 258–262.
Polarized light and angle of stimulus incidence in the compound eye of *Limulus*.

551 WEBER, H., 1924. *Zool. Anz.*, **60**, 261–269.
Ein Umdreh- und Fluchtreflex bei *Nassa mutabilis*.

552 WEIS, I., 1930. *Z. vergl. Physiol.*, **12**, 206–248.
Versuche uber die Geschmacksrezeption durch die Tarsen des Admiral, *Pyrameis atalanta*.

553 WEIS-FOGH, T., 1949. *Nature*, **164**, 873–874.
An aerodynamic sense organ stimulating and regulating flight in locusts.

554 WEIS-FOGH, T., 1950. *8th Int. Congr. Ent.*, **1948**, 584–588.
An aerodynamic sense organ in locusts.

555 WELLINGTON, W. G., 1949. *Sci. Agric.*, **29**, 210–215.
The effects of temperature and moisture upon the behaviour of the spruce budworm, *Choristoneura fumiferana*. I. The relative importance of graded temperatures and rates of evaporation in producing aggregations of larvae.

556 WELLINGTON, W. G., 1949. *Sci. Agric.*, **29**, 216–229.
The effects of temperature and moisture upon the behaviour of the spruce budworm. *Choristoneura fumiferana*. II. The responses of larvae to gradients of evaporation.

557 WELLINGTON, W. G., 1950. *Trans. roy. Soc. Can.*, **44**, Section 5, 89–101.
Variations on the silk-spinning and locomotor activities of larvae of the spruce budworm, *Choristoneura fumiferana*, at different rates of evaporation.

558 WELLINGTON, W. G., 1953. *Nature*, **172**, 1177.
Motor responses evoked by the dorsal ocelli of *Sarcophagus aldrichi*, and the orientation of the fly to plane polarized light.

559 WELLINGTON, W. G., 1955. *Ann. ent. Soc. Amer.*, **48**, 67–76.
Solar heat and plane polarized light versus the light compass reaction in the orientation of insects on the ground.

560 WELLINGTON, W. G., SULLIVAN, C. R. and GREEN, G. W., 1951. *Canad. J. Zool.*, **29**, 339–351.
Polarized light and body temperature level as orientation factors in the light reactions of some hymenopterous and lepidopterous larvae.

561 WELLS, G. P., 1949. *J. mar. biol. Ass. U.K.*, **28**, 465–478.
The behaviour of *Arenicola marina* in sand, and the role of spontaneous activity cycles.

562 WELLS, M. J., 1958. *Behaviour* (in the press).
Factors affecting the reaction to *Mysis* by newly hatched *Sepia*.

563 WELLS, M. J. and WELLS, J., 1957. *J. exp. Biol.*, **34**, 131–142.
The function of the brain of *Octopus* in tactile discrimination.

564 WELSH, J. H., 1931. *Biol. Bull.*, **61**, 497–499.
Specific influence of the host on the light response of parasitic water mites.

565 WELSH, J. H., 1933. *Biol. Bull.*, **65**, 168–174.
Light intensity and the extent of activity of locomotor muscles as opposed to cilia.

566 WEVER, E. G. and BRAY, C. W., 1933. *J. comp. cell. Physiol.*, **4**, 79–93.
A new method for the study of hearing in insects.

567 WEVER, E. G., 1935. *J. comp. Physiol.*, **20**, 17–20.
A study of hearing in the sulfur-winged grasshopper (*Arphia sulfurea*).

568 WEYRAUCH, W., 1929. *Z. vergl. Physiol.*, **10**, 665–687.
Sinnesphysiologische Studien an der Imago von *Forficula auricularia*.

569 WEYRAUCH, W., 1936. *Rev. suisse Zool.*, **43**, 455–465.
Untersuchungen und Gedanken zur Orientierung von Arthropoden. 7. Teil. Uber starke und schwache Orientierungsreize.

570 WEYRAUCH, W., 1936. *Zool. Anz.*, **113**, 115–125.
Orientierung nach dunklen Flachen.

571 WHITMAN, C. O., 1898. *Biol. Lect.*, 285–338.
Animal behaviour.

572 WIESER, W., 1956. *Limnology and Oceanography*, **1**, 274–285.
Factors influencing the choice of substratum in *Cumella vulgaris*.

573 WIGGLESWORTH, V. B., 1941. *Parasitology*, **33**, 67–109.
The sensory physiology of the human louse *Pediculus humanis corporis*.

574 WIGGLESWORTH, V. B. and GILLETT, J. D., 1934. *J. exp. Biol.*, **11**, 120–139, 408–410.
The function of the antennae of *Rhodnius prolixus* and the mechanism of orientation to the host, and, Confirmatory experiments.

575 WILLIAMSON, D. I., 1951. *J. mar. biol. Ass. U.K.*, **30**, 73–99.
Studies in the biology of Talitridae.

576 WILSON, E. B., 1891. *Amer. Nat.*, **25**, 413–433.
The heliotropism of *Hydra*.

577 WILSON, D. P., 1948. *J. mar. Biol. Ass. U.K.*, **27**, 723–760.
The relation of the substratum to the metamorphosis of *Ophelia* larvae.

578 WILSON, D. P., 1953. *J. mar. biol. Ass. U.K.*, **32**, 209–232.
The settlement of *Ophelia bicornis* larvae. The 1952 experiments.

579 WILSON, D. P., 1955. *J. mar. biol. Ass. U.K.*, **34**, 531–543.
The role of microorganisms in the settlement of *Ophelia bicornis*.

580 WOLF, E. 1926. *Z. vergl. Physiol.*, **3**, 209–224.
Physiologisch Untersuchungen über das Umdrehen der Seesterne und Schlangensterne.

581 WOLF, E., 1926. *Z. vergl. Physiol.*, **3**, 615–691.
Das Heimkehrvermögen des Bienen. I.

582 WOLF, E., 1928. *Z. vergl. Physiol.*, **6**, 221–254.
Das Heimkehrvermögen der Bienen. II.

583 WOLF, E., 1933. *Z. vergl. Physiol.*, **20**, 151–161.
Das Verhalten der Bienen gegenüber flimmernden Feldern und bewegten Objekten.

584 WOLF, E., 1937. *J. gen. Physiol.*, **20**, 511–518.
Flicker and the reactions of bees to flowers.

585 WOLTER, H., 1936. *Zool. Jb., Abt. allg. Zool. Physiol.*, **56**, 581–612.
Beiträge zum Lichtsinn von *Carcinus maenas*.

586 WREDE, W. L., 1929. *Tijdschr. ned. dierk. Ver. Leiden.*, **3**, 109–112.
Versuche über die Chemoreception bei *Eupagurus bernhardus*.

586a WULFF, V. J., 1956. *Physiol. Rev.*, **36**, 145–163.
Physiology of the compound eye.

587 YERKES, R. M., 1902. *Amer. J. Physiol.*, **6**, 434–449.
A contribution to the physiology of the nervous system of the medusa *Gonionemus murbachi*. I. Sensory reactions of *Gonionemus*.

588 YERKES, R. M., 1906. *J. comp. Neurol.*, **16**, 457–463.
Concerning the behaviour of *Gonionemus*.

589 YERKES, R. M. and AYER, J. B., 1903. *Amer. J. Physiol.*, **9**, 279–307.
A study of the reactions and reaction times of the medusa *Gonionemus murbachi*.

590 YONGE, C. M., 1947. *Phil. Trans. roy. Soc.*, B., **232**, 443–518.
The pallial organs in the Aspidobranch Gastropoda and their evolution throughout the Mollusca.

591 ZERRAHN, G., 1933. *Z. vergl. Physiol.*, **20**, 117–150.
Formdressur und Formunterscheidung bei der Honigbiene.

SPECIES INDEX

(Figures in heavy type indicate references either to figures or tables)

PROTOZOA

RHIZOPODA

Amoeba proteus, 89, 242, 244, 246

CILIATA

Colpoda cucullus, 215; *Colpidium campylum*, 215; *Diophrys hystrix*, **240**, 241; *Loxodes*, 19, 20, 196; *Paramecium* sp., 40, 41, **42**, 47, 181, 182, 196, 241, 245, 251, 313; *P. aurelia*, 215, 246; *P. bursaria*, 41; *P. calkinsi*, 246; *Spirostomum*, 241; *Stentor caeruleus*, 41, 47, 242; *Tetrahymenea gelei*, 241

FLAGELLATA

Euglena viridis, 6, **6**, 41, 42, **43**, **44**, 47, 48, 49, 82, 89; *Pouchetia*, 6; *Polytoma uvella*, 215

COELENTERATA

HYDROZOA

Chlorohydra viridissima, 90; *Corymorpha* sp. 243; *Hydra* sp. 243, 249, 316; *Hydra fusca* (see *Pelmatohydra oligactis*); *Hydra littoralis*, 293; *Hydra viridis* (see *Chlorohydra viridissima*); *Obelia sp*, 197; *Pelmatohydra oligactis* (see *Hydra fusca*), 90

SCYPHOMEDUSAE

Aurelia aurita, 197, 293; *Cassiopea* sp, 197; *Chrysaora hyoscella*, 198; *Cotylorhiza tuberculata*, 197; *Cyanea capi-llata*, 197, 198, 293; *Gonionemus murbachi*, 36, 197, 198, 243; *Rhizostoma pulmo* (see *Rhizostoma octopus*); *Rhizostoma octopus*, 197; *Sarsia tubulosa*, 293; *Tiaropsis indicans*, 242

ACTINOZOA

Anemonia sulcata, 244, **292**, 293; *Bunodes* sp., 90; *Calliactis para-*

COELENTERATA—*contd.*

ACTINOZOA—*contd.*

sitica, 316; *Cereactis aurantiaca*, 90; *Cerianthus membranaceus*, 90, 208; *Metridium marginatum*, 293

CTENOPHORA

Beröe ovata, 198; *Pleurobrachia pileus*, 198; *Pleurobrachia pileata* (see *P. pileus*)

PLATYHELMINTHES

TURBELLARIA

Convoluta roscoffensis, 199; *Dendrocoelum lacteum*, 38, **39**, 40; *Dugesia gonocephala*, 37; *Dugesia tigrina*, 37; *Mesostoma lingua*, **240**; *Otoplana*, 200; *Plagiostomum*, 37; *Planaria alpina*, 252; *P. gonocephala* (see *Dugesia gonocephala*); *P. lugubris*, 272, 274; *P. maculata* (see *Dugesia tigrina*)

TREMATODA

Opisthorchis felineus, 296

NEMERTEA

Lineus, 250

ANNELIDA

OLIGOCHAETA

Eisenia foetida, 291; *Lumbricus terrestris*, 6, **6**, 90, 313; *Tubifex* sp., 296

POLYCHAETA

Alciopa sp., 8, **10**, 123; *Arctonoë* sp., 276; *Arenicola marina*, 198, 199, 200, 202, 327; *Branchiomma*, 133, 199; *Branchiomma vesiculosum*, 45, 91; *Nereis*, 247; *Nereis diversicolor*, 65, 69, **70**; *Ophelia bicornis*, 250; *Serpula contortuplicata*, 91; *Tomopteris*, 215

367

N

SUBJECT INDEX

(Figures in heavy type indicate references either to figures or tables)

GEORGE ALLEN & UNWIN LTD

London: 40 Museum Street, W.C.1

Auckland: 24 Wyndham Street
Bombay: 15 Graham Road, Ballard Estate, Bombay 1
Buenos Aires: Escritorio 454-459, Florida 165
Cape Town: 109 Long Street
Calcutta: 17 Chittaranjan Avenue, Calcutta 13
Hong Kong: F1/12 Mirador Mansions, Kowloon
Karachi: Karachi Chambers, McLeod Road
Madras: Mohan Mansion, 38c Mount Road, Madras 6
Mexico: Villalongin 32-10, Piso, Mexico 5, D.F.
New Delhi: 13-14 Ajmeri Gate Extension, New Delhi 1
Sao Paulo: Avenida 9 de Julho 1138-Ap. 51
Singapore: 36c Princep Street, Singapore 7
Sydney, N.S.W.: Bradbury House, 55 York Street
Toronto: 91 Wellington Street West

ANIMAL NAVIGATION

J. D. CARTHY

The history of human navigation is one of a long struggle to produce instruments and devices to help men to find their way across the Earth's surface. Yet for thousands of years, unaided by gadgets, ants have returned to their nests, birds have migrated for hundreds of miles and eels have swum back to the continents from the depths of the Atlantic. Usually their navigation is accurate, for otherwise they die. The ways in which animals make use of the signposts in the world around them, signs unperceived by humans, for example, the pattern of polarized light from the sky, or smells so diluted in the air or in water that we do not realize their existence, makes a fascinating and original study.

Dr. Carthy has done much research into the homing abilities of ants as an approach to the general problem of the navigating animal. Taking into account the many new discoveries throughout the animal kingdom, he has written an absorbing and rewarding description of the complexities of animals' senses.

'To anyone even averagely curious about the unsolved problems of the world we live in, investment in this fascinating book will return a rich dividend.' *News Chronicle.*   *Demy 8vo. 18s. net*

THE EVOLUTION OF AN INSECT SOCIETY

DEREK WRAGGE MORLEY

In an absorbing manner the author sets out the fascinating story of a commune of British Wood Ants, composed of five separate but friendly nests. These nests are joined one to another by recognizable trails along which thousands of worker Wood Ants scurry to and fro throughout the summer months.

The commune is first described, then the origins of the Wood Ants' behaviour is traced forward from the days of their barely social ancestors whose small colonies of a dozen or twenty individuals lived in simple cave-like hollows dug out of the earth. The coming of the Ant Queens, the development of ant economy, the growth of the Nursery, the development of the communal food-basket for carrying home food to the nest, and the manner in which the work of the colony is apportioned amongst its individuals, are in turn described, and the recent history of the commune is recounted.

'For the ordinary reader this book provides a connection story, careful psychological observation, and strange kindred images to which we readily adjust our minds.' Sir Harold Nicholson. *Observer.*

Illustrated. Demy 8vo. 18s. net

GEORGE ALLEN & UNWIN LTD